Ann...

Anna K... ...ope and California
and comp... ...gland. She married and
lived for a ... ...ere she began to write. Her
first marriag... ...her second ended in divorce. A
heroin addict ...ost of her life, she continued to write
even during bouts of mental illness. Out of this period
came *Asylum Piece* (1940) and *I Am Lazarus* (1945), stories
that give an astonishing insight into the subjective reality of
schizophrenia. During the 1940s she lived in New York,
where she did research for a military psychiatric unit. For a
time she worked on Cyril Connolly's *Horizon*, in which
some of her stories were published. Anna Kavan wrote eleven
books, among them the novels *Sleep Has His House* (1948)
and *Ice* (1967). She died in London in 1968. She was found
holding a syringe, which she had always referred to as her
'bazooka'.

PICADOR *Classics*

My Madness

the selected writings of
ANNA KAVAN

edited and with an Introduction by
Brian W. Aldiss

PICADOR *Classics*

published by Pan Books

This selection first published as a Picador Classic
by Pan Books Ltd, Cavaye Place, London SW10 9PG

9 8 7 6 5 4 3 2 1

This selection © Brian W. Aldiss 1990
Introduction © Brian W. Aldiss 1990

ISBN 0 330 34532 8

Photoset by Parker Typesetting Service, Leicester
Printed and bound in Great Britain by
Richard Clay Ltd, Bungay, Suffolk

Contents

20th. June 90.

Dearest Correne,

Madness and heroin
addiction is trivial compared
to what we will have to
endure, oh well thats
Wilde for you honey. Hope
you had; have a good
life baby.

Best wishes
and
snoggies

Robbie

XXXXX

Introduction:
Kafka's Sister

'How cold it is in the exploding world'
Julia and the Bazooka

When Franz Kafka wrote his famous letter to his father, one of his accusations was that his father did not keep the commandments he imposed on his son. Hence, said Kafka, his world had become divided into three parts.

In the first world, he felt himself a slave. The second world was a world of power, remote from him. The third was where everyone else lived happily and free from orders. Kafka's lifelong guilt feelings arose from his oppressive sense of these divisions, brought about by his father's transgressions. Kafka, in the words of one of his editors, Erich Heller, had 'an irresistible tendency to fall apart', contained only by his writing. Writing was his way of survival.

The parallels with the writer calling herself Anna Kavan are strong. Her quarrel was with a mother who would not keep her own commandments. Like Kafka, Kavan seems as a child always to have felt herself in the wrong; and this feeling, as she reached adult years, also matured, into the prevailing sense that somehow her existence was unjustified, insubstantial. Like Kafka, she suffered in her struggle to come to terms with other people, and with herself.

'It is as if I were made of stone, as if I were my own tombstone,' complains Kafka in his diary for 1910.

'What exactly is it that's wrong with me? What is the thing about me that people can never take?' asks the narrator in Kavan's wartime story, 'Glorious Boys'.

'And where am I to find a little warmth in this?' asks the narrator in 'My Madness', as she becomes her own tribunal.

Implicitly, these and similar questions are asked in story after story. The 'I' character, a mirror image of Kavan, always expresses the same gamut of anxiety. The search is on, for something lost in childhood to be found in adult life. Insidious as a serpent comes the fear of others, the fear of relationships, but, most destructively, the fear of the self with its inadequacies, the first of Kafka's three dreaded divisions.

'Once and for all, I've declared myself against life and people, on the side of otherness and indifference, isolation, the mineral beauty of the non-human world' – so says a character in 'High in the Mountains', speaking in the voice of alienation.

'All we see of the mentally ill,' says Carl Jung, 'regarding them from the outside, is their tragic destruction, rarely the life of that side of the psyche which is turned away from us.' Kavan shows us the hidden side, and it has its beauty, as it struggles to make sense of an illogical world. Extracts similar to the ones quoted above can be taken almost at random from Kavan's writings, showing her alienation, her madness.

Yet, as her friend Raymond Marriott warns us, she was in many ways an ordinary and a pleasant creative person, chic, generally fun to be with. The fiction remains at least at arm's length from the facts of her life. Writers have many reasons for using a persona not entirely congruent with their own natures, for fact is more complex than fiction. What rises from the printed page is part of an elaborate game of hide-and-seek which a writer plays, perhaps unconsciously, not necessarily with the reader but with herself or himself. Kavan is dextrous in the use of symbols, and symbols are easily mistaken for the real thing.

Although she often looked outwards with a shrewd and witty eye – 'the church clock is calling the hour again in its dull country voice', as she says in 'My Madness', and we have all heard that particular chime – all roads lead back, like the strands of a web, to the spider of her self-obsession.

Yet hers is not a fiction of claustrophobia. The prose is too fine-spun for that. Her longing for abstraction takes refuge in its symbols: Madness, Ice, China – as one should say Trial, Castle, Amerika. Her narcissism flew to another universe, ethereal and 'on the side of otherness'. Hence Kavan's great attraction, that she sees beyond the personal to an impersonal infinity. She is not a victim but a creator, not a mad thing but a winged thing.

Her literary evolution is of remarkable interest. Born somewhere at the turn of the century (the imprecision is necessary, for she would never reveal her age), she was then plain Helen Edmonds. That did not satisfy her. A divine discontent was on the move in her.

The chilly sexuality in the novel *Let Me Alone*, in its very title, perhaps conveys something of what was happening to Helen Edmonds. In that novel, Anna is the protagonist, taken to the East against her wish. Findlay, Anna's lover, finally holds her in his arms. The night of the country now called Sri Lanka is about them. 'For the moment, she was open to him.' Yet they do nothing; not so much as a kiss is exchanged. The isolation is unbridgeable. 'They were in different worlds.'

That seems to have been a lifelong problem, not merely for the fictional Anna but also for the real one.

After the ineffectual encounter with Findlay, Anna is raped by her husband, Matthew. She suffers atrociously, yet her spirit remains cold; 'nor did he ever become real to her.'

That sense of unreality, perhaps the heart of symbolism, was a lifelong problem. And here indeed the fictional character – as a vampire is supposed to take over the living – becomes imposed upon the form of the author.

A contemporary reader of *Let Me Alone* feels a shock when the irreconcilable Matthew and Anna are introduced at an up-country club in Burma as 'Mr and Mrs Kavan'. The very words seem ill-assorted. But *Let Me Alone* was first published in 1930, and the author's name on the title page given as Helen Ferguson, her married name.

Helen Ferguson evidently felt that she had defined herself in the character of Anna, who so courts yet fears isolation. Shortly there- after, her own marriage failing, she encountered the writings of Franz Kafka, and changed her name by deed poll to that of the character she had invented, Anna Kavan. Art inundated nature.

This change of name, so full of masochism and pride, followed a period in a mental hospital, the period brilliantly defined in 'My Madness'. It represented a transformation, the crossing of a frontier away from the real. Anna Kavan had converted herself, as writers sometimes do, but rarely so deliberately. From now on, the realm of fantasy commanded her, and she it.

The discontinuity of personality is reflected in the discontinuities of Kavan's prose. The prose is always lucid, without Latinate constructions, without long words or literary allusions; the complexity lies in what is omitted. Often the discontinuities are nothing short of terrifying, as for instance in some of the stories in the collection *Julia and the Bazooka*, made soon after Kavan's death. That is to say, they may terrify the reader, although to the 'I' character they are merely the stuff of life. Living somewhere on an unnamed continent, you may find friends turn into tigers.

Much of the strength of the laconically entitled story, 'A Visit', in that same collection, derives from the proffered discontinuity of its opening sentence: 'One hot night a leopard came into my room and lay down on the bed beside me'. We are at once in the unknown territory of the Douanier Rousseau, where communication between human and animal happens as punctually as the full moon.

'A Visit' is included in this section to dispel the notion that Anna Kavan's writings are merely depressing. Such is not the case; and the luminosity of even the dark pieces gives light enough. In her sudden transitions of mood and feeling we see the kinship with Kafka, and perhaps even something of that concealed humour which was Charles Dickens's gift to Kafka.

Many people are surprised to learn that when Kafka first read extracts from *The Trial* to Max Brod and their circle of friends, he could sometimes hardly continue for laughter. Similarly, Chekhov was first played outside his own country for tragedy, not comedy. Kavan's reputation is at present for gloom, madness and paranoia. Not undeservedly. Yet the whisper of mocking laughter is often to be heard, even in the sibylline *Sleep Has His House*.

Kavan in person, too, did not always project her shadowed side. In conversation with her English publisher, Peter Owen – it's to be doubted if there would be an Anna Kavan without a Peter Owen – I said something of this kind, having enjoyed her friendly company. Owen agreed. It took a while to see through the camouflage of normality; or perhaps, human nature being so diverse, one should rather say that the camouflage of tortured romanticism concealed much that was no more or less than normal. In either event, Anna was of smart, cheerful appearance. She enjoyed male company.

Neither in her appearance nor her behaviour did she reveal her incurable heroin addiction. As Peter Owen admits, it was a while before the fact of that addiction dawned on him.

When I met her, towards the end of her life, I too knew nothing of the heroin. By then, she had been on the habit for some thirty years. Heroin was her accomplice, her truce with reality. I saw only another dedication: to literature, and to that I responded.

Raymond Marriott, another long-term friend of Anna's, emphasizes her worldly, everyday side, reminding us that she was a good gardener, an excellent painter, and a skilled designer of small houses.

Anna was friendly and welcoming, in the small house of her own design in Hillgate Street, in the Kensington district of London. I had selected *Ice* as the best science fiction novel of 1967, less from any firm conviction that it was science fiction, or from a desire to dismay rivals, than to draw attention to a splendid piece of writing which might have been overlooked in the face of more noisy claimants for public attention. We talked in the ordinary way of two strangers waiting to get to know each other, and I gave her a novel of mine which, I felt, also operated in the same regions of otherness as *Ice*.

Anna had some complaint about Cyril Connolly, the editor of *Horizon* for whom she had worked in the war years. He could have been more supportive of her with regard to her own writing, she felt. It was the sort of remark anyone might make. She longed to have a reputation, and thought that perhaps my attention marked a new start; she liked the idea of being regarded as a science fiction writer. It sounded modern. One sees in her work the sort of modernism – love of cars and speed and so on, not to mention the 'fast set' – which surfaces in Aldous Huxley's novels.

Little financial reward had followed from the publication of her novels and stories. She was reduced to selling some paintings (of which the house seemed still full), including a Graham Sutherland she had liked; and there was the tiresome business of designing houses or their interiors for other people.

No doubt her eye for design was sharp. She showed me over her house, walking with a stick. I supposed her to be in her late sixties. Her home was cunning and discreet, garden and house interlocked. It would have been no great matter for a leopard to enter her bedroom. Exotic plants grew everywhere, indoors and out, and mirrors basked mistily among paintings. A pleasant place in which to exist, with a flavour of the admired Henri Rousseau about it.

I offered to do something about American publication for *Ice*, since she had no agent. I sent a copy of the novel to Lawrence P. Ashmead, then my publisher at Doubleday. Larry was – is – a fine and understanding editor, but it took him some while to work through the Doubleday machine.

Finally, he sent me a letter saying that Doubleday accepted *Ice*. Anna had just died. She died of heart disease on 6 December 1968; I read of her death in the obituary columns of *The Times*. It was not suicide. Only a week earlier, I had received a letter from her which concluded with the words, 'Sorry this is such a disjointed note. I really don't feel human at present.' The ice was closing in fast.

Doubleday's hardcover edition was followed in the States by a funny little Popular Library (New York) paperback edition, which proclaimed on its cover, 'Sci-Fi at its Best'. Of course, *Ice* is not sci-fi, and only marginally science fiction, existing as it does in that fertile area – increasingly fertile as the century diminishes – where unreality prevails and life strategies are not those of the false everyday world we have constructed between ourselves and what Kavan calls 'no-times'.

'Reality had always been something of an unknown quality to me,' she says at the start of *Ice*.

If one plays the game of categories, then Anna Kavan ranks as a symbolist, one of the few English symbolists. It is a rare breed, which is perhaps why she has found no protagonist to speak up for her. A slightly coterie publisher published and nourished her. She formed no alliances with other authors. Her name does not appear in *The Oxford Companion to English Literature*. Symbolism is not a part of the solid English mainstream of writing. We prefer our fictional protagonists to turn into successes or failures rather than leopards.

The characters in *Ice* are designedly symbolic and nameless. The girl, the hero, the warden. The countries through which they travel are anonymous. Their decisions are makeshift, their actions almost random, their circumstances as arbitrary as the advance of the ice. Their world is ramshackle, and under sentence of death. In such a situation, war attains a positive value: 'By making war we asserted the fact that we were alive and opposed the icy death creeping over the globe.'

The maddened military activity, the nameless nations, everything contributes to a sense of doom. Yet all is lively, mobile, even joyous after a fashion, since catastrophe for such affectless people is just a way of life. The response to catastrophe can only be indifference. 'Once prominent states had simply dropped out of existence.' States of mind also.

This vertiginous sense is counterpointed by the business of personal disintegration. 'Something in her demanded victimization and terror, so she corrupted my dreams, led me into dark places I had no wish to explore. It was no longer clear to me which of us was the victim. Perhaps we were victims of one another.'

Ice lures us to the heart of Kavan's writing, and to the peak of her achievement, where personal concerns become universalized.

That relationship with Kafka. What are we to make of it? 'Helen Ferguson's' instinct to ally herself with the Czech writer was a true one. Kafka is clearly her literary and spiritual mentor. Both were self-torturers, both aspired to dissolve themselves into literature. 'I have no literary interests, but am made of literature,' said Kafka. Their own personalities, deprived of self-respect through nature or more probably nurture (overweening fathers and mothers), sought an established basis in a projected writing self; the writing self became what could be cherished.

In comparison with Kafka, Kavan is a watercolourist. Yet direct comparison is unfair; Kafka remains one of the great dark beacons of twentieth-century literature. She still offers her original torments, and we do not forget that she was a painter as well as a writer, her canvases also offering wry comment on her state of mind. Headless creatures hug one another, becoming one body. One head out-Januses Janus, its three faces perhaps girl, hero, warden, the watcher. And there was also the life of the drug addict, that decades-long communion with otherness. By the end, Kavan had created herself even more decidedly than her literary mentor. Hers is the honourable position of Kafka's sister.

Anna Kavan is at present that uncomfortable thing awaiting final judgement, a cult figure. Her situation is as ambiguous as she could desire.

Indications are that her reputation may belatedly spread further. At the University of Tulsa, her newly discovered journals and diaries are being edited for publication. A biography is on its way. Kavan's friend, Rhys Davies, wrote a novelized version of her life, *The Honeysuckle Girl*, which it would be good to have reprinted.

Other novels of Kavan's have still to see the light of day. This generous selection of her writing may be regarded as a bridging loan, with 'My Madness' in particular a good down-payment on her life, work and themes.

Yet perhaps she would perversely become hostile to the world's acclaim. It would not bring back the lost hours or the lost Sutherland. In one of her stories, 'A Summer Evening', she yearns towards a final grand gesture of alienation.

'I can never go back to the living world unless I am changed completely ... If this whole structure could be transmuted into something hard, cold, untouchable, unaffected by any emotion ... then and then only, indifferent to isolation and independent of time, I might endure the world.

'... Inexhaustible and impervious, I would stride all over the world, seeing everything, knowing everything, needing nothing and nobody ... finally leaving earth and the last human being behind me and turning away to the most remote galaxies and the unimaginable reaches of infinite space.'

Brian Aldiss
Boars Hill, Oxford
August 1989

My Madness

This selection has been edited by Frank Hatherley from
Asylum Piece (1940) and *Sleep Has His House* (1948)

1938.
Anna K is at work in her small, cold, damp, dark English study.
She feels the cold.

one

It is not easy to describe my mother. Remote and starry, her sad stranger's grace did not concern the landscape of the day. Should I say that she was beautiful or that she did not love me? Have shadows beauty? Does the night love her child?

We lived in a house full of things kept brightly polished, but all the shine of the house was quenched by my mother's sadness.

It was lonely in those rooms dark with my mother's sadness and with the rain on the windows. My parents seldom had time for talking to me. No one talked to me much: but the rain often used to whisper to me.

In time I found out what it was that the rain whispered. I learnt from the rain how to work the magic, and then I stopped feeling lonely. I learnt to know the house in the night way of mice and spiders.

Hidden by curtains, sheltered in cupboards, ambushed in fox-holes between the tables and chairs, I transmuted flat daylight into my night-time magic and privately made for myself a world out of spells and whispers.

two

For a long time I have been lonely, cold and miserable. It is months since I have seen the sun. In the low-lying streets near the river where I live there is fog all through the winter. When I go to bed at night it is so cold that the pillow freezes my cheek.

Suddenly, one morning, all this becomes intolerable to me. It seems that I can no longer bear the cold, the loneliness, the eternal fog – no, not for another hour – and I decide to visit my Patrons and ask them to help me. It is a desperate resolve, but once I have made it I am filled with optimism as I put on my best dress and carefully make up my face.

At the last moment, just as I am ready to start, I remember that I ought to take a present with me. I have no money with which to buy a gift worthy of such great people: is there anything in the house that will do? In a panic I hurry from room to room, as if expecting to discover some valuable object, the existence of which I have overlooked all the time I've been living here.

Some apples on the kitchen shelf catch my eye because even in this gloomy half-light their cheeks show up yellow and red. The simple fruit may please palates which have grown too accustomed to the flavour of hot-house peaches and grapes. I hastily fetch a cloth and polish four of the yellowest apples until they shine. Then I line a small basket with fresh paper, arrange the apples inside, and set out.

Soon I am in a lift, being whirled up towards the skies. A manservant in white stockings and purple knee-breeches shows me into a magnificent room. Here one is above the fog, the sun is shining outside the windows draped in soft veils of net, or, if it is not, it makes no difference, for the room is full of artificial sunshine from the concealed lights. The floor is covered by a carpet softer than moss, there are chairs and great sofas upholstered in delicate brocade, beautiful flowers are arranged in vases some of which are shaped like shells and some like antique urns.

After the foggy gloom to which I have grown accustomed it is like being transported to summer, to paradise.

Before very long my Patron appears. He is tall and fine looking as such an important man ought to be. Everything about his appearance is perfect: his shoes gleam like chestnuts, his shirt is of finest silk, he wears a red carnation in his buttonhole and in his breast-pocket is a handkerchief bearing a monogram embroidered by holy women. He greets me with charming courtesy and we sit talking for a while on general topics. He addresses me as an equal. I begin to feel quite elated at such a promising start. Surely everything is going to turn out as I wish.

The door opens and my Patroness enters. We both rise to meet her. She is dressed in deep blue velvet, and on her hat perches a small bird as vivid and rare as a jewel. There are pearls round her neck and diamonds on her smooth hands. She speaks to me with rather stilted brightness, smiling with narrow lips that do not unclose easily.

Diffidently I offer my humble present, which is graciously accepted and then laid aside. My spirits fall somewhat. We sit down again in our cushioned seats and for a few minutes continue to maintain polite conversation. There comes a pause. I realize that the preliminaries are over and that it is time for me to state the object of my visit.

'I am freezing with cold and loneliness down there in the fog! Please be kind to me. Let me share a little of your sunshine and warmth. I won't be any trouble to you.'

My companions glance at one another. A look of the deepest significance passes between them. My Patron leans back in his chair and places the tips of his long fingers together. His cuff-links glitter, his hair shines like silk.

'We must treat this question objectively.'

His voice has a reasonable, impartial sound, and I start to feel hopeful again. But as he goes on talking I perceive that the air of consideration which has impressed me so favourably is really nothing but a part of his perfect ensemble, and no more to be relied upon than the flower in his buttonhole.

'Don't think that I am accusing you, or setting myself up as your judge, but you must admit that your conduct towards us in the past has been far from satisfactory.'

He looks again at my Patroness who nods her head. The little bird in her hat seems to wink at me with its brilliant, blind eyes.

'Yes,' says she, 'you have caused us a great deal of sorrow and anxiety by your behaviour. You have never consulted our wishes about anything but have obstinately gone your own way. It is only when you are in trouble that you come here asking us to look after you.'

I am ashamed to feel tears in my eyes. 'But you don't understand. It's a matter of life and death this time. Please don't bring the past up against me now. I'm sorry if I've offended you; but you have everything and you can afford to be generous. It can't mean very much to you. But, oh, if only you knew how I long to live in the sunshine again!'

I am plunged into despair because I see that neither of my hearers is capable of comprehending my appeal. I doubt if they are even listening to me. They do not know what fog is like; it is only a word to them. They do not know what it means to be sad and alone in a cold room where the sun never shines.

'We don't intend to be hard on you. No one will ever be able to say that we have not treated you with patience and forbearance. We will do our best to forget and forgive. But you, on your side, must promise to turn over a new leaf, to make a clean break with the past and give up your rebellious ways. You must prove yourself worthy of our generosity.'

His voice goes on, but now I am the one who is not listening. I have heard enough to fill me with hopeless disappointment. It is useless for me to attempt any further approach to people who are utterly inaccessible, utterly out of sympathy with me.

Almost at my last gasp, I come to throw myself at their mercy, and a lecture is all they can find for me in their empty hearts. Through a glaze of tears I catch sight of my yellow apples pushed into a corner behind an enormous box of liqueur chocolates.

'And where am I to find a little warmth in all this?' What an incongruous sound the words have between these serene walls and how the fastidious flowers seem to toss their heads in disdain.

I have thrown away my last chance. There is no object in waiting a moment longer, so I get up and fly from the room. And at once the lift is swooping away with me, carrying me down to the cold, foggy streets where I belong.

three

When my mother died I knew why the house had always been quiet. The house had been waiting and watching from the beginning, listening to the steps my mother danced with death.

My father never told me about what had happened. No one said anything to me about the death of my mother and I never asked anyone. It was a question which could not possibly ever be asked.

But I often wondered. At night, especially, I used to wonder.

Sometimes I got afraid in the night, wondering about death and myself and my mother, and wishing that I could ask someone. But of course I knew my mother's death was the one thing I would never be able to speak of to anyone, no matter how frightened I was. That was the last thing I would ever do.

four

Somewhere in the world I have an implacable enemy although I do not know his name. I do not know what he looks like, either. In fact, if he were to walk into the room at this moment, while I am writing, I shouldn't be any the wiser.

For a long time I believed that some instinct would warn me if we ever came face to face: but now I no longer think this is so. Perhaps he is a stranger to me; but much more probably he is someone whom I know quite well – perhaps someone I see every day. For if he is not a person in my immediate environment, how does he come to possess such detailed information about my movements?

It seems quite impossible for me to make any decision – even concerning such a trifling matter as visiting a friend for the evening – without my enemy knowing about it and taking steps to ensure my discomfiture.

The fact that I know absolutely nothing about him makes life intolerable, for I am obliged to look upon everybody with equal suspicion. There is literally not a soul whom I can trust.

Whenever I speak to anyone I catch myself scrutinizing him with secret attention, searching for some sign that would betray the traitor who is determined to ruin me.

What act of mine can possibly have given rise to such a relentless persecution? I go over and over my past life without finding any clue.

But perhaps the situation has arisen through no fault of my own but merely on account of some fortuitous circumstances that I know nothing about.

Perhaps I am the victim of some mysterious political, religious or financial machination – some vast and shadowy plot, whose ramifications are so obscure as to appear to the uninitiated to be quite outside reason, requiring, for instance, something as apparently senseless as the destruction of everybody with red hair or with a mole on his left leg.

Because of this persecution my private life is already practically in ruins. My friends and family are alienated, my creative work is at a standstill, my manner has become nervous, gloomy and irritable, I am unsure of myself, even my voice has grown hesitating and indistinct.

You would think that my enemy might take pity on me now; that, seeing the miserable plight to which he has reduced me, he would be content with his vengeance and leave me in peace.

But, no; during the last few weeks I have received almost certain indications that he is starting to lodge false accusations against me in official quarters.

The time can't be far off when I shall be taken away. It will be at night, probably, that they will come for me. There will be no revolvers, no handcuffs; everything will be quiet and orderly with two or three men in uniform, or white jackets, and one of them will carry a hypodermic syringe.

I am only telling you this so that when you do not see me any more you will know that my enemy has finally triumphed.

five

My mother's death made no difference to the house except that her outward presence had gone away. Her sadness and her boredom stayed in the quiet rooms where I lived along with shadows. As if they felt lonely, these two ghosts attached themselves to me and entered my night-time world.

Sometimes I thought they had taken me for my mother, and I felt nearer to her through their nearness. Sometimes her nearness was like a hand on my shoulder; then I felt frightened, and ran and jumped and turned somersaults even, trying to shake off her hand. But the hand always stayed on my shoulder as long as it wished to.

Sometimes, looking out of an upstairs window, I could feel my mother looking out of my eyes.

One day when I combed my hair in front of a mirror, my mother looked out at me with her face of an exiled princess.

That was the day I knew I was unhappy.

six

Yesterday I went to see my official adviser. I have visited him fairly often during the last three months in spite of the inconvenience and expense of these interviews. When one's affairs are in such a desperate state as mine, one is simply obliged to make use of any possible help; and this man – I shall call him D – has been my last hope. He has been the only source of advice and assistance available to me, the only person with whom I could discuss my affairs: in fact, the only person to whom I could speak openly about the intolerable situation in which I have been placed.

Even with D I have always been on my guard. There have been days when something seemed to warn me that he was not altogether to be trusted. But what was to become of me if I were deprived even of his support, unsatisfactory as it might be? No, I really couldn't face the future entirely alone, and so, for my own sake, I *must* not distrust him.

At our early meetings he always treated me with extreme consideration, even with deference, listening with the closest attention to everything I had to say, and in general impressing me with the grave importance of my case. It was this very attitude of his which aroused my first vague suspicions.

If he were really looking after my interests as thoroughly as he asserted, why was it necessary for him to behave in this almost propitiatory way which suggested either that he was trying to attract my attention from some possible negligence on his part, or that matters were not progressing as favourably as he affirmed?

Yet he had a knack of inspiring confidence, and with a few encouraging, convincing phrases he could dispel all my tenuous doubts and fears.

But presently another cause for suspicion pricked my uneasy mind. Ever since my introduction to D I had been aware of something dimly familiar about his face with the very black brows accentuating deep-set eyes into which I never looked long enough or directly enough to determine their colour but which I assumed to be dark brown.

Then one day, just as I was leaving his house, the complete memory which had eluded me for so long, suddenly came to me with an impact sharp as a collision with a fellow pedestrian.

As soon as I got home I started to search through the newspapers and periodicals which, in my preoccupied state of mind, I had allowed to accumulate in untidy piles. It was not long before I found what I was looking for. The face of the young assassin, gazing darkly at me from the page, was, in all essentials, the same black-browed face that had confronted me a short time previously in the curtained seclusion of his handsome room.

Why did this accidental likeness make such an impression on me, I wonder? One has only to think of D's responsible position, to look at his controlled, serene, intelligent face, to realize the fantastic nature of the comparison. The whole sequence of ideas is utterly grotesque, utterly illogical. And yet there it is; I can't banish it from my mind.

As a result, I decided to put my case in the hands of a different adviser. This was a serious step, not to be taken lightly, and I expended a great deal of time considering the subject before I finally sent off my application. In wording my letter I was particularly careful to avoid any statement that could possibly be taken as detrimental to D, merely stressing the point of how expensive and awkward it was for me to be continually undertaking the long journey to his house, and asking for my case to be transferred to someone in the university town near my home.

For several days I waited anxiously for an answer, only to receive at the end of that time a bundle of complicated forms to be filled up in duplicate. These I completed, sent off, and then waited again.

How much of my life lately has consisted of this helpless, soul-destroying suspense! The waiting goes on and on, day after day, week after week, and yet one never gets used to it.

Well, at last the reply came back on the usual stiff, pale blue paper, the very sight of which I have learned to dread. My request was refused. No explanation was given as to why a favour which had been granted to hundreds of people should be denied to me.

But of course one can't expect explanations from these officials; their conduct is always completely autocratic and incalculable. All they condescended to add to the categorical negative was the statement that I was at liberty to dispense altogether with the services of an adviser should I prefer to do so.

I was so cast down after the receipt of this arbitrary communication that for two whole weeks I remained at home, absolutely inactive. I felt utterly wretched in body as well as in mind, exhausted, listless and depressed as if after a severe fever.

At last – yesterday – I reached a point where I could no longer endure so much tension. There was only one person in the whole world to whom I could unburden my mind, only one person who might conceivably be able to relieve my suspense, and that was D who was still, when all was said, my official adviser.

On the spur of the moment I decided to go and see him again. I was in a condition in which to take action of some sort had become an urgent necessity. I put on my things and went out to catch the train.

The sun was shining, and I was astonished to see that during the period I had remained indoors, too preoccupied with my troubles even to look out of the window, the season seemed to have passed from winter to spring. From the train I saw hares playing among the fine, emerald green lines of the winter wheat: the newly ploughed earth in the valleys looked rich as velvet.

Even in the city there was a feeling of gladness, of renewed life. People walked briskly towards appointments or dawdled before the shop windows with contented faces. Some whistled or sang quietly to themselves under cover of the traffic's noise.

As I walked along, I determined to put the whole matter of the letter and its answer frankly before D, to conceal nothing from him, but to ask him what he thought lay behind this new official move.

After all, I had not done anything that should offend him; my request for a change of adviser was perfectly justifiable on practical grounds. Nor had I any real reason for distrusting him.

I reached his house and stood waiting for the door to be opened. A beggar was standing close to the area railings holding a tray of matches in front of him, a thin, youngish man of middle-class appearance, carefully shaved, and wearing a very old, neat, dark blue suit.

Of course, the whole town is full of destitute people, one sees them everywhere, but I couldn't help wishing that I had not caught sight, just at this moment, of this particular man who looked as though he might be a schoolmaster fallen on evil days. We were so close together that I expected him to beg from me; but instead of that he stood without even glancing in my direction, without even troubling to display his matches to the passers-by, an expression of complete apathy on his face that in an instant began to dissipate for me all the optimistic influence of the day.

As I went inside the door, some part of my attention remained fixed on the respectable looking beggar. The thought crossed my mind that perhaps one day I, no longer able to work, my small fortune absorbed in adviser's fees, my friends irreparably alienated, might be placed in the same situation as he.

The manservant informed me that D had been called out on urgent business but that he would be back before long. I was shown into a room and asked to wait.

After the spring-like air outside, the room felt close and oppressive. An enormous grandfather clock in the corner didactically ticked the minutes away.

Listening to that insistent ticking, a sense of abysmal futility gradually overwhelmed me. The fact of D's absence, that he should choose today of all days to keep me waiting in this dismal room, created the worst possible impression on my overwrought nerves. A feeling of despair, as if every effort I might make would inevitably be in vain, took possession of me. An apathy, similar to that displayed by the beggar outside, had come over me.

Suddenly the servant returned to say that D was at my disposal. But now I no longer wanted to see him. It was only with the greatest difficulty that I forced myself to stand up and follow the man into the room where my adviser sat at his desk.

I don't know why the sight of him sitting at his accustomed pose should have suggested to me the idea that he had not really been called out at all, but had been sitting there the whole time, keeping me waiting for some ulterior motive of his own; perhaps to produce in me just such a sensation of despair as I now experienced.

We shook hands, I sat down and began to speak, driving my sluggish tongue to frame words that seemed useless even before they were uttered. Was it my fancy that D listened less attentively than on previous occasions, fidgeting with his fountain-pen or with the papers in front of him?

I heard myself advancing the old argument of inconvenience, explaining in hesitant tones that in order to spend less than an hour with him I must be nearly six hours on the double journey. And then I heard him answer that I should no longer have cause to complain of this tedious travelling, as he was just about to start on a holiday of indefinite length and would undertake no further work until his return.

If I felt despairing before, you can imagine how this information affected me. Somehow I took leave of him, somehow found my way through the streets, somehow reached the train which carried me across the now sunless landscape.

How hard it is to sit at home with nothing to do but wait.

To wait – only to wait – the most difficult thing in the whole world. To wait – with no living soul in whom to confide one's doubts, one's fears, one's relentless hopes. To wait – not knowing whether D's words are to be construed into an official edict depriving me of all assistance, or whether he intends to take up my case again in the distant future, or whether the case is already concluded.

Sometimes I think that some secret court must have tried and condemned me, unheard, to this heavy sentence.

seven

Out of the night-time magic I built in my head a small room as a sanctuary from the day. Phantoms might be my guests there, but no human could enter. Human beings were dangerous to me, like tigers prowling at large in the daytime world. Inside my secluded room I felt safe from these tigers, though I sometimes envied them.

Sometimes a savage beauty lured me into the sun and I would start to love the danger a little. On these occasions I felt the reluctant love drained painfully from me as blood drains from a deep wound. The tigers lapped my love's blood and remained enemies.

The inhabitants of the day laughed at the gift I wanted to bring them, and I shut myself back in my inner room to escape the betrayal of their arrogant mouths.

Had my mother been afraid of the tigers? Was that the theme of the music she danced to with death in our quiet house?

eight

Already the church clock is calling the hour again in its dull country voice, half stupefied with the cold. I lie in bed, and like a well-drilled prisoner, an old-timer, I resign myself to the familiar pattern of sleeplessness. It is a routine I know only too well.

My gaoler is in the room with me, but he cannot accuse me of being rebellious or troublesome. I lie as still as if the bed were my coffin, not wishing to attract his attention. Perhaps if I don't move for a whole hour he will let me sleep.

Naturally, I cannot put on the light. If only I could see my gaoler it would not be so bad. The room is as dark as a box lined with black velvet that someone has dropped into a frozen well.

At first I fancy that he is standing like a dark curtain beside the door. The ceiling is lifted off the room and he is towering up, taller than an elm tree, up towards the icy mountains of the moon. But then it seems to me that I have made a mistake and that he is crouching on the floor quite close to me.

An iron band has been clamped round my head, and just at this moment the gaoler strikes the cold metal a ringing blow which sends needles of pain into my eye sockets. He is showing his disapproval of my enquiring thoughts; or perhaps he merely wishes to assert his authority over me. At any rate, I lie motionless, hardly daring to breathe, under the bedclothes.

To occupy my mind I begin to run through the formulae which the foreign doctor taught me. I repeat to myself that there is no such person as a *victim* of sleeplessness, that I stay awake simply because I *prefer* to continue my thoughts.

I try to imagine myself in the skin of a newborn infant, without future or past. If the gaoler looks into my mind now, he cannot raise any objection to what is going on there.

Now I am almost on the point of falling asleep. My body feels limp, my thoughts have become strands of weeds, of no special colour, slowly undulating in colourless water.

My left hand twitches, and again I am wide awake. It is the striking of the church clock that has called me back to my gaoler's presence. Did I count five strokes or four? I am too tired to be certain. In any case, the night will be over soon.

The iron band on my head has tightened and slipped down so that now it presses against my eyeballs. And yet the pain does not seem so much to come from this cruel pressure as to emanate from somewhere inside my skull: it is the brain itself which is aching.

All at once I feel desperate, outraged. Why am I alone doomed to spend nights of torment, with an unseen gaoler, when all the rest of the world sleeps peacefully? By what laws have I been tried and condemned, without my knowledge, and to such a heavy sentence, too, when I do not even know of what or by whom I have been indicted? A wild impulse comes to me to protest, to demand a hearing, to refuse to submit any longer to such injustice.

But to whom can one appeal when one does not even know where to find the judge? How can one ever hope to prove one's innocence when there is no means of knowing of what one has been accused?

No, there's no justice for people like us in the world: all that we can do is to suffer as bravely as possible and put our oppressors to shame.

nine

'The trouble with you is that you're always avoiding responsibility.'

I kept hearing D's agreeable, soft, sympathetic voice, so out of keeping with the heartless words it was speaking, and seeing his dark-browed face which always vaguely reminded me of some other face I had seen long ago, I couldn't remember quite where, perhaps in a painting or a newspaper photograph.

'This is a case where you must act on your own initiative. I'm sorry if I appear unkind, but you must believe me when I say that it will do you far more good in the long run to see this through by yourself than blindly to follow outside advice – whether mine or anyone else's . . .'

I was so hurt by D's unexpected attitude that I believe I was thinking more about him than about my own trouble as I went out into the wintry London twilight. I had given myself away and D must be despising me or laughing at me.

What was I going to *do* about the interview at which I was shortly supposed to be present? Should I go to the hotel, as I had agreed to do, to meet my husband and the young woman whom he proposed to introduce into our home? Was I capable of accepting emotionally the situation to which, in discussion, I had already given an intellectual acceptance? With what smile, with what words, should I greet this stranger, younger, more beautiful, more fortunate than I? With what unnaturally hardened gaze should I observe glances, gestures, long familiar to my heart, directed towards a new recipient?

The recurring sequence of these questions, to which I seemed fundamentally incapable of replying – to which, indeed, I did not hope or expect to find any answers – began to assume by its very monotony a quality of horror and torment impossible to describe. I began to feel that if I did not succeed in breaking out of the loathsome circle I should suddenly become mad, scream, perpetrate some shocking act of violence in the open street.

But worst of all was the knowledge that the laws of my temperament would forbid me even a relief of this kind; that I was inexorably imprisoned behind my own determination to display no emotion whatever.

I was cold and tired. I realized that I must have been walking for a long time without taking any notice of my direction. Now I saw that I was in a street which I did not know very well. Night had fallen, the lights glowed mistily through a thin haze. I looked at my watch and saw that the hour arranged for the interview had almost arrived.

No sooner had I discovered this than a change seemed to come over everything. It was as though, in some mysterious way, I had become the central point around which the night scene revolved. People walking on the pavement looked at me as they passed; some with pity, some with detached interest, some with more morbid curiosity. Some appeared to make small, concealed signs, but whether these were intended for warning or encouragement I could not be sure. The windows, lighted or unlighted, were like eyes more or less piercing, but all focused upon me. The houses, the traffic, everything in sight, seemed to be watching to see what I would do.

I turned round and began to walk quickly in the direction of the hotel. I hurried in order not to be late for my appointment, but the idea of taking a taxi for some reason never occurred to me.

In my head I could hear D's pleasant voice telling me that I must act on my own initiative. His face, with the black eyebrows that always recalled an elusive memory, floated before me, and then vanished away.

I came to the hotel entrance which was brilliantly lighted. People were going in and out of the revolving doors. I walked slower and finally stood still. Even now I half believed that I would go inside, keep the appointment, and behave creditably, too, at the interview.

But then my feet were carrying me away, and I knew, what I think the watching eyes had known all the time, that rather than face the situation I would escape anywhere, into no matter what shame, what guilt, what despair.

ten

Things at school began going wrong. I broke rules and was often in the detention room. People started saying how difficult I'd become.

'She does not concentrate ... Does not adapt ... Does not co-operate ... Does not compromise ... Not satisfactory ... unsatisfactory ... Does not ... Un ... Dis ... Does not ... Non ... Un ... Non ... No ...'

At the start I had tried to fit in. Now I'd stopped trying because I knew it was hopeless. The daylight world was my enemy, and to the authorities of this world who had rejected me I would not submit. They had insulted and damaged me and I would never surrender to them.

By the time I went to the university I had become more skilful in my dealings with day. The secret the rain had whispered to me years before, the secret of living apart from the daylight world, had now taught me to avoid conflicts without endangering my seclusion.

Working from my hidden base in the dark, I warily reconnoitred the territory of the light, and learned to describe what I found there. Stimulated by danger, I changed my anxiety into written words, words to build a bridge which might not be cut down.

eleven

There is some quite trivial, distant noise; a sound, moreover, which has nothing to do with me, to which there is not the slightest need for me to pay any attention: yet it suffices to wake me, and in no gentle way, either, but savagely, violently, shockingly, like an air-raid alarm. The clock is just striking seven. I have been asleep perhaps one hour.

Roused in this brutal fashion, I jump up just in time to catch a glimpse of the vanishing hem of sleep as, like a dark scarf maliciously snatched away, it glides over the foot of the bed and disappears in a flash under the closed door. Useless, quite futile, to dash after it in pursuit: I am awake now for good, or rather, for bad; the wheels, my masters, are already vibrating with incipient motion.

'Stop! Wait a little – it's so early – Give me a little respite! Only let me have a little more sleep – an hour – half an hour – that's all I ask.'

What's the good of appealing to senseless machinery? The cogs are moving, the engines are slowly gathering momentum, a low humming noise is perceptible even now. How well I recognize every sound, every tremor of the laborious start.

The loathsome familiarity of the routine is almost the worst part of it, intolerable and inescapable at the same time, like a sickness inside the blood. This morning it drives me to rebellion, to madness; I want to batter my head on the walls, to shatter my head with bullets, to beat the machines into pulp, into powder, along with my skull.

I hear myself calling out – to what, to whom, heaven alone knows. 'It's horribly unjust! I can't work so many hours on so little sleep. Doesn't anyone know or care that I'm dying here amongst all these levers and wheels? I can hardly open my eyes —'

Suddenly I notice that the light which hurts my eyes so much comes from the sun. Yes, the sun is actually shining outside. Instead of snow, there is dew sparkling all over the grass. Crocuses have spread their neat, low fire of symmetrical flames under the rose bushes. Winter has gone; it is spring.

In astonishment I hurry to the window and look out. What has happened, then? I feel dazed, bewildered. Is it possible that I am still living in a world where the sun shines and flowers appear in the springtime? I thought I had been exiled from all that long ago.

I rub my tired eyes; still there is sunlight, the rooks flap noisily about their nests in the old elms, and now I hear how sweetly the small birds are singing. But even as I stand there all these happy things start to recede, to become phantasmal, transparent as the texture of dream plasma, banished by the monstrous mechanical outlines of pulleys, wheels, shafts, which in their orderly, remorseless and too-well-known evolutions now with increasing insistence demand my attention.

Like a fading mirage in the background I can still, straining my eyes, faintly discern the sunlit grass, the blue, blue arches of sky across which a green shape flies in remote parabola, the ghost of an emerald dagger spectrally flung.

'Oh, stop – stop! Give me another minute – just a minute longer to see the green woodpecker!'

But my hands already, in automatic obedience, are starting to perform their detested task.

What does a machine care about green woodpeckers? The wheels revolve faster, the pistons slide smoothly in their cylinders, the noise of machinery fills the whole world. Long since cowed into slavish submission, I still draw from some inexorable source the strength to continue my hard labour although I am scarcely able to stand on my feet.

In a polished surface of metal I happen to notice my reflected face; it wears a pale, beaten, lonely look, eyes looking out at nothing with an expression of fear, frightened and lonely in a nightmare world. Something, I don't know what, makes me think of my childhood; I remember myself as a schoolchild sitting at a hard wooden desk, and then as a little girl with thick, fair, wind-tossed hair, feeding the swans in a park.

And it seems both strange and sad to me that all those childish years were spent in preparation for this – that, forgotten by everybody, with a beaten face, I should serve machinery in a place far away from the sun.

thirteen

R is one of my oldest friends. Once, long ago, we used to live in flats in the same building, and then, of course, I saw a great deal of him. Afterwards the circumstances of our lives altered, wider and wider distances divided us, we could only meet rarely and with difficulty – perhaps only once or twice in a whole year – and then only for a few hours or at the most for a weekend. In spite of this our friendship – which was purely platonic – continued unbroken.

A particularly long interval had elapsed since our last encounter, so I was delighted when we were at length able to arrange a new meeting. It was settled that we should meet in town, have dinner together, and travel by train later in the evening to the suburb where R was living.

Our appointment was for seven o'clock. I was the first to arrive at the restaurant, and, as soon as I had put my bag in the cloakroom, I went upstairs to the little bar which I often visited and where I felt quite at home.

I noticed that a waiter was helping the usual barman, and in the idle way in which one's thoughts run when one is waiting for somebody, I wondered why an assistant had been brought in that evening, for there were not many customers in the bar.

R appeared almost immediately. We greeted each other with happiness, and at once fell into a conversation which might have been broken off only the previous day.

We sat down and ordered our drinks. It was the waiter and not the barman who attended to us. As the man put down the two glasses on the table, I was struck by his ugliness. I know that one should not allow oneself to be too influenced by appearances, but there was something in this fellow's aspect by which I couldn't help feeling repelled.

The word 'troglodyte' came into my head as I looked at him. I don't know what the cave dwellers really looked like, but I feel that they ought to have been very much like this small, thick-set, colourless individual. Without being actually deformed in any way, he seemed curiously misshapen; perhaps it was just that he was badly proportioned and rather stooping.

Extraordinary as it seems, I must have been paying more attention to the waiter than to my friend, for it was not until after we had lifted our glasses that I noticed a certain slight alteration in R's appearance. He had put on a little weight since our previous meeting and looked altogether more prosperous. He was wearing a new suit too, and when I complimented him upon it, he told me that he had bought it that day out of a considerable sum of money which he had received as an advance on his latest book.

I was very glad to hear that things were going so well with him. Yet at the same time a small arrow of jealousy pierced my heart. My own affairs were in such a very bad way that it was impossible for me not to contrast my failure with his success, which seemed in some indefinable manner to render him less accessible to me, although his attitude was as friendly and charming as it had ever been.

When we had finished our drinks we went down to the restaurant for dinner. Here I was surprised, and, I must admit, rather unreasonably annoyed, to see the same waiter approaching us with the menu.

'What, are you working down here as well as upstairs?'

R must have been astonished by my disagreeable tone, for he looked sharply at me. The man answered quite politely that his work in the bar was finished for the evening and that he was now transferred to the restaurant. I would have suggested moving to a table served by a different waiter, but I felt too ashamed to do so. I was very mortified at having made such an irrational and unamiable display of feeling in front of R, who, I felt sure, must be criticizing me adversely.

It was a bad start to the meal. All on account of this confounded waiter, the evening had acquired an unfortunate tendency. Although we talked without any constraint, some essential spark, which on the other occasions had always been struck from our mutual contact, now withheld from us its warmth. It even seemed to me that the food was not as good as usual.

I was glad when the waiter brushed away the crumbs with his napkin and set the coffee before us. Now at last we should be relieved of the burden of his inauspicious proximity.

But in a few minutes he came back, and putting his repulsive face close to mine, informed me that I was wanted outside in the hall.

'But that's impossible – it must be a mistake. Nobody knows I'm here.'

He unemphatically and obstinately insisted that someone was asking for me.

R suggested that I had better go and investigate. So out I went to the hall where several people were sitting or standing about, waiting to meet their friends. The waiter led me up to a man of late middle age, neatly and inconspicuously dressed, with a nondescript, roundish face and a small grey moustache. He might have been a bank manager or some such respectable citizen. I think he was bald-headed. He bowed, and greeted me by my name.

'How do you know who I am?'

In reply, he began to reel off quite a long speech; but all so fast and in such a low voice that I could only catch a word here and there and these did not make sense. Totally unable to follow what he was saying, I only vaguely got the impression that he was asking me to accompany him somewhere. Suddenly I saw that the suitcase standing on the floor near his feet was my own.

'What are you doing with my bag? How did you get it . . .? The attendant had no right to let you take it out of the cloakroom.'

Before I could reach it he picked up the bag himself with a deprecating smile, and carried it out of the door.

I followed him, full of indignation and eager to reclaim my property. In the street, pedestrians came between us and I was unable to catch up with him until he had turned the corner into a narrow alley full of parked cars. It occurred to me that the man was out of his mind: I couldn't believe he intended to steal the suitcase; he looked far too respectable for that.

'What's the meaning of all this? Where are you taking my bag?'

I caught hold of his sleeve. We were just beside a large black limousine which stood in the rank of waiting cars.

For the first time he spoke clearly so that I could really hear what he was saying: 'Here is my authorization. It was merely out of consideration for you that I refrained from producing it inside where everyone would have seen it.'

He took a pale blue form out of his pocket and held it towards me. But in the uncertain cross light from the street lamps and the cars I only had time to make out some unintelligible legal phrases, and my own name embellished with elaborate scrolls and flourishes in the old-fashioned style, before he hastily put the stiff paper away again.

Now for the first time I observed the official coat-of-arms emblazoned on the glossy black door panel of the car, and I saw too that the windows were made of frosted glass.

I spoke quietly and in a reasonable tone to the elderly man, telling him that I was not blaming him in the least, but that a mistake had certainly been made; I was not the person mentioned on the document he had shown me which probably referred to somebody of the same name.

I picked up my suitcase and walked rapidly back to the restaurant. He did not attempt to stop me, nor, as far as I could see, was he following me, and I congratulated myself on having escaped so easily. It seemed as if boldness were what was most needed in dealing with officialdom.

R was still sitting at the table where I had left him. My spirits had now risen high, I felt cheerful, lively and full of confidence as I sat down – bringing my bag with me this time – and related the peculiar incidents that had just taken place. I told the story quite well, smiling at the absurdity of it; I really think I made it sound very amusing. But when, at the end, I looked for R's smile of appreciation, I was astonished to see that he remained grave. He did not look at me, but sat with downcast eyes, drawing an invisible pattern on the cloth with his coffee spoon.

'Well – don't you think it was funny that they should make such a mistake?'

Just at that moment I noticed the ugly waiter hovering near, almost as if he were trying to overhear our conversation, and now a feeling of dread slowly distilled itself into my veins.

'Why don't you say something? Surely it's not possible that you think that there was no mistake? That I am the person they really wanted?'

My friend put down the spoon and laid his hand on my arm. The affectionate touch, so full of sympathy and compassion, demoralized me even more than his words.

'I think, if I were you I would go and find out just what the charge is against you. After all, you will easily be able to prove your identity if there has really been a mistake. It will only create a bad impression if you refuse to go.'

Now that I have so much time on my hands in which to think over past events, I sometimes wonder whether R was right: whether I would not have done much better to keep my freedom as long as possible and even at the risk of prejudicing the final outcome of the affair. But at the time I allowed him to persuade me.

I have always had a high opinion of his judgement, and I accepted it then. I felt, too, that I should forfeit his respect if I evaded the issue. But when we went out into the hall and I saw the neat, inconspicuous man still impassively, impersonally waiting, I began to wonder, as I have wondered ever since, whether the good opinion of anybody in the whole world is worth all that I have had to suffer and must still go on suffering.

fourteen

These people could not all be tigers, surely? They smiled at me, they wanted me for a friend; how could they all be on the enemy side? I almost trusted them.

But a barrier always stood between us, preventing friendship. I didn't know what this barrier was, though sometimes I thought it was my mother's shadow that divided me from everything that went on in sunshine.

Later I was thankful the barrier had not fallen. I found out that people were not what they appeared; they were different from myself although they spoke a similar language. They were traitors who had betrayed their dark and magical origin for a cheap citizenship of the day.

When I discovered this my confidence vanished. I felt afraid and ashamed. It was a terrible disappointment, a dreadful humiliation. When I saw how nearly I had been tricked into an alliance with traitors, I resolved to hide myself away in my secret room where no treacherous sight or sound could deceive me again.

Now from this dark and solitary place where I belong I will not stir again.

When voices call to me I refuse to answer, I stop my ears with the black robe of night and pull the folds of darkness about my head.

And in the night my mother comes to meet me, strange, solitary, splendid with countless stars, my mother Night.

Mine, lovely, mine. My home.

Who Has
Desired the Sea

The late autumn sun came into the ward about two in the afternoon. There wasn't much strength in the sun which was slow in creeping round the edge of the blackout curtains so that it took a long time to reach the bed by the window.

He lay on the bed fully dressed and watched the sun clamber feebly from one empty bed to another all down the ward, rasping the folded dark army blankets with bristles of light. When it had investigated each iron bedstead the sun slipped down and stretched itself on the floor. The floor was polished and shiny, but where the sun lay a film of dust was revealed. Bars of shadow crossed the pale sun on the floor because of the paper strips pasted over the window. He noticed, as he had noticed on previous afternoons, how the horizontal lines looked like the shadows of prison bars. The association was vaguely unpleasant, and a vague uneasiness disturbed his preoccupation. There was no sense in the paper, anyhow, he thought. It wouldn't prevent the glass splintering if a bomb dropped anywhere near.

He turned his head to the window and the uneasiness disappeared. On the window itself the paper strips were translucent and honey coloured and no longer suggestive of prison bars.

Outside the window he could see the park with trees and grass and a drive curving through. There was a white board shaped like an arrow at the edge of the drive, pointing to the hospital with the words Neurosis Centre painted on it. The tall trees were practically leafless and their black branches swayed gravely and delicately in the wind. The short grass underneath was patched with tarnished brown-gold by the fallen leaves. In summer it would be an agreeable English scene; but now the dying autumnal leaves and the sea wind gave it some desolation.

The man on the bed knew that he ought to be with the other patients, many of whom were walking about outside, their bright hospital trouser-legs showing under their khaki greatcoats. He ought to get up and put on his own overcoat which hung neatly on the hook by his bed, folded in the regulation way with the buttons fastened. He knew this was what he should do. But the knowledge had no relevance. It did not seem to apply directly to him. Something like glass came in between, dividing him from it. He lay quietly looking out of the window.

It was pass day, the day visitors were allowed, and some of the soldiers out there had civilians with them, friends and relatives with whom they were going out for the afternoon. Some couples walked arm-in-arm, and there were a few family groups with children scuffing their feet through the fallen leaves. Most of those who had no visitors stepped out briskly towards the road leading to the shops and the cinema. Only here and there an isolated patient walked slowly, with bent head, looking down on the ground, or wandered aimlessly on the grass as if he did not notice where he was going.

Before the eyes of the man in the ward the scattered figures outside moved in a pattern as remotely impersonal as that of the weaving branches or the seagulls circling against the sky.

He saw these things with his blue, away-looking eyes, but he was not attending to them. He was looking for something, or rather someone, quite different: he was looking for a young man with thick brown awkward hair and a small scar on his cheek. For a long time he had been looking for this young man. It was absolutely necessary that he should find him. The man on the bed did not know how it was that he, whose life had become a lonely uncertainty, was so certain of this one thing. He did not at all understand it, but he did not question it either. He only knew with complete conviction that it was essential to him that this man be found. Then, and not till then, he himself would be able to get outside the glass.

The sun was crawling weakly across the ward. The man stretched out and held his hand in the sun. He saw the sunshine on the back of his brown strong-fingered hand and felt the faint warmth. He felt the sunshine and saw it, but it was beyond the glass, it was not touching him really. After a moment he put his hand down again on the blanket beside him. He did not feel disappointed or troubled about the glass. He was used to it. It was queer how you got used to things, even to living inside a glass cell.

A picture of a clock drifted in front of him. It was an electric clock that had belonged to one of his aunts, it was made of brass with all its works showing, a skeleton of a clock inside a glass dome, and it never required winding. When he was a small boy there had seemed to him to be something horrific and fascinating and pathetic about the sight of the pendulum frantically swinging, swinging, swinging, perpetually exposed and driven in that transparent tomb.

A gust of wind rattled the window and blew the clock thousands of miles and days back to its mantelpiece. The man on the bed listened for the sound of waves in the wind. Although the sea was a good distance off it was possible sometimes to hear the waves break on the rocky shore. Now, as on every occasion when he was aware of the sea, a vague disquietude, restlessness, creased his forehead in anxious lines.

Now he was not able to attend to his watching, was the fear behind the anxiety. Now if the young man came near he might not be aware. The sea-sound was a distraction, interrupting his vigil.

The wind died down again and the noise of the waves was no longer distinguishable. With the patients all out on passes the hospital seemed unnaturally still. The murmurous confusion of steps and voices, the opening and closing doors which normally went unnoticed became in absence obtrusive.

Without moving his body the man turned his head from the window and looked down the empty ward. The sun had now reached the wainscot and was starting to pull itself up the wall. Soon it would catch his greatcoat and mount above it and move on up to the ceiling. Then it would go altogether and leave the ward to the strengthening shadows. But before that happened he himself would be gone. There was something which had to be done. Something immensely difficult that had to be done by him while the afternoon sun still shone. It was something he would not be able to do. It was too difficult. It was impossible. But it was required of him. He would be obliged to attempt this impossible thing. He would not be allowed to evade the foredoomed attempt. They would come to the ward and fetch him away to make it.

So for these last few minutes he must wait with his whole attention for the young man with the thick untidy hair and the little scar. So he must hope that his twelfth-hour arrival would make everything plausible. Since the sea was quiet he had no more anxiety, and with the anxiety and the restlessness gone all that he felt was a great preoccupation and longing that the young man should appear. From the effort he would soon have to make he was now dissociated. For a moment it had seemed urgent; but now the glass shut it off. It was strange how dim and unurgent the glass made it.

If only he would come now, the man thought. He was looking along the length of the ward, and watching the door. He always felt that the young man with the scar was more likely to come when there was no one about. Maybe he had something private to say, and that was why he would come when things were quiet. Well, the place was deserted enough now.

But then, inside the glass, the pendulum began madly swinging, swinging, making him feel confused. Pictures and confusion crowded inside the glass.

Now in the distance he saw the beach at Mairangi and the young man was standing there very tanned in his bathing slips and that was the small scar on his cheek that he had got from the oyster shell on the rock swimming under water when he was eight years old. That was one of the things he was seeing, with, in the background, Cape Promise and all the islands, the Sugar Loaf and The Noises, the little ones where the penguins went, and the one which was an extinct volcano. It was the strong southern sun that made the wattle burn like a yellow fire all along the creek. In Mairangi at Christmas time the sun was so strong it hurt your eyes for the first few seconds when you came out of the bach in the morning and ran down the beach to swim. That was the place where they dragged the boat over the warm sand, shells sharply warm on the foot soles, and where they had those great fishing trips out to the Barrier, the water as smooth and solid to look at as kauri gum and as blue as sapphires, and he remembered the clean splashless opening of the water as you dived into it like a knife.

But then the water was piled-up and ugly, another colour, another ocean, and that was another thing in the sky he was seeing and Shorty asking him if it were an FW and he looking up at it over the gun and saying, No, that's one of the escort planes. We're not in the range of the FWs yet. And Shorty repeating to the boys on the gun, No, it's one of ours. We're not in the range yet, and the others all saying, Must be one of the escorts. But it was a Focke-Wulf all right swooping over the evil water and it delivered them to it when the tanker's deck twisted, splintered and pulped and exploded in flame, and he remembered how the black water towered up and then the thousand-ton icy weight of it smashing down on them like a whale, the freezing, murderous bastard.

And now suddenly there was nothing but the skeleton in the transparent cell, brass midriff and spine, wheels and frangible springs, the hollow man, bloodless, heartless, headless; only the crazy pendulum swinging in place of head.

'Why are you up here? Don't you feel well?' the nurse said, coming into the ward.

'I'm all right,' he said. He looked at her and was glad because it was this nurse who had come for him, the pretty fair one, who would not make a fuss or ask too many questions.

'You haven't forgotten you've got a visitor, have you?' she said. 'You surely haven't forgotten about your fiancée coming? She's downstairs now and you ought to have been there to meet her. Did you forget today was visiting day?'

So he thought, here it is: it's come now, the time when I have to do the impossible thing. And for a second he felt sick inside, but that passed, and he was behind the glass and feeling nothing at all.

'No, I hadn't forgotten,' he said.

He swung his legs off the bed and stood up tall and lean, and unhooked his coat while the nurse straightened the pillow and then came with him down the ward and waited while he held his comb under the tap at the wash-basin and tugged at the unmanageable brown hair that never would lie flat whatever he did to it with water or brilliantine.

He saw the nurse watching, and said, 'This is a kind of experiment, isn't it? To see how I get on with Nora, I mean.'

'Doctor thinks it will do you good to see her,' she said. 'That's why he told her she could come down from London today. It's not going to be very easy for her, you know. She's been awfully worried about you. It's up to you to show her that you're going to be quite all right.'

'Yes,' he answered, out of the glass.

They were downstairs now at the door of the waiting-room. The nurse opened the door and stepped back and he went into the room which was empty except for the girl standing close to the window; quick-smiling face and tapping heels, he watched her come quickly towards him now. Again he felt hollow sick because of the hopeless attempt, the effort which had to be made, thinking inside himself, Do I have to do this? Is it absolutely necessary to try this impossible thing? But then it passed, he felt her breath and her light kiss on his cheek, it was over, he was in his glass cell and it seemed quiet there and he felt nothing at all.

'It's a lovely afternoon,' the girl said presently. 'Shall we go for a walk?'

'All right.'

She was nervous, not knowing how to begin knowing him again, and, remembering his loose colonial stride and how he liked being out in the open places, she walked with him away from the town and the cinema where she would have felt at home.

She's a sweet girl really, he thought with a vague pang that was gone almost before he felt it at all. It was not her fault that he could not even feel sorry because she had come to him when he was no longer there. She was not in the least to blame. How could she know that he was a hollow thing; only wheels and a pendulum working inside a case? Because he had not found the young man with the scarred cheek he could not come to her through the glass.

She was talking to him as they walked in the thin sunshine beyond the hospital grounds. The sun was getting very low and the seagulls were flying low over the downs where they walked. He looked at her face between him and the sky. She was walking with her head turned to him and the sinking sun shone on her pleasantly powdered face and he could see that she was trying hard to make contact with him. He heard the sea make a noise just over the rise of the hill.

'No further,' he said, standing still. 'I don't want to go on any further.'

She looked at him with surprise and said, 'Don't you want to look at the sea? Let's just walk up to the top where we can see it now that we're here. It's quite close now.'

He felt the bad feeling come on him again, but this time there was no sickness, only a sudden sinking and emptiness, as when a small ship lurches and rolls suddenly, so that he waited for the crash and slither of loose objects falling: but there was only the wind and the gulls and the waves breaking below the edge of the hill. It passed, and he started to walk on again up the slope, because it did not matter really. Nothing mattered, he thought, because nothing could reach him while he was inside the glass.

'All right,' he said. 'Let's go and look at the sea.'

And really when he saw it it did not matter: it was quite easy to look at the agitated empty pale sea that was faintly touched with lilac feathers under the sunset sky. Except that he would rather not have seen the breaking waves on the rocks at the foot of the cliff. It was quite a high cliff to which the track had led them over the downs. The girl was looking out to sea and smiling with the wind blowing back the short bits of hair round her face.

'It's fine up here, isn't it?' she said to him.

'No,' he said, 'it's the wrong sea.'

He saw the bewilderment and distress and incomprehension come instead of the smile on her face because of what he had said; and he thought that he ought to try and explain something, but it was impossible because there was nothing but the swinging pendulum with which to explain.

And at the same time he saw on sunnier cliffs barelegged girls, perhaps his sisters, riding barebacked on ponies with rough manes flying, he saw the bleached gilt hairs on the brown girls' legs and heard girls' high voices calling and laughing often.

'You've always been mad on the sea,' a girl's voice was saying.

Yes, the sea was the one thing he had always been crazy about. But what had become of those other oceans? What had become of the sapphire blue deep water, the quick, clear small waves on the beaches, the purple submerged peninsulas of the reefs? Now he remembered the steady smooth rush of the sailing boat through blue sunlit water and the satisfactory slap of water on the sides of the boat. He remembered the huge seas marching past the tanker, huge and heavy and whale coloured, marching in manic persistence, the staggering deck, the water bursting endlessly over the catwalk. And for a second he remembered the time on the gun when they brought the plane down at sunrise, and for a second he was that young gunner triumphant and in his glory, the sea lunging pink-stained into oblivion past the gun sights. Then he remembered the horror that came later, the freezing, strangling, devilish masses of water, the horror of blazing oil on the water and Shorty screaming out of the flaming water. Then the cold blankness settled again and he could not remember whether he had known these things or what had become of them.

Now it was this town girl he had met on leave in the city to whom he had to attend. She was a good-looking girl; and perhaps before the glass closed round him he had felt something for her, but now there was just this impossible thing, this effort he could not make. He knew he ought to explain something. She was trying to be sweet and kind to him. But he knew he could never do the impossible thing. And just then it occurred to him that he was shaking under his khaki coat.

'What is it, Lennie?' she asked him.

'Nothing,' he said. 'It's cold standing around. Let's walk into town and get tea there. Let's get away from the sea.'

'Don't you like the sea any more?' she asked. She was looking at him walking away from the cliff, and biting her lip.

'No,' said the man. 'I don't think so. I think I hate it.'

But then, feeling the hollow, vague coldness inside the glass, and going away from the sea, there was nothing at all left and nothing mattered at all.

'I don't feel anything about it,' he said. 'I don't feel anything about anything.'

On the way to the town she took his arm and they walked like that for a bit while he thought of the effort which he was required to make. He had known all the time he would not be able to make it. He knew that he had to do this tremendous thing and he wanted to do it and it was his duty to do it; but he knew that it was impossible, that he would never make the attempt now, and soon she unlinked her arm and began telling him about a picture with Spencer Tracy.

In the tea place where they sat down together it was half dark already and lamps were lighted. Drinking strong tea, with no anxiety left except the ache of the unmade and abandoned effort, the girl pouring the tea, the warmth of it spreading through him, he could feel the beginning of comfort after the dusk and the sea wind. While the waitress fastened the blackout they drank and just as the blackout was fixed and it was impossible to see out any longer, something thundered outside with a noise like a heavy sea and the man started and slopped his tea in the saucer.

'The buses stop just outside here,' the girl said. 'It's the market place and they all stop here.'

'What a filthy row,' he said, feeling the evil sickness on him again, knowing that he was shaking again under his coat. So this was how he lived now, getting jittery because a bus pulled up near. Well, he was not going on like that. It was not good enough. The one person who could help him had not appeared. He probably never would. But there must be some other way. He knew that there was another way although for the moment he couldn't think what it was. Soon it would come back to him, in a minute he would remember the way out, the way where he was going.

'Are you feeling all right?' the girl said. She had put her arms on the table and was leaning towards him.

'Of course.'

'Why don't you eat your cake?'

'I'm going to.'

The cake was too dry. He had to hold it in his mouth after he'd chewed it and then by taking a gulp of tea he was just able to wash it down without retching.

He put the cup carefully back on the saucer so that it didn't rattle. The girl touched his hand with her fingers.

'Don't you like me any more either?' she said.

'I can't explain,' he said. 'I can't help it.'

The sickness had come up in his throat now and his lungs, and he could feel it strangling him and he was drowning again in the four-mile-deep icy horror of sickness or water. He looked at the girl and saw that she was crying.

'It's no good. I can't do it,' he said.

Then he pushed back his chair and stood up quickly because, just then, he saw the young man's face in a mirror up on the wall, he saw the thick wind-ruffled hair and the little scar on the cheekbone. The face moved in the mirror and when he looked round he could not see it anywhere in the room, and when he wanted to call out the sickness choked him, and now he tried to fight off the icy sickness, but like whales the waves of it fell on him till he was pounded and drowned, and while he froze suffocating and could not move or breathe, he heard the girl say, 'Where are you going?' and then he was able to move suddenly, and he got out of the tea-room.

It was evening and too dark to distinguish faces when he was in the street.

I wouldn't recognize him even if I knew which way he had gone, the man thought, hurrying along the dark streets, looking at the strange people he passed in the dark, who passed without looking at him. Once a bus went roaring by with a smell of burnt oil and he felt the sickness coming at him again but he fought it back and walked faster and it was all right and he was only a hollow man walking in the darkness without objective. Once a stranger asked him where he was going, but he went on without stopping to think that he did not know the answer. And once somewhere far off in the dark something hurt for a second because of the girl left alone and crying: but that was over immediately.

Then he was out of the town and the moon was up but behind cloud and it was less dark, and then he was walking on grass and he could see the heavy black swelling shapes of the downs, and the clouds sculptured in towers and bastions and battlemented with the light of the climbing moon. Then there was first the smell and then the sound of the sea. Then there were cliffs and the cold tumultuous restless water beneath.

Then instead of hurrying he was standing still, he was very tired now and sweating under the heavy coat, and looking up he saw a white shining fan, spreading over the sky, like light from a door slowly opening, and he knew the moon was coming out of the clouds. Then he looked over the sea and there were islands it seemed, and then a great migration of birds thickened the air and he was in a rushing of wings, the wings beat so dark and fast round him he felt dizzy like falling and the moon disappeared. And then it was clear again, brilliant moonlight, and there, ahead, bright as day, were all the small islands, Cape Promise, and the bay of Mairangi, wide, still, unbelievably peaceful under the full moon. And then he did know where he was going.

The Birds
Dancing

It was late and quite dark when I got to the place, too tired to care about anything after the long journey; though I was favourably impressed by the comfort of the hotel, and the manageress seemed particularly attentive.

But in the morning I was definitely disappointed. Of course, it was still only early spring, but this dull grey day held out no promise of future sunshine, and, in its indeterminateness – neither warm nor cold, belonging to no special season – was more depressing than the winter I had left at home. And the town was also a disappointment, much larger than I'd been led to expect, and devoid of interest.

Instead of the small place I had been imagining, surrounded by open country, with plenty of pleasant walks through the fields and woods, I found endless streets of ugly houses, all exactly alike, covering such a wide area that the country seemed quite out of reach. Far away at the ends of some of the roads, I could just make out the faint line of distant hills, with the still leafless woods clinging to them like purplish shadows. But, when I asked about the transport to get me there, I was told it did not exist. And this, incredible as it seemed, turned out to be the actual truth.

Trains and buses, I was told, stopped only at the large towns.

I asked the manageress to arrange for a car to take me to some suitable starting point for my country walk. But, to my astonishment, her manner now changed completely, she was like another and far less amiable woman, hostile, obstructive and disapproving. Country walks, she curtly informed me, were out of the question, all pasture and woodland being private property, and trespassing severely punished. She went on to ask reprovingly why I was not satisfied, like everyone else, with the town; its cinemas, theatre and museums – if I wanted exercise, why couldn't I, like other people, walk by the lake? Then she stalked off, positively radiating displeasure, giving me no time to answer. She refused ever to discuss the subject after this, keeping out of my way as much as she could, and, when she had to speak to me, adopting a cold distant tone, as if I had mortally offended her. And, as the rest of the staff imitated her attitude, I found myself practically ostracized, my predilection for the country evidently regarded by everyone as something abnormal and reprehensible.

Of course, the sensible thing would have been to move on somewhere else, and this I fully intended to do. But such unanimous opposition aroused some contrariness in me, and I wanted to get my own way first. I *would* reach the country somehow – on foot, since none of the drivers (intimidated or bribed, I supposed by the manageress) would take me there. But, though I walked steadily for several hours each day, I never seemed to get any nearer to those faraway hills – I was amazed by the length of the dull streets, which seemed literally to have no end.

Instead of becoming discouraged, however, my resolve developed into a fixation. I am not naturally obstinate; I think I would have soon given up, if I hadn't been continually irritated by the grim censorious faces of the hotel people, whose stubborn disapproval seemed to breed stubbornness in me. In more congenial circumstances, I should not have been affected by their antagonism. But marooned here, in this uninteresting town where I knew nobody, I couldn't help reacting to the perpetual silent hostility of those around me. Not that I minded being left to my own devices; I have never been gregarious, and, fortunately, I had plenty to read.

But I soon began to get bored with my unrewarding routine of plodding along dull roads day after day, towards the hills that seemed to recede as I advanced. And, though I forced myself to keep it up for a while, a morning came when the whole thing got on my nerves to such an extent that I felt I should scream if I were to pass those endless rows of dull little houses again. Impelled by a sudden impulse, I started walking the opposite way, relieved to have turned my back on the scene of my futile daily pilgrimages.

So far, I had not explored the lake, or even seen it, partly because the manageress had told me I ought to walk there, partly because I had devoted all my energies to reaching the country; and I now found myself on the way to it with no very high expectations. I'd been so consistently disappointed in everything here (including the weather, which had remained always overcast ever since my arrival, so that I'd almost ceased to hope for a sunny day) that I thought it would probably prove to be a mere pond, as unimpressive and uninteresting as the town.

Anticipating – in view of my previous experiences – a long walk before I got there, I was amazed to reach the lake in a few minutes.

Though the shallow basin in which it lay might have been hundreds of miles away from the hotel, completely hidden from the town-side by a thick wide belt of evergreens: tall firs, cypresses, cedars, and pines, entwined closely with a thicket of lower trees and bushes, so interwoven as to form an impenetrable screen; a dense lofty rampart, which followed the curves of the shoreline, towering above the water in a gloomy unbroken wall, as far as the eye could reach. In addition to this barrier of dark leaves, the fall of the land helped to seclude the sunken lake, which was at a considerably lower level than the town, and to exclude any street noises.

In spite of the manageress's remark, the place did not appear to be very popular, for it was completely deserted, and, in any case, inaccessible to traffic, only a footpath skirting the forest of last year's canes, sere and brown, that stood, with a few tattered withered leaves clinging to them, in the shallows. The total effect could not be called unimpressive; but it was distinctly sad. The melancholy aspect of black trees and forsaken water was increased by the curious flat level light, which cast no shadows and seemed to dissolve all colours; the tremendous grey arch of the sky, devoid of tonal gradations, mirrored itself exactly in the glassy expanse of the lake, into which it merged, with no trace of horizon line, the other shore being hidden behind the low clouds.

What struck me most forcibly in the scene was the absence of life; not a single living thing – not a fly, not an insect between the stones – moved in all this monochrome vista, upon which the very light seemed to fall dead. Several minutes passed before I realized that animation of a kind *was* present, though in a suspended state, in the form of some distant shapes, which because they were so far out, I had taken to be of vegetable origin, only now identifying them as aquatic birds, compactly curled up, floating on the still water, presumably fast asleep. Though I walked on hoping to see them better, I was prevented from doing so by the densely packed canes, which for some time also concealed from me the other more active life form down there on the mud.

I thought the swarms of drab little creatures were field-mice until I saw their wings; which seemed vestigial and almost useless, for, when I clapped my hands, most of them ran about frantically on their thin twinkling legs, with tiny squeaking twitters of agitation, only a few attempting a broken sort of flutter. But I never really observed them with any care, as I had a slight horror of them, for some reason; they were altogether too numerous and too fragile-looking for my liking.

On my return from this expedition, I had just entered the hotel, when the manageress abruptly confronted me, and asked what I thought of the lake. It was such a surprise to be addressed spontaneously, and even quite affably, by her, that I was too taken aback to wonder how she knew where I'd been. I believe I made some conventional response about the lake's melancholy romantic charm, which was meant as a compliment, though she seemed to take it quite differently.

'Melancholy!' she repeated scathingly: 'Just wait till you see it with all the birds dancing,' immediately walking off as before, in an aura of haughty disdain, giving me no chance, either then, or later on in the dining-room, to ask what she meant by the dancing birds.

However, the incident was not without its effect. Precisely as if a spell had been broken by her speaking to me, I seemed to come back to my senses, suddenly deciding to leave the very next day. Now I couldn't imagine why I had stayed so long. What on earth was I doing here in this dismal town where I had no friends and nothing to do? All at once I was so impatient to get away that, in the morning, I started packing before breakfast, determined to catch the first train – only to hear that there wasn't one until mid-afternoon.

Having already practically finished packing, and faced with this unwelcome interval that had to be filled somehow, I went out, far too restless to stay indoors, and again took the road to the lake. The manageress's words must have left some lingering curiosity at the back of my mind, for I approached the water thinking how impossible it was to associate dancing, or any other form of activity, with those strange somnolent birds. Surely there were more of them than there had been yesterday? And I noticed that many were now in pairs, as if some current had wafted them together while they slept. Yes, I could see now that there were certainly many more on the lake, not only far out, but quite close to the shore.

I strolled down to the edge of the mud, to inspect the queer floating shapes, which, in their neat compact glossiness, resembled so many round satin cushions scattered upon the water. As I watched, one of them startled me considerably by uncurling (though without really waking up), stretching out a long snake-like neck, rearing up, and clapping its wide wings once or twice with a loud indescribable sound. Then it resumed its former position, immediately becoming exactly the same as all the others, so that I could not be sure which had moved; it seemed incredible that any one of them should really have come to life, but I couldn't doubt it, with that weird clapping still echoing in my ears.

Today, there seemed to be something peculiarly depressing about the mournful grey scene, and the flat neutral light, coming from everywhere and nowhere; the still air seemed to me to stagnate, like air enclosed in a box. How glad I was to be going away – I was longing to escape from this monotonous grey sky – to see sunshine and movement again. I distinctly remember this thought because it was my last – it was actually in my head, when all thought was arrested by an amazing outburst of sound, quite unlike any other on earth, and a scene still more astounding; so spectacular that, even forgetting my imminent departure, I stood blankly staring.

All over the lake, the birds were now waking, unfurling in bursts of spray, to grapple and battle with one another, or, tangling their snakenecks, to intertwine them in orgiastic coupling; at the same time beating their mighty wings, which produced this increasing volume of strident unearthly sound, in which the air itself appeared to dissolve.

The whole sky was starting to break up, its uniform greyness split into fire-edged towers, which hurtled against each other, exploding in whirling transparency, which, while the thunderous collision still shook the air, dispersed, vanishing into the vivid blue spreading in from all sides. The sun, appearing momentarily as a milky disc, sprinkled the water with countless shimmering scales; instantly they became points of fire, I was almost blinded, as sunshine blazed forth in its full potency, pouring down a resplendent flood of brilliance.

Too dazed by the speed and violence of this sensational transformation scene to perceive the approach of a new disturbance, I only became aware of it when I recognized, far back in the woods I had never managed to reach, the yelling of the great trees, through which a hurricane was now tearing. This was my only warning before a terrific blast struck me down, passing over my head in a tempest of dust and debris, flattening and smashing the reeds, and lashing the lake into a chaos of foam and spray.

By the time I had picked myself up, and rubbed the grit out of my eyes, the force of the gale had subsided into a high wind, which continued to blow steadily through a scene grown fantastic beyond belief, where all that for so long had been calm and colourless was now the exact opposite – agitated and brilliant.

I had adjusted myself so thoroughly to perpetual grey quiet, that a form of dizziness attacked me now, when I saw the formerly pale placid lake a turmoil of leaping foam-topped waves, blue-green with deep purplish shadows; and all seething, absolutely alive, with the incredible numbers of coupled birds, orgiastically dancing amid the spray, serpentine necks entwining and frenziedly undulating in their erotic transports. I think the abrupt change to universal motion and colour alone would have dazed me; even without this sensational horde of madly dancing creatures, which were constantly rocketing up, showering trails of white water, to settle again, in fresh fountains of spray, among struggling bodies and slashing bills somewhere else. The noise of their hoarse or shrill screeching cries, filling the air, completed my utter confusion. I was too stupefied to tell whether angels or more birds were descending from heaven, until the new shapes came planing on taut widespread wings, to join the collective love-dance.

Between the innumerable waterspouts everywhere bursting up, I fancied I occasionally caught sight of the opposite shore, which had hitherto remained hidden behind the clouds. But it seemed far away and unreal, I was by no means sure the solitary building these glimpses revealed existed outside my imagination; for its colossal size and outlandish architecture – monstrous windowless towers linked by threadlike laddery webs as delicate as the rigging of an old schooner – seemed to belong to the fantasia of hallucination, with all that delirious tumult intervening.

While I stood watching the participants in this watery saturnalia, that was half battlefield, writhe and flounder in their ecstatic loves, or, with savagely ripping beaks, stain the water blood-red, I gradually grew aware of being no longer alone. Looking round then, I thought, in my bewilderment, the whole population of the district must be congregating on the previously deserted waterfront. Nor was it only the size of the crowd that surprised me, but also the animation displayed by these people, whom I had always considered as a dour stolid lot – now they were laughing and calling to one another in excited jubilant tones.

How like a dream things were getting! The prodigious flood of sunshine, pouring down in such unstinted abundance, instead of illuminating, seemed to obscure things in front of my eyes, I felt I was losing sight of reality in the dazzle.

It hardly surprised me when the manageress appeared, smiling and friendly as she had been when I first arrived, and, standing beside me, said teasingly, 'Well, do you think our lake looks melancholy now?'

I was glad she didn't seem to expect an answer; for I was incapable of collecting my wits, amazed by the utterly false picture I seemed to have formed of her in my mind – how could I ever have seen her as cold and stern, or failed to see that she was a young and attractive woman? A strand of hair, escaping from her bright headscarf, kept blowing across her cheek, glinting in the sun; and I wondered if it could be this tiny disorder that gave her such a curiously abandoned look; almost a look of intoxication.

A new surge of excitement distracting my attention, I glanced at the surrounding people; and it immediately struck me that every face had something of the same almost drunken expression, as if the human beings were taking part, to some extent, in the orgy of the birds. All at once, as though really intending to join the mad dance on the water, everybody surged towards the lake, trampling into the slimy mud any unfortunate individual who fell or was knocked down in their mad stampede, as casually as they crushed underfoot the small flightless birds, great numbers of which had been stunned or killed outright when the canes crashed down on them.

All my life I have detested crowds and their behaviour, and, even in my present confusion, I was surprised at my own indifference to this disgusting scene; it only troubled me because I was afraid the manageress might leave me to join the mad rush – to prevent this, I encircled her with my arm ... immediately becoming oblivious of everything but the ardent physical attraction of her body pressed against mine.

Yet, even as I accentuated this pressure far beyond the requirements of protection, so that we could scarcely have come closer in an embrace, I felt a sort of aversion from what I was doing. It was only some primitive part of me that desired the amorous contact – this realization made me aware that I was not immune to the crowd's hysteria. But before I had time really to grasp the fact, I heard my companion's voice, strange and rapt-sounding, not speaking to me, but, as it seemed, reciting, out of a trance or dream, the words of some ritual magic, which reached me above all the commotion.

'. . . the planners travelled all over the country in search of the ideal site, finally choosing this headland, then a flourishing suburb of our town. As soon as the inhabitants heard the decision, they demolished their homes with their own hands . . .'

Unable to see the lake, since she was blocking my view, I could only guess that she was gazing at the building on the other shore. But now, with startling abruptness, she threw off her entrancement, detaching herself from me with hurried, irritable impatience, casually and almost roughly, as she might have done from a briar that had caught her dress. And, in fact, she seemed to regard me as an inanimate object, leaving me without a word or a glance, and plunging straight into the crowd.

Now, for the first time, I saw the new activity on the water: where the waves were not only teeming with the innumerable couples of frantically dancing birds, but also crowded with boats of all shapes and sizes, hastily put out with the object of snaring these crazed wild things, which seemed to have lost all sense of danger, and did not attempt to escape. A boat would hardly have pushed off before it was beached again, its heaving net bulging as with a giant Medusahead, extruding everywhere the bloodied, slimy, twisted, entangled serpents which were the necks of the captured birds, dumped out and left just as they were on the mud, in a mad, smashed, writhing, suffocating agglomeration, while the hunters set off insatiably for a fresh load.

Amidst all the uproar, dazzle and movement, I caught sight of the manageress, making for one of these boats, already launched and riding the waves, through which she was wading, indifferent to the water splashing above her waist – at the last moment, when she was almost out of her depth, helped up by those on deck, she triumphantly climbed aboard. And my last glimpse was of her face of impassioned delight, as she helped, with savage delight, to manipulate the great seine.

It is only in my memory that I see her like this, for ever since that day of the dancing birds, she has been the aloof, efficient disciplinarian I knew before, a figure so irreconcilable with the other that it is hard to believe they could be the same person.

Yet that primitive part of me, which the crowd evoked, which is responsive to mass emotion, must believe in the wild aspect of her nature, and expect her to reappear as she stood then, maenad-like, bloodstained and drenched with spray, her hair loosened and streaming out on the wind like a flag, in the dangerously rocking boat. I can think of no other reason why I continue to stay here, long after I should have been back at my work. Unless, subconsciously, I prefer this explanation, degrading as it is, to some other I won't even formulate; a possibility made plausible by my reluctance to consider the matter objectively. Most of the time I feel only a slight surprise that it should be possible to drop out of one's life so easily, by accident as it were, and without attracting any attention. By now, no doubt, my post has been filled, my flat taken over by a new tenant, my friends – but I had no intimate friends, and any acquaintance who may have noticed my protracted absence must have ceased long ago to give it a thought.

Here, summer is nearly over already. Tall green canes hide the lake's muddy shore. No reminder is left of birds stamped underfoot, or struggling and strangling to death in the bloody nets, except the survivors, apparently none the worse, cruising about, plumply complacent, above the reflected building.

Of it I know no more than I did on the day of their murderous love-dance. There are things into which it is inadvisable to inquire. So I ask no questions – they would not be answered in any case – about those who obligingly destroyed their homes so that it could be built, or about the others who have succeeded them there. Doubtless some good reason exists for making that whole shore a closed area no one may visit, from which no one may come across to the town. These matters are no business of mine. Yet sometimes I cannot help feeling uneasy, when I think of a whole community lost, displaced, as I am myself.

If a flourishing suburb can disappear, why not a country? a continent? a whole world? Perhaps one day our world will slip out of its place in the vastness of infinity as unobtrusively as I left all that was known and familiar to come here, and so lost my place in life, without meaning to do so, or even knowing it could be done, without making the slightest stir.

A Visit

One hot night a leopard came into my room and lay down on the bed beside me. I was half asleep, and did not realize at first that it was a leopard. I seemed to be dreaming the sound of some large, soft-footed creature padding quietly through the house, the doors of which were wide open because of the intense heat. It was almost too dark to see the lithe, muscular shape coming into my room, treading softly on velvet paws, coming straight to the bed without hesitation, as if perfectly familiar with its position. A light spring, then warm breath on my arm, on my neck and shoulder, as the visitor sniffed me before lying down. It was not until later, when moonlight entering through the window revealed an abstract spotted design, that I recognized the form of an unusually large, handsome leopard stretched out beside me.

His breathing was deep though almost inaudible, he seemed to be sound asleep. I watched the regular contractions and expansions of the deep chest, admired the elegant relaxed body and supple limbs, and was confirmed in my conviction that the leopard is the most beautiful of all wild animals. In this particular specimen I noticed something singularly human about the formation of the skull, which was domed rather than flattened, as is generally the case with the big cats, suggesting the possibility of superior brain development inside. While I observed him, I was all the time breathing his natural odour, a wild primeval smell of sunshine, freedom, moon and crushed leaves, combined with the cool freshness of the spotted hide, still damp with the midnight moisture of jungle plants. I found this non-human scent, surrounding him like an aura of strangeness, peculiarly attractive and stimulating.

My bed, like the walls of the house, was made of palm-leaf matting stretched over stout bamboos, smooth and cool to the touch, even in the great heat. It was not so much a bed as a room within a room, an open staging about twelve feet square, so there was ample space for the leopard as well as myself. I slept better that night than I had since the hot weather started, and he too seemed to sleep peacefully at my side. The close proximity of this powerful body of another species gave me a pleasant sensation I am at a loss to name.

When I awoke in the faint light of dawn, with the parrots screeching outside, he had already got up and left the room. Looking out, I saw him standing, statuesque, in front of the house on the small strip of ground I keep cleared between it and the jungle. I thought he was contemplating departure, but I dressed and went out, and he was still there, inspecting the fringe of the dense vegetation, in which huge heavy hornbills were noisily flopping about.

I called him and fed him with some meat I had in the house. I hoped he would speak, tell me why he had come and what he wanted of me. But though he looked at me thoughtfully with his large, lustrous eyes, seeming to understand what I said, he did not answer, but remained silent all day. I must emphasize that there was no hint of obstinacy or hostility in his silence, and I did not resent it. On the contrary, I respected him for his reserve; and, as the silence continued unbroken, I gave up expecting to hear his voice. I was glad of the pretext for using mine and went on talking to him. He always appeared to listen and understand me.

The leopard was absent during much of the day. I assumed that he went hunting for his natural food; but he usually came back at intervals, and seldom seemed to be far away. It was difficult to see him among the trees, even when he was quite close, the pattern of his protective spots blended so perfectly with the pattern of sun-spots through savage branches. Only by staring with concentrated attention could I distinguish him from his background; he would be crouching there in a deep-shaded glade, or lying extended with extraordinary grace along a limb of one of the giant kowikawas, whose branch-structure supports less robust trees, as well as count-less creepers and smaller growths. The odd thing was that, as soon as I'd seen him, he invariably turned his head as if conscious that I was watching. Once I saw him much further off, on the beach, which is only just visible from my house. He was standing darkly outlined against the water, gazing out to sea; but even at this distance, his head turned in my direction, though I couldn't possibly have been in his range of vision. Sometimes he would suddenly come indoors and silently go all through the house at a quick trot, unexpectedly entering one room after another, before he left again with the same mysterious abruptness. At other times he would lie just inside or outside, with his head resting on the threshold, motionless except for his watchful moving eyes, and the twitching of his sensitive nostrils in response to stimuli which my less acute senses could not perceive.

His movements were always silent, graceful, dignified, sure; and his large, dark eyes never failed to acknowledge me whenever we met in our daily comings and goings.

I was delighted with my visitor, whose silence did not conceal his awareness of me. If I walked through the jungle to visit someone, or to buy food from the neighbouring village, he would appear from nowhere and walk beside me, but always stopped before a house was in sight, never allowing himself to be seen. Every night, of course, he slept on the bed at my side. As the weeks passed he seemed to be spending more time with me during the day, sitting or lying near me while I was working, now and then coming close to gaze attentively at what I was doing.

Then, without warning, he suddenly left me. This was how it happened. The rainy season had come, bringing cooler weather; there was a chill in the early morning air, when he returned to my room as I finished dressing, and leaned against me for a moment. He had hardly ever touched me in daylight, certainly never in that deliberate fashion. I took it to mean that he wished me to do something for him, and asked what it was. Silently he led the way out of the house, pausing to look back every few steps to see whether I was coming, and into the jungle. The stormy sky was heavily clouded, it was almost dark under the trees, from which great drops of last night's rain splashed coldly on my neck and bare arms. As he evidently wanted me to accompany him further, I said I would go back for a coat.

However, he seemed to be too impatient to wait, lunging forward with long, loping strides, his shoulders thrusting like steel pistons under the velvet coat, while I reluctantly followed. Torrential rain began streaming down, in five minutes the ground was a bog, into which my feet sank at each step. By now I was shivering, soaked to the skin, so I stopped and told him I couldn't go on any further. He turned his head and for a long moment his limpid eyes looked at me fixedly, with an expression I could not read. Then the beautiful head turned away, the muscles slid and bunched beneath patterned fur, as he launched himself in a tremendous leap through the shining curtain of raindrops, and was instantly hidden from sight. I walked home as fast as I could, and changed into dry clothes. I did not expect to see him again before evening, but he did not come back at all.

Nothing of any interest took place after the leopard's visit. My life resumed its former routine of work and trivial happenings. The rains came to an end, winter merged imperceptibly into spring. I took pleasure in the sun and the natural world. I felt sure the leopard meant to return, and often looked out for him, but throughout this period he never appeared. When the sky hung pure and cloudless over the jungle, many-coloured orchids began to flower on the trees. I went to see one or two people I knew; a few people visited me in my house. The leopard was never mentioned in our conversations.

The heat increased day by day, each day dawned glassily clear. The atmosphere was pervaded by the aphrodisiac perfume of wild white jasmine, which the girls wove into wreaths for their necks and hair. I painted some large new murals on the walls of my house, and started to make a terrace from a mosaic of coloured shells. For months I'd been expecting to see the leopard, but as time kept passing without a sign of him, I was gradually losing hope.

The season of oppressive heat came round in due course, and the house was left open all night. More than at any other time, it was at night, just before falling asleep, that I thought of the leopard, and, though I no longer believed it would happen, pretended that I'd wake to find him beside me again. The heat deprived me of energy, the progress of the mosaic was slow. I had never tried my hand at such work before, and being unable to calculate the total quantity of shells that would be required, I constantly ran out of supplies, and had to make tiring trips to the beach for more.

One day while I was on the shore, I saw, out to sea, a young man coming towards the land, standing upright on the crest of a huge breaker, his red cloak blowing out in the wind, and a string of pelicans solemnly flapping in line behind him. It was so odd to see this stranger, with his weird escort, approaching alone from the ocean on which no ships ever sailed, that my thoughts immediately connected him with the leopard: there must be some contact between them; perhaps he was bringing me news. As he got nearer, I shouted to him, called out greetings and questions, to which he replied. But because of the noise of the waves and the distance between us, I could not understand him. Instead of coming on to the beach to speak to me, he suddenly turned and was swept out to sea again, disappearing in clouds of spray. I was puzzled and disappointed. But I took the shells home, went on working as usual, and presently forgot the encounter.

Some time later, coming home at sunset, I was reminded of the young man of the sea by the sight of a pelican perched on the highest point of my roof. Its presence surprised me: pelicans did not leave the shore as a rule, I had never known one come as far inland as this. It suddenly struck me that the bird must be something to do with the leopard, perhaps bringing a message from him. To entice it closer, I found a small fish in the kitchen, which I put on the grass. The pelican swooped down at once, and with remarkable speed and neatness, considering its bulk, skewered the fish on its beak, and flew off with it. I called out, strained my eyes to follow its flight; but only caught a glimpse of the great wings flapping away from me over the jungle trees, before the sudden black curtain of tropical darkness came down with a rush.

Despite this inconclusive end to the episode, it revived my hope of seeing the leopard again. But there were no further developments of any description; nothing else in the least unusual occurred.

It was still the season when the earth sweltered under a simmering sky. In the afternoons the welcome trade wind blew through the rooms and cooled them, but as soon as it died down the house felt hotter than ever. Hitherto I had always derived a nostalgic pleasure from recalling my visitor; but now the memory aroused more sadness than joy, as I had finally lost all hope of his coming back.

At last the mosaic was finished and looked quite impressive, a noble animal with a fine spotted coat and a human head gazing proudly from the centre of the design. I decided it needed to be enclosed in a border of yellow shells, and made another expedition to the beach, where the sun's power was intensified by the glare off the bright green waves, sparkling as if they'd been sprinkled all over with diamonds. A hot wind whistled through my hair, blew the sand about, and lashed the sea into crashing breakers, above which flocks of sea birds flew screaming, in glistening clouds of spray. After searching for shells for a while I straightened up, feeling almost dizzy with the heat and the effort. It was at this moment, when I was dazzled by the violent colours and the terrific glare, that the young man I'd already seen reappeared like a mirage, the red of his flying cloak vibrating against the vivid emerald-green waves. This time, through a haze of shimmering brilliance, I saw that the leopard was with him, majestic and larger than life, moving as gracefully as if the waves were solid glass.

I called to him, and though he couldn't have heard me above the thundering of the surf, he turned his splendid head and gave me a long, strange, portentous look, just as he had that last time in the jungle, sparkling rainbows of spray now taking the place of rain. I hurried towards the edge of the water, then suddenly stopped, intimidated by the colossal size of the giant rollers towering over me. I'm not a strong swimmer, it seemed insane to challenge those enormous on-coming walls of water, which would certainly hurl me back contemptuously on to the shore with all my bones broken. Their exploding roar deafened me, I was half-blinded by the salt spray, the whole beach was a swirling, glittering dazzle, in which I lost sight of the two sea-borne shapes. And when my eyes brought them back into focus, they had changed direction, turned from the land, and were already a long way off, receding fast, diminishing every second, reduced to vanishing point by the hard, blinding brilliance of sun and waves.

Long after they'd disappeared, I stood there, staring out at that turbulent sea, on which I had never once seen any kind of boat, and which now looked emptier, lonelier and more desolate than ever before. I was paralysed by depression and disappointment, and could hardly force myself to pick up the shells I'd collected and carry them home.

That was the last time I saw the leopard. I've heard nothing of him since that day, or of the young man. For a little while I used to question the villagers who lived by the sea, some of them said they vaguely remembered a man in a red cloak riding the water. But they always ended by becoming evasive, uncertain and making contradictory statements, so that I knew I was wasting my time.

I've never said a word about the leopard to anyone. It would be difficult to describe him to these simple people, who can never have seen a creature even remotely like him, living here in the wilds as

they do, far from zoos, circuses, cinemas and television. No car-
nivora, no large or ferocious beasts of any sort have ever inhabited
this part of the world, which is why we can leave our houses open all
night without fear.

The uneventful course of my life continues, nothing happens to
break the monotony of the days. Sometimes, I suppose, I may forget
the leopard's visit. As it is I seldom think of him, except at night
when I'm waiting for sleep to come. But, very occasionally he still
enters my dreams, which disturbs me and makes me feel restless
and sad. Although I never remember the dreams when I wake, for
days afterwards they seem to weigh me down with the obscure
bitterness of a loss which should have been prevented, and for
which I am myself to blame.

One of
the Liberated?

My wife has agate eyes and the whitest skin. Her eyes are like precious stones under very clear water, and they sometimes turn a mysterious deep jade green. Her hair is long, lustrous, dark brown, so dark it is almost black. People often describe her appearance as striking. But although she always attracts attention wherever she goes, she's not in the least spoilt or conceited. On the contrary, she is a nice, quiet, natural, affectionate girl.

We have been married just over a year, and we live in the country, but not very far from the town where she works. Five mornings a week, she drives to the station in my old Vauxhall. Outside our gate, the road runs through some trees, emerges, and keeps straight on for a little way, then curves round, skirting the base of the hills. She always waves to me when she gets to the bend (she knows I'll be standing there, watching her out of sight), just before the car leaves the road and becomes airborne, heading north, soaring up over the beechwoods over the tops of the hills, until it disappears on the other side. In five minutes she'll be at the station, catching the nine-fifteen. It would take her a good twenty minutes longer if she kept to the road.

Five days a week, she works in a publisher's office. The firm prints books on Hydraulics, the Function of Method Analysis, Kinky Kars – that sort of thing. She's a very intelligent girl. Soon after six she comes back to me, sailing serenely south, high over the wooded hills. I rush out to meet her and put the car away in the garage. I can hardly wait for the evening we're going to spend together. Just to sit in the room with her fills me with happiness. But what about her? Is *she* equally happy? I don't know. She never speaks of her feelings; though that may be simply because she is always quiet. At first I thought she would become more confident as she got to know me better; but no, she still says very little, almost nothing about herself. Often I long to ask questions. I like to know about things, to understand them; I have an enquiring mind. But so far the questions have never been spoken. Certain things are too difficult to ask.

I imagine her sitting in the publisher's office all day like a captive princess in a tower; and I feel guilty because I'm free to go where I like, do whatever I please. I feel I'm to blame for letting her work so hard, although we agreed on the arrangement at the start, so that I could go on painting. Unfortunately, no one buys my pictures, so she has to support both of us. If only I could make it up to her in some way; do something to please her. I sometimes try to prepare little surprises. Not long ago, thinking she must be tired when she gets home, I decided to do the housework. How carefully, thoroughly, industriously I swept and polished, until the rooms shone.

Gravely, in silence, she looked all round, went through the whole house, examining everything. I followed and watched her. A compulsion seemed to be forcing her to inspect my work closely, in every detail. She even looked inside the oven, ran her finger along high window sills, normally out of reach – and she's not exactly what you'd call domesticated herself, in the ordinary way. I became nervous, suspecting her disapproval. But she said nothing, either in criticism or praise.

About this time last year, we found some fritillaries in the fields, and she was delighted by the queer little snake's head flowers, which I thought rather sinister with their murky purple and green petals. So when the milk boy told me the other day they were starting to flower in the Lodden meadows, I walked over, six miles each way, and after long searching, collected a small bunch; it took me the whole afternoon. I carried them home in a plastic bag, the stems wrapped in damp moss, and just had time to arrange them in one of her favourite vases before she opened the door. I expected an exclamation of pleasure. But she made no comment at all, only gave them a long, rather strange look I couldn't fathom, and then gazed at me with the same queer expression in her pellucid eyes. Those of variegated chalcedony can be so baffling. All of a sudden, I felt an utter fool. After all, if she wanted, she could . . . couldn't she . . .?

Now I've come to the real heart of the problem. For I can't deny that a problem exists in our relations. My guilt is only a minor issue, on which I've tended to concentrate for obvious reasons. I may as well admit now that it's the car business I find disturbing: that, and the white mice she keeps in her bosom (why there? I'm afraid they may do her some injury). I was looking at our wedding photograph, at her radiant nice girl's face. Can there, I wondered, be something about her at a deeper level – something I don't understand? Is it possible that she is – that she can do things other people can't do?

Come to think of it, quite a number of things have happened since we've been married which need explaining. It's slightly worrying if I let myself dwell on it.

You could say I've become addicted to her. She's essential to me, I can't do without her, she keeps me going. Her quiet sensible ways are my antidote to the pretensions of the smart art set, to the whirling antics of modish psychedelia. But I'm beginning to think I know nothing about her. I don't understand why she never tells me anything about herself. She dominates me, I think about her all the time, even when I'm working. There's been a change lately in the way I paint, I don't mean the technique. I look at my recent compositions with a sense of alienation, as if they had been inspired by somebody else; and there's not the least doubt in my mind who this is. Does she want me to paint unsaleable pictures so that I'll be dependent on her? But what am I saying? Where can I have got such a crazy notion? She *is* a nice, normal, uncomplicated girl who's devoted to me. But her eyes are so strange sometimes.

After dinner, our usual routine, she washes the dishes and I dry them. I was thinking all the time about the questions I'd never asked. Things of this sort can break up a marriage if they go on too long. It seemed to me that the time had come when we had to discuss everything openly; otherwise our whole relationship would be endangered.

This conclusion hit me with such violence that I dropped a plate. At the crash, she looked around, not at the shattered bits on the floor as most people would have done, but straight at me, so that our eyes met. Hers had that strange deep green tint they get sometimes; which seemed to overflow and fill the space between us with a bright jade green light, so dazzling that I had to lower my own eyes. To hide my confusion, I stooped down, collected the remains of the broken plate and took them out to the dustbin. It was a moonless night and quite dark, but I felt so disturbed that I stayed outside, walking blindly about on the common, until I walked into a gorse bush. Then I went back to the house.

She was in the living-room, watching television. Automatically, I sat down and stared at the screen, without seeing the picture. I felt tired, depressed by all the things I couldn't understand, and by knowing I ought to ask her about them. I was on the verge of saying,

'If only you'd keep on the road all the way to the station,' when she twisted round in her chair. At that moment I saw the white mouse clinging to her sleeve with its sharp little claws, having been dislodged, presumably, from some more comfortable and secure place by her movement. Almost at the same time, I caught sight of another tiny white whiskered snout and two bright black sequin-eyes, peering out of the front of her dress, between two of the buttons.

'What's that, for God's sake?' I shouted idiotically, jumping up, making such a row that the creatures were gone in a flash.

I was shocked, absolutely appalled. I can't even begin to express my horror at the idea of the disgusting pink crinkled claws scrabbling over her skin. 'Those mice ... what are you doing with them ...? Do they *live* there ...?' I hardly knew what I was saying, I was almost frantic. Their hateful little pink claws ... her lovely white skin ... The thing was a nightmare. Obscene. I couldn't stand it. 'Throw them out – now, this instant!' I yelled like a lunatic, lunging forward as if I meant to turn her upside down and shake them out of their hiding place. She must have been frightened, she moved so fast. She was out of her chair, her skirt brushed my leg, in a second the door had shut, and directly afterwards the front door banged too.

If I'd been in my normal senses, I'd have gone after her. But it seemed useless just then, I was certain I'd lost her – that she would never come back. At the same time, I had the somewhat bizarre notion that I only existed in relation to her, as if, quite literally, I couldn't live without her. Since that was the case, I should just have to kill myself. There was nothing else to be done. Means were not lacking either. Even a choice was at my disposal. A bottle three-quarters full of barbiturates up in the bathroom. My shotgun. The car exhaust. Razor blades.

While I was considering the alternatives without enthusiasm, I heard her come back indoors. It was no relief, for some reason. I expected her to come into the room and speak to me, became indignant when she went straight upstairs. Then, exhausted by emotion, I sat down in the easy chair, leaned back, stared up at a motionless spider. A web of fine cracks turned the ceiling into the map of an enemy country, its capital the black blob of the spider. The house, which had always seemed safe and friendly before, full of friendly familiar things, had become a hostile sinister place full of unseen traps, unknown dangers. There was absolute silence. What could she be doing up there? Going to bed as if nothing had happened? I started feeling indignant again, but fell into an uneasy doze.

Later, when I woke I was cold, my left leg had gone to sleep. I rubbed it to restore circulation, saw the spider still on the ceiling; it hadn't moved. Then, while I was looking at it, it suddenly darted off, quickly and stealthily, like a mouse; and I thought, I don't *have* to think about mice, I won't let myself. I sat up straight, got up out of the chair. Why had I been considering suicide? Death was pointless, it solved no problems; I'd be no better off, I should just be dead. Now it seemed quite insane to stay down here, thinking of dying, when there was a perfectly good bed with a beautiful girl in it in the room above. I locked the front door, put the lights out, and got undressed in the dark.

Nothing moved in the dark bedroom, there was no glimmer of light, not a sound. I said out loud to the silence, to the universe, to the night: 'I don't understand a thing. And I don't care. I refuse to think any more.' Her hand came out of the bed, took hold of mine, pulled me in. There was no light at all, not the faintest gleam, we dived through the pitch-black tunnel of love together. Kiss, kiss. That's better. Smile in the dark, my love. At the other end was the morning, bright sunshine and birds. She was still asleep. Lovely she looked, her eyes closed, her dark hair on her shoulder.

I went down to get the breakfast. The house felt familiar and cheerful, already warm. The clock was ticking, I touched it with love because she had wound it up. My feet were not on the ground, I drifted around the ceiling-map of a friendly country, floated upstairs with the tray. She was sweet and smiling, she said kind things, her agate eyes seemed to smile. I wished it was the weekend so that we could be together all day. But she said: 'I must hurry, or I shall miss the train.' She wore her blue dress, not the one she'd had on yesterday. This one too fastened down the front; but I could only think how beautiful she was in the morning sun. It almost seemed possible that I'd imagined those hateful creatures, that she *was* a nice quiet natural girl, no different from other nice girls. Well, I should know in a minute.

I watched her drive away in the old Vauxhall, reach the bend in the road. Would she . . .? or wouldn't she . . .? I held my breath. As usual, she turned there to wave to me; and then went soaring up, northwards, over the hill tops, and away out of sight.

Sleep
Has His House

Foreword

Life is tension or the result of tension: without tension the creative impulse cannot exist. If human life be taken as the result of tension between the two polarities night and day, night, the negative pole, must share equal importance with the positive day. At night, under the influence of cosmic radiations quite different from those of the day, human affairs are apt to come to a crisis. At night most human beings die and are born.

Sleep Has His House describes in the night-time language certain stages in the development of one individual human being. No interpretation is needed of this language we have all spoken in childhood and in our dreams; but for the sake of unity a few words before every section indicate the corresponding events of the day.

... in a strange land, on the borders of Chymerie ... the god of sleep has made his house ... which of the sun may naught have, so that no man may know aright the point between the day and night. ... Round about there is growing on the ground, poppy which is the seed of sleep ... a still water ... runs upon the small stones ... which gives great appetite for sleep. And thus full of delight the god of sleep has his house.

John Gower

It is not easy to describe my mother. Remote and starry, her sad stranger's grace did not concern the landscape of the day. Should I say that she was beautiful or that she did not love me? Have shadows beauty? Does the night love her child?

What a fearful thing it can be to wake suddenly in the deepest hours of the night. Blackness all round; everything formless; the dark pressing against the eyeballs; the darkness a black thumb pressed to the starting eyeballs distended with dread. At first I don't know what I am to become. I am like an embryo prematurely expelled from the womb. I remember nothing, know nothing: I haven't the least idea what is making me tremble all over like a person suffering the effect of shock. It happens to be the cruellest shock of all I am suffering from: the brutal violence of the birth shock.

I must find myself, I cannot drown in so black a sea, and I begin to strike out, threshing about desperately, this way and that, in pursuit of the images which appear, transparent as the shadows of icicles, incorporated in the night-plasma. Floundering among the waves, my head just above water, the most shapeless water, I plunge into a picture: but at once the outlines disintegrate, coldly ... coldly ... no frost flower decorating a window-pane vanishes more inexorably in the sun. Into the ephemeral images I dive, one after the other: sometimes one crystallizes into a brief sharpness – never to permanence. At last I dive with extraordinary accuracy into my own body, which I see laid out, high and dry, above the receding tide. I am lying there like a long white fish on a slab. Is it a bed or a bier that I'm lying on? Or have I really been washed up on some beach or other?

I feel the sides of the thing I'm lying on with my hands. Yes, it's a bed, no doubt of that. I'm myself, alive on a bed, not drowned or exposed in a morgue. Nor am I a fish on a fishermonger's marble slab.

So far so good. But what bed it is that I'm lying on I'm not able to say. What room is this? I look round for a window. Is it there . . .? Or there . . .? Or perhaps over there, where, in any case, I feel a door ought to be? There's not a single gleam, not a glimmer, to give me a clue. The whole room is as black as pitch. In fact, I'm not at all sure that it is a room. Something suggests to me now that I'm on board ship; I might be floating adrift on some tranquil sea. And yet there's no sound, no motion, nothing to indicate either sea or land. Like a ghost train my life streams through my head, and I don't know which point of the compass I'm facing.

How dark it is. The moon must have stolen away secretly. The stars have thrown their spears down and departed. There seems to be nothing except primordial chaos outide the window. Utterly still, utterly alone, I watch the darkness flower into transient symbols. And now there is danger somewhere, a slow, padded beat, like cushioned paws softly approaching. What an ominous sound that is to hear in the night.

The first place I remember was warm and sunny. I remember the flowers that grew there, and trees smelling of summer. The sun always seemed to shine in that country. I don't remember seeing my parents often. A Japanese houseboy looked after me most of the time. He was kind and told me many beautiful stories. He drew pictures to please me, plants and magical fishes.

Up, up, up swings the little boat, gently, languidly climbing the enormous swell, like drifting thistledown, scarcely seeming to move. The tiny boat hardly seems to be moving at all, but up it climbs on the huge blue undulation, up, up, towards the solemn clouds standing in tall arcades, far too bright for the eyes. In a dazzle of utter blue, the boat climbs to the wave's shoulder. And down, down, down, it begins to travel, with emerald facets glittering on the blue. The descending swell burns translucent, a fiery barrow, entombing the amethyst shades of sea-lions, over which the little boat glides with blithe unconcern.

Painted ultramarine, with embossed eyes vigilant for water demons, the boat itself is the centre, the focal point, of a vast sea dream. And it is dreamlike and noticeable that the boat is oarless, sailless, motorless, moving apparently of its own volition and without any help from the yellow man who sits in the stern, smiling down at his drawing of coloured inks. Held in fingers the colour of old piano keys, his brush traces the lines which are finer than hairs. The smooth progress of the boat does not disturb the accuracy of his touch. Intent, with the sun glistening like a second reflected sun on his bowed head, he placidly continues to map out a spidery complex of strokes, paying no attention to the course on which he is being carried. And now the swells rear into monsters plunging thunderously to the shore; but the boat has passed the protecting reef and floats on the shallow water. Here through a sparkling window the sea-floor can be seen, coral citadels, battlemented with shells of peculiar shapes and colours, parks and thickets of weed and gardens of lacy crimson sea-fern. The inhabitants of these subaqueous regions pass under the boat serenely on their mysterious business. Some are beautiful creations, some grotesque, some delicate as spun glass, others clumsy like the outcome of a bungled experiment; some baleful, some amusing, some benign; some fearsome or weird in their exaggerated strangeness. They are equipped with every conceivable variation of colour, texture and form: with frills, fans, fringes, spines, tentacles, filaments, helmets, swords; with appendages like trailing banners; with veils, periscopes, carapaces, suckers, pincers, razors, nets. This is clearly the source from which the yellow artist in the boat draws his inspiration. The picture is finished. He holds it up and smiles at the complicated fantasy evolved by his brush-strokes. He smiles, the smile growing unclear as a breaker shatters its glassy curve on the reef, and a miniature rainbow, a storm-dog, slowly dissolves in spray over his head.

The dream foreground which reappears is obscured by mantles of nostalgic melancholy. A soft antique rain falls. Twilight. The colours lavender to pigeon and pearl grey with the delicate green of a weeping willow tree on the left. Behind the willow hangs the suggestion of a cascade. In the middle distance, centrally placed, a small hill with a tomb – a simple shrine, it looks like – at the top.

The remote voices of antiquity whisper quietly together: the willow; the rain; the cascade. Presently a shadow moves on the lower slopes of the hill; at first a blur, gradually becoming distinguishable as the back view of a fox, belly close to the ground, long brush extended, cautiously stealing upwards. It moves along so secretly that it appears to creep like a snake. When it has almost reached the top, the fox stops, turns its head, and looks slowly from side to side. With its head turned, it crouches there for a while in furtive forlornness, then suddenly disappears. In its place stands a young girl with long and very lovely hair who clasps her grave-clothes with one hand, runs to the tomb and vanishes inside.

Immediately the light changes and brightens, the rain stops; there is a stir of suppressed excitement, an impression of movement, although no new shapes appear. The mists in the foreground weave and divide, expanding, convolving, coagulating, in the middle air where they remain suspended and faintly vibrant, transfused with rosy light which grows stronger and stronger as if the sun were rising behind them. As brightness culminates, the mist breaks into countless shimmering flakes, a swarm of petals speckles and flutters the air, a charming group of cherry trees is nodding gracefully in full flower.

Plangent music is heard as a crowd of courtiers enters, escorted by attendants who at once retire unobtrusively into the background, while the ladies and gentlemen arrange themselves under the cherry trees as if for the opening movement of a ballet. These are people of brilliance and distinction; it is impossible to imagine anything more decorous than their behaviour, at once natural and ceremonial, or more elegant than their elaborate garments 'in which, down sleeve and skirt, fold chimes with fold in every imaginable harmony of texture and hue'. A sort of masque is now played out among them, with much gallantry on the part of the gentlemen and many exchanges of formal gifts, each with its appropriate message, sprays of blossom concealing love notes, caskets no less sparkling than the epigrams they contain. From time to time someone sings or plays on the lute or the zithern, or recites a poem fitting the situation of the moment. There is nothing in the least stilted about all this, and one gets the impression that it is not really a charade that is taking place, but a recognized ritual of conduct, the genuine expression of cordiality among these cultured and decorative exquisites.

Several moon-faced children are moving about here and there, and they are made a great fuss of, caressed and petted by everybody. The whole party is continuously in a state of fluidity, groups forming and breaking and re-forming with different units, so that the effect is that of a dazzling and constantly changing colour design, like those boxes of coloured beads which can be shaken into innumerable shining patterns. Two figures only remain static, the hub around which all this brilliance revolves. Perhaps it is Prince Genji himself with long hanging sleeves, the bright scarlet of his underrobe showing through the flowery tissue of his mantle, who is smiling so enigmatically at the First Princess in her clove-dyed silk dress.

Gradually the picture starts to fade out. Light, which has all the time emanated from some point behind the cherry trees, for several minutes has been imperceptibly fading and is now no longer rosy; the blossom-cloud has lost its lamplike glow and is mere pale flowering cherry. There is a general lowering of tone and tempo so that the figures of the courtiers seem less alive, their clothing less gay, their voices less melodious, as they slowly disperse. The music lingers a little while after the last one has vanished; but the notes diminish and dwindle into the tinkling of a child's musical-box.

Silence. Livid swaths of light fall as if cut by a scythe. The trunks of the trees are obliterated, but the blossom can still be seen, a compressed blizzard, pallidly churning and milling. The unobserved and forgotten guards in the distance now suddenly assume drastic importance as they begin to converge on the centre. They wear bulky dark clothes and their faces are obscured as by masks or helmets. Each is an incipient catastrophe, intensely ominous in his stiff hierarchic motions.

A loudening rush of noise like escaping steam hisses out of the spinning mass in mid-air and seems to draw the figures together. As they finally gather in a compact group under this pallid magnet, they are caught in a funnel of dead lead-grey light flaring down from it, and for the first time are to be seen in detail. They are small, dressed in some indeterminate uniform, their faces under their helmets formally, flatly, impersonally evil. They are looking straight ahead, as if posed for a picture. Their expressions set, childish and racially inaccessible. After a while darkness steadily and methodically plucks them out of sight one by one.

The ashy remnant of what was once cherry blossom continues to rain through the blackness while the accompanying noise expands, spouts and crackles into an ear-splitting engine-roar. As this shattering thunder becomes quite unbearable, it explodes into silence. At the same instant the whirling formlessness bursts into a shower of leaflets which are catapulted in all directions. They drift downwards, and there is a momentary glimpse of them sucked and eddying madly in the up-draught of a flaming jungle village, fired palm trees ablaze and streaming. Vacuum.

Later we crossed the sea to a colder country where my mother was bored and sad. We lived in a house full of things kept brightly polished. Visitors admired the house and everything in it. Most of all they admired my mother. She was like a queen in the house – a princess in exile. All the shine of the house was quenched by my mother's sadness. It was not a gay house in spite of the bright things in it. No, the house was not really gay at all.

The dream scene comes to light as a comprehensive view of a garden suburb seen from the air. The whole layout is visible. At one extremity the conglomeration of city outskirts: slums, factories, converging tram, train, bus routes, arterial roads. At the other end the opening countryside: fields, scattered industrial areas, a golf course, a few hills and small woods. Then a closer view of the suburb. It's a high-class residential district. The streets are wide and planted with trees, the geometrical rows of houses stand in neat gardens, there is a busy shopping centre, solid neo-Georgian municipal buildings, a crescent of fake Tudor houses in herring-bone brick disguises, business premises. It's summer. A windy and sunny day. All the gardens are spick and span with orderly flower-beds and lawns carefully mown. A few have tennis courts; others have pools, rockeries, sundials, effigies of rabbits, toadstools or gnomes. Some, not many, tradesmen's vans and shiny private cars sliding along the roads. A bus draws itself smoothly past the public gardens. Smoke rises in fat curlicues from prosperous chimneys. More insistent than anything, dwarfing the whole scene of papier-mâché cuteness, the enormous blue undisciplined sky with robustious clouds bucketing across.

A straight view of one of the widest streets from ground-level follows.

A dark limousine, an eight-year-old model, but beautifully kept, is being driven along this street by a chauffeur in hogskin gloves. A white gate with THE ELMS painted on the top bar. Appropriate elm trees at each side. The gate is hooked open. The car makes a careful curve and drives in. A glimpse of lawn; cutting the edge of the grass with long-handled shears, a gardener, who glances up with skimming non-interest. The front door comes into prominence with porch and flanking hydrangeas in pots. The car stops; chauffeur gets out of his seat, rings the door bell, comes back and opens the door of the car from which emerges a lady of no particular age, dressed for paying a call. Her dress and hat are expensive, very much toned-down versions of the season's fashionable styles. A maid in white afternoon apron and cap opens the house door for her.

All these people, the lady, the chauffeur, the gardener, the maid, have the same face which they wear as if it were a mask, indifferent, decorous, nondescript, and quietly, negatively repressive. If the chauffeur and his employer were to change clothes no one would notice the difference.

Meanwhile, a door opens into the usual drawing-room, arranged with half-taste, too many knick-knacks, too many vases of flowers. The casement windows have chintz curtains and the same material has been used for covering the sofa and chairs. The room only differs from other suburban drawing-rooms because a good deal of the bric-à-brac comes from the East.

The visitor sits down with her feet close together. She has been in the room before. As she takes off her gloves and smooths the creases out of them, she glances about the room, stamping it with the tepid pass of her recognition.

After a minute the door opens and the mistress of the house – for the sake of economy she may as well be called A – comes in. She is nearing forty, her still young face is attractive in spite of the discontent harassing it. During a rather long-drawn-out pause she stands in the doorway at the far end of the room. There is plenty of time to observe her. The details of her appearance become clearly defined; narrow neurotic face under bright curled hair, uneasy hands, plain light dress very simple compared with the visitor's outfit. This woman's restless, artistic personality is considerably over-emphasized by contrast with the mediocre, phlegmatic mask-face worn by all the others. However, she seems a little too dramatic to be quite convincing. There is a suggestion of planned exhibitionism about her pose in the doorway which is so prolonged as to produce an effect of tension. As she at last shuts the door quietly and comes forward, in dream fashion the room gradually heightens and elongates: at the same time an invisible sponge passes over it, eliminating detail; windows are blotted out one after another till only a single tall window remains, admitting a flat neutral light, between stiff fluted curtains: so that she advances into a long, cold, lofty, uncoloured room which is empty except for the unaltered chintz chair where the visitor sits and one or two other indistinct objects which symbolize furniture.

With each step A takes, a modification, corresponding to what's happening in the room, progresses in her own appearance. All her tragic potentialities are brought out and accentuated. She grows taller and thinner, her face chalk-white and haggard, her hair curls into a stiff sacrificial crown. Even her dress changes colour, turning red-black, so that she eventually stands like a dark pillar in front of the blank window. She has her back to the room and to the visitor who has remained sitting in the flowery armchair, feet side by side, smoothing the creases out of her folded gloves.

How you must miss it all, the visitor says.

Synchronizing with her perfectly commonplace voice, the light starts to grow dim, diminishing steadily until the room becomes quite dark except for the luminous window against the lower part of which, in the exact centre, A's sombre silhouette remains standing throughout, absolutely motionless.

How you must miss it all, the visitor says.

The romance of the East, a precisely similar voice says, answering, in precisely the same ladylike, banal, superficial tone. From different parts of the room other identical voices eject similar comments: The colour, The mystery, The gay social life, and so on. As each voice speaks, a pasty finger of light rambles towards it, just barely indicating repetitive replicas of the original caller and establishing the existence of a chorus distributed round the dark room. Every time the light touches a new speaker she is shown sitting with consciously crossed ankles, consciously ladylike, her face tilted to vacancy, smiling the conventional vapid smile of the afternoon visitor.

While this goes on, the view outside the window, materializing from nothing, presents a sequence of Far-Eastern scenes dissolving into one another, tremendously fast, immensely disorganized. It is never possible to grasp these visions completely (they are partly hidden by the black shape standing with her back to the room) because of their speed and the confused way in which they evolve themselves at all angles and on different size scales.

For instance: a minuscule landscape with palms and temples, instantly smothered by the overflowing of a gigantic yellow river in spate; slither of water yeastily regurgitating refuse and half-seen domestic objects; rafts on which families are living, fishing, washing, cooking, sleeping, engaging in intimate occupations of all descriptions, suddenly soar upwards like magic carpets: a tangle of upside-down horses' legs racing; intersecting arcs of swung polo-sticks swooping: ambiguous smiling bland oriental faces: gathering of Very Important People (white, most of them, but a sprinkling of highly decorated and jewelled nabobs in magnificent costumes for picturesque local colour); personages with orders; uniforms; elaborately dressed women. Then, getting more tangled and chaotic, a crazy avalanche of flowers, mosquito nets, champagne bottles, electric fans: hands carrying trays, golf bags, rackets, wraps; guns, whips; white hands, brown hands, yellow hands; hands lighting cigarettes, cigars; holding weapons, holding glasses, holding reins, rackets, bats, sticks, clubs; holding other hands: mouths with lipstick, with moustaches, with thick lips, with thin lips; Eastern mouths, Western mouths; mouths shouting orders, kissing, singing, drinking, whispering: liners, trains, cars, tongas, traps; baggage, horses, mules, bullocks, sampans, rickshaws; children, dogs, coolies, ayahs: ships sailing, troops marching, storms breaking, doors opening, moons rising, suns setting, trees blowing; duststorms, thunderstorms; meetings, intrigues, assignations, partings.

Immediately after this the somewhat more stabilized formality of a black tree-trunk, of which A's body forms a part, with perfectly naked bilateral boughs, immediately sprouting several huge white trumpet-shaped flowers.

There is an infinitesimal break in continuity as the dream angle changes a little. The comments of the chorus veer, but scarcely, and continue

you must find it a great change living here
very different indeed
perhaps a trifle dull after all your travels
although we have our own interests too
there's always plenty going on in a quiet way
the bridge parties
the tap dancing at the health class
the sale of work
the Women's Institute meetings
the garden fête at the vicarage
dinner at Dr Moore's (such a charming man).

The accompanying pictures outside the window by contrast with the previous sequence are very slow and definitive; their materialization is painstakingly realistic and they follow the spoken phrases meticulously, with strict, but not exaggerated, attention to rigorous suburban respectability, dullness.

And then it's so easy to run up to town for a theatre or a film.

Quick in the vision the closed car sliding along, a man with a white silk scarf at the wheel, a woman beside him wearing an evening wrap of some kind; their dummy figures sitting stiffly erect, their white faces calcified in boredom. Branching out of the car fading, the black arterial road with lateral streets swings back to the black tree, the black woman's body clamped to the tree. This time the flower-spurting is reversed, the petal wreckage dripping down flaccid, a slimy tatter of dissolution, semi-liquid decay.

The light goes back sharply to normal, returning to the dream the suburban drawing-room, the chintzes, the knick-knacks, the vases of flowers. A has just sat down on the sofa. Under polite composure her limp attitude protests against hard reality. The visitor, sitting exactly as she has sat from the start, is saying something indistinguishable to her as the maid comes in at the door pushing a trolley with bright crested silver tea-service, plates of thin bread and butter, absurdly small cucumber sandwiches, macaroons.

A little girl with fair hair – she is unmistakably the child of her mother and so could be called B – peeps in through the open door, unnoticed by the grown-ups; then tiptoes away.

Our house always seemed especially quiet, as if people spoke there only in lowered voices. My parents seldom had time for talking to me. No one talked to me much: but the rain often used to whisper. It rained a lot and the rain kept whispering to me. In the long afternoons when the rain filled each window and shadows met together in every corner, I sometimes thought of the sun and the Japanese houseboy. It was lonely in those rooms dark with my mother's sadness and with the rain on the windows. The rain shut off the house by itself in a lonely spell.

In time I found out what it was that the rain whispered. I learnt from the rain how to work the magic and then I stopped feeling lonely. I learnt to know the house in the night way of mice and spiders. I learnt to read the geography of the house bones. Invisible and unheard I scampered down secret tunnels beneath the floor-boards and walked a tightrope webbing among the beams.

After that I never wished for children to play with, or for the Japanese houseboy to tell me fantastic stories. Hidden by curtains, sheltered in cupboards, ambushed in foxholes between the tables and chairs, I transmuted flat daylight into my night-time magic and privately made for myself a world out of spells and whispers.

The pre-realist fantasia opens up in an inchoate sort of Marie Laurençin dream of delicate tints. No form to speak of. Just a pearly billowing and subsiding of fondant chromatics; baby blue, candy pink, lemon-icing yellow, all sweetly harmonious and insipid like a débutante's bon-bon box tied up in cellophane and big satin bows. After a sufficiency of this things begin to take shape, but as we are taking a long view of the time-stream and creation hasn't occurred yet, there's naturally a lot of fluidity. A tinkling twinkling musical-box tune, with accompanying Tyrolean or Swiss dancers, fancy peasants, rose-wreathed cupids, angels with night-gowns and cheeks like pomegranates, is liable to translate any minute into a Brahms symphony and the austere discipline of the *ancien corps de ballet*.

In the same way the mountain which presently arches itself up like a cat's back is perhaps Mount Olympus, or perhaps Mount Sinai, or perhaps it is a cat's back and not a mountain at all. Assuming that it's a mountain, as a closer view seems to confirm, one gets an impression of pellucidity more appropriate to a mirage. There are crystalline snow slopes, diaphanous groves of trees, hyaline rocks, and, in the immediate foreground, a small lake, clear as glass, the translucent waters of which have surely never been contaminated by so much as a minnow.

Perhaps it is an extreme northern latitude that gives such rarefied transparency to the scene, lighted, as it appears to be, by the limpid coruscations of the aurora borealis. And this is a theory which gains a certain amount of support from the arrival of a party of hikers, of a truly Scandinavian robust comeliness, who proceed to picnic by the water's edge. Every one of these picnickers, old as well as young (for there are several elderly people among them), is remarkable for his or her splendid physique, and for a skin tanned to a glorious golden brown. As might be expected of such magnificently fit specimens, they are full of abounding gusto and energy. Every now and then members of the group, unable to contain their *joie de vivre*, go off to run races or engage in contests of strength, calling aloud to each other by oddly familiar names. A good deal of indiscriminate neck-ing, of a specially exuberant, whole-hearted and unself-conscious variety, also goes on; and this gives rise to sudden jealousies, apt to culminate in violence or in malicious pranks and practical jokes. It is noticeable that these childishly evanescent loves and quarrels spring up and are forgotten with equal ease; and perhaps this has something to do with the wine with which all the haversacks seem to be well supplied.

The irresponsible holiday atmosphere has a good innings before certainly pronouncedly killjoy clouds, gathering censoriously over the lake, begin to deluge the picnickers with torrential rain. It's no ordinary mountain storm that comes on, but an absolute cloud burst, a cataclysmic jet of watery disapproval, a purge which attacks the gay party with dank tenacity, never letting up until it has succeeded in washing them out of the picture entirely.

And now that the clouds clear away the whole aspect of the mountain has changed. Vanished the lake, the roseate dream-light, the ethereal snows. Instead, a prosaic materialism illuminates a dado of arid crags behind a laboratory where a scientist is working, an old fellow with a grubby grey beard reminiscent of those superannuated physicians who dodder out their last days at obscure Continental spas. He is wearing a voluminous white overall tied with strings at the back, and this gives him a grotesque likeness to a stout elderly *bonne*. The overall, beneath which his broad-toed black boots poke out like obstinate tortoises, is none too clean, being spotted, not only with spilled food and gravy, but by traces of the various experiments with which he is grumpily occupied. Back and forth he lumbers between his microscope and his reports, frequently pausing to consult a huge reference book, so massive that it might almost be made of stone, but without ever seeming to find the formula that he wants. A specially baffling point teases him, he paws at the great tome, shakily turning the pages with his vein-knotted hands.

He doesn't see the face watching him through the window, the cretinous grin under the shapeless straw hat full of holes. The village idiot peeps in round the post of the open door, grows bold seeing the old man so absorbed, and cautiously tiptoes into the room. The idiot boy advances in shambling stealth a little nearer the table where something is spluttering over a burner; cunningly keeps his eye on the reader; jerks himself nearer still. He is attracted by the bubbling mess in the tube; then fascinated by it; his hand stretches slyly towards it, draws back, fumbles to it again; he twitches in violent excitement, grimacing at it; clutches it.

The whole bag of tricks flashes up at his touch in an explosion of glittering dust. There's a split second's glimpse of the vast sad blackness of infinity before the perfectly bare void is spattered by this glittering exsurgence, this bursting fountain of molecules, instantly crystallizing to sequins of differing size. And now at once begins the fiery development of comets, suns, planets, nebulae; constellations are clotted together; worlds rush forth on their immense navigations, the monstrous efflorescence of the universe burgeons in the flick of an eyelash. Creation is under way. The solar system is off. Larger and more brilliant blaze the globes, the stars roar past like stratoliners to destinations not checked in quadrillions. The billiard-ball earth swings up and flattens colossally underfoot. The thunderous revving of the cosmic machines settles to the steady beat of eternity.

Right in the middle of all this, in a quiet place, the little girl B sits reading a book. She is sitting on short fresh green grass, leaning against a tree, where it is quiet and cool. Everything here is springlike and very much simplified; just the grass and the innocent green tree and the child. Before long several other children appear and begin to play with red and green bean bags. They stand in two rows and each child throws the bag over his shoulder to be caught and passed on by the child behind. Their conduct is orderly, ritualistic, almost obsessional. They are completely concentrated on their serious attention to the rules of the game, their occasional subdued exclamations barely disturb the hush. Under the tree, B puts down her book and looks on. It's clear that she would like to join in, but she feels shy and needs some encouragement. The others pay no attention to her, they are quite absorbed in their game. At last B gets up and goes towards them. Play stops for a moment. A boy with a polite blank public-school face steps out and gravely invites her into the game.

Perhaps B is nervous, perhaps she doesn't understand the rules, perhaps she just means to introduce an innovation. Anyway, when it comes to her turn, she throws the red bean bag forward instead of back. The game breaks up at once, as if by telepathic agreement. The faces of the other children grow astonished and hostile. The polite boy in particular wears an outraged expression as he marshals his companions away.

Left alone, B stands bewildered, looking in the direction where the players have vanished. After a moment, quickly and hopefully, her eyes are drawn to a man (it's her father, as a matter of fact) who walks along fast, dressed in dark town clothes and carrying a dispatch case and an umbrella. Her face turns upwards in expectation. But he is in too much of a hurry to notice her. He has important things on his mind, he passes on and scurries into an enormous office building which at this moment snaps up like an opera hat out of the ground to the right of the tree. As soon as he's in, the ornate double doors close behind him; but still, through the wrought-iron scrolls, he can be seen diminishing down room after room full of clerks, typists, desks, telephones, green-shaded lamps; door after transparent door shutting behind his back, till he is at last inaccessibly entombed as if in the heart of a gigantic formicary.

B, who has taken a few steps towards the building as if she meant to follow him, drifts back to the tree, on the other side of which a plain stone wall with a door in the centre has now erected itself. From some distance off, A approaches aloofly, her hand already outstretched to the door. On this narrow door, with her left hand, with a blue-flashing ring, she raps in a deliberate fashion. While she is waiting for the door to open she turns her eyes slowly upon the child, at whom she looks directly and pensively. Then her eyes move, sliding without eagerness to the door which, opening, displays a dark space where it is just possible to distinguish the sculptured pallor of urns in the deep shadow. A goes inside. With two final, distinct clicks, the door is shut and locked. The little girl watches with the acceptance of perfectly uncomprehending fatalism, then sits down in her original place at the foot of the tree. As she picks up her book and starts reading, the wall and the office building dissolve unobtrusively, restoring the dream picture as it was to begin with. The only difference being that its vernal simplicity now holds a definite suggestion of loneliness, isolation.

When my mother died I knew why the house had always been quiet.
The house had been waiting and watching from the beginning, listening to
the steps my mother danced with her death.

My father never told me about what had happened. No one said anything
to me about the death of my mother and I never asked anyone. It was a
question which could not possibly ever be asked. But I often wondered.
At night, especially, I used to wonder. Sometimes I got afraid in the night,
wondering about death and myself and my mother, and wishing that I
could ask someone. But of course I knew I would never be able to ask such a
question. My mother's death was the one thing I would never be able to
speak of to anyone, no matter how frightened I was. That was the last
thing I would ever do.

Day time. Night time. Night the dark time: the time for wonder; the time for the question in daylight not to be spoken.

The question starts under the chest of drawers. At first it's impossible to be sure; there's still the chance that it may be something else. Perhaps a moth is attacking the thick winter sweater that's kept in the bottom drawer. The tough coarse ropes of wool are almost too much for him, but he won't give in, he won't admit that it's one too many for him, he tussles on in really heroic style, not taking abrasions and setbacks into any account at all. Or perhaps a beetle is boring into the wood. The bottom drawer sticks, it has to be pulled quite hard before it will open, and after a specially sharp tug a sprinkle of powdery shavings falls from the soft wood. A worm or a beetle could certainly dig himself in very cosily there; and without having to work unduly hard either.

However, it is not a moth in the bottom drawer, it isn't a beetle, it isn't the floor-boards stretching themselves in the dark. It's the question moving under the chest of drawers. It moves a little way on its belly, then craftily keeps still for a while like a tiger waiting to spring. Like a tiger the question crouches under the chest of drawers; a tiny tiger about the size of a mouse, and its striped coat black as velvet instead of tawny. Now it's moving again, flattened against the floor. Out in the room it crouches, expanding, accumulating its force. Soon it will be ready to pounce; its muscles bunch and ripple fearfully inside its skin. Larger and larger it grows: easily, beautifully, the tautened muscles levitate, launch the dark body into the air. The awful, lovely, stylized bow of the spring; effortless, almost languid, inevitable.

Where? Not the bright upstairs room that the morning shines through?

Mirror bevels, catching the sunlight, spit prisms so brilliant they seem cut out of rainbow diamonds. Held in a medallion of net-filtered sun, a white tallboy with elaborate mouldings; ornate, capacious and expensively Edwardian. Drawers glide silently in and out with glimpses of rolled stockings, gloves, blouses, underwear. The garments are lacy or hand-embroidered, there are scent sachets and lavender bags in the corners of the drawers. A travelling clock in its open morocco case chimes a light silver sound. Fluted silver candlesticks, crested, at the mantelpiece ends: the candles in them are pink. Monogrammed silver brushes and boxes yield smothered prismatic gleams. They are laid out on a wide white dressing-table in the bay window. The dressing-table matches the tallboy, the drawer fronts and the frame of the oval mirror criss-crossed with moulded ribbons and wreaths, the table-top, under its glittery paraphernalia, covered by a runner embroidered with pink roses. A similar flowered cloth on the table beside the bed, with a vase of carnations, bottle of Eno's fruit salts, harmless pillbox and water carafe arranged on a silver tray, all very clear in the sun. The net-curtained light coming through the window is candidly and peaceably laid over the pale, shiny, smooth satin bedspread. The sunlit effect is not sharp and not harsh, but insistent enough to give a frank innocuousness, openness, to everything in the room.

The door shuts on this and opens again, slowly, under the same ringed hand which we have seen already. A enters the same room; the only change is that now the sun is setting. Red sunset light fills the room so that it seems to be floating inside a druggist's beaker of coloured water. Red in this sunset danger-light, her head held back tensely, the neck muscles tensing, the fragile exposed curve of the vulnerable white neck, taut, a vulnerable flower-stalk in the red room. With quick red springing wide and away from the neck, a vaporous darkening within the room, the silver suddenly blackened, the window rusted. The left hand leaps to the throat, convulsing, and flashing its dulled ring. Red sprays and stipples the bedspread with the delicacy of fine rain. Red cascades mistily from the open drawers of the tallboy, gingerly spreading fanwise over the whole floor, creeping towards the door

which opens and closes softly and carefully under A's hand as she goes out.

She closes the door with abstracted and almost tender attention, walking slowly away. It's a narrow gallery that she steps out into, a gallery running round three sides of a hall. Everything is very dark, the only light comes from an antique lantern down in the body of the hall which grudgingly emits a dusty glimmer through its horn windows. The gallery is in deepest shade. The panelling, the row of shut doors, are really nothing but guesswork. The hall roof is as high as a church, it wouldn't be out of place to see bats flitting about, or an owl roosting up on one of the rafters. The main part of the hall, down where the light is, presents a queer conflict between the florid and the austere. The bare lofty walls, the grim perspectives of shadow, the uncurtained and ecclesiastically shaped windows, have a severe monastic look. But this asceticism doesn't agree at all with the arsenic-green carpet, or with the sumptuous throne-like chair, glowing with scarlet silk under the lantern. The two colours, the arsenical carpet, the scarlet chair, the only visible colours, burn with the suppressed, dangerous intensity, the theatrical violence, with which occasional colours are overemphasized in the usually neutral-tinted dream scene. There is a chemical suggestion about these tints, reminiscent of fires examined through smoked glass. One feels that they are too strong to be faced without some sort of screen.

A man is sitting in the chair, closely occupied with papers which he can barely see to read. Papers are stacked on a small table beside him: papers are in his hands, on his knees. Because of the position in which he is sitting, bent over his work, it's quite impossible to distinguish clearly anything about him. (But it's a pretty safe bet that he's the man who on a previous dream occasion was too busy to notice that his daughter wanted to ask him for his support.)

The general effect produced by all this is sinister and at the same time slightly phoney. What really introduces the sinister element is that the dramatic trappings are somehow unconvincing. The massive walls might quite possibly be made of paper, the whole place might taper off into a flimsy tangle of wires and screens just out of eyeshot. And yet nothing positively suggests this. It's simply the ominous dream-feeling that appearances may suddenly slip out of themselves into something entirely different.

Visual reality might here be only a mask held in front of the face of some much more frightening reality in another dimension.

And this applies too in some way to A who, wrapped in a long dark garment, slowly starts to walk down the stairs. She is aware of the man sitting near the lamp without being disturbed by his presence. She walks quietly, but without making any special effort to avoid his notice; anyway, he is too far off to hear her. He is much farther away than he could possibly be. Glancing at him, her face is depersonalized, the face of someone seen in a photograph. When she gets to the foot of the stairs, coming into the lamp's radius, the shadows of the banisters fall on her in successively widening strokes, like the flails of a threshing machine. At the foot of the stairs she stands still. She now has to embark on the arsenic sea, incandescent with mineral fires. It's a hard step for her to take. (Why are these endings called acts of weakness?) She stands on the last stair, her hand on the carved newel-post.

She puts one foot in front of her. As her foot touches the carpet, the newel-post, very abnormally tall and massive, rears up behind her like a black tree. In an instantaneous flashback of association comes the vaguely disturbing sensation of *déjà vu*— Has this happened already . . . where . . .?

A takes a step forward; then another. She goes on to a door at the left of the lantern: that it is an outer door is shown by its numerous heavy fastenings; but the bolts are not bolted, the iron chain is hanging unhooked.

(*For a fractional moment, far off in the sea of universal identity, the slave, broken by torture, gravely and quietly speaking his antique wisdom: Is there smoke in the room? If only a little I will remain; but if it is a very great smoke I will go out. For that door is always open. Slow smoke rising solemn and funnel-shaped, as from a censer, conceals him, drifts him away.*)

A has only to turn the handle in order to go out. As she proceeds to do this, there is a perceptible increase in tension. She is set on holding herself aloof and dedicated to her purpose. She seems now definitely not to wish to attract the notice of the man sitting near. Nevertheless, there is a moment, just before she turns the handle, when something forces her to look at him, she even seems to make an unspoken appeal, though cynically without hope, as if to the indifferent and insensitive masses who understand nothing, see nothing. He, not absolutely unconscious, shuffles his documents, moves his feet on the carpet, roughening the bright pile. As tension accumulates, he looks up with a reluctant, resentful, only incipiently aware expression. Does he hear something unusual? Is it raining outside? Has the wind got up suddenly? He doesn't see A. He would have to turn his head right over his shoulder to get her into his field of vision. For a few seconds he is restless, more irritated by the interference with his concentration than anything else. Soon he brushes the whole intangible interruption aside and goes on reading.

A slowly turns the door handle. And this door too she shuts very carefully and quietly behind her as she goes out into the garden of THE ELMS, where the gardener is cutting the edge of the grass with a pair of long-handled shears. She stands on the lawn quite close to him, watching the snipped grass blades fall on the gravel. She has the air of wishing to know with some part of her attention just how the shears are manipulated: but from this fractional escape her real ego stands always dissociated. The gardener does not look up. He wears an old soft-brimmed straw hat, his back is stiff, his head bent, the snicking rhythm of the shears does not hesitate.

While he stolidly goes on clipping, a car pulls up in front of the porch, the chauffeur gets out and rings the bell, the suburban lady steps down from the car, the maid comes to open the door of the house. These four people, the visitor, the gardener, the chauffeur, the maid, each wearing a similar mask-face under straw hat, hat with bird in it, peaked cap, muslin cap, are grouped together a few yards from A. The tableau holds in suspense while all the masks slowly swing towards A and remain fixed. Fright starting to appear on her face, A looks from one to the other, turns round, hurries away. As she goes out of the gate, the branches of the elms at each side reach out fumbling at her, their long arms fingered with groping leaves. A leaf falls: she begins running; others fall. Magnified, not in size but in prominence, dead leaves eddy to and fro on the ground, cluster in dusty drifts, scamper singly away.

And against a lead sky the bare tree-tops are labouring.

Are you afraid of the tigers? Do you hear them padding all round you on their fierce fine velvet feet?

· The speed of the growth of tigers in the nightland is a thing which ought to be investigated some time by the competent authority. You start off with one, about the size of a mouse, and before you know where you are he's twice the size of the Sumatra tiger which defeats all comers in that hemisphere. And then, before you can say Knife (not a very tactful thing to say in the circumstances anyhow), all his boy and girl friends are gathered round, your respectable quiet decorous docile night turns itself into a regular tiger-garden. Wherever you look, the whole night is full of tigers leaping and loping and grooming their whiskers and having a wonderful time at your expense. There isn't a thing you can do about it apparently.

The wilder the tricks of the tigers, the more abandoned their games and gambols, the more diversely dreadful become the dooms of the unfortunate A in this dream. Her fugitive shape, black-swathed, vanishes at the end of every cul-de-sac. Through the cities of the world she pursues her fate, in streets where the dead eyes of strangers are no colder than the up-swarming lights which have usurped the brilliance of the stars. From shrouded platforms among the clouds she hurtles down. She plunges from towers strict and terrible in their stark fragile strength, delicate as jerboa's bones on the sky, perdurable with granite and steel. Slumped on his stained bar, Pete the Greek, beneath flyblown Christmas festoons which no one will ever remove, hears the screaming skid of wheels spouting slush with her blood. Limp as an old coat not worth a hanger, she is to be found behind numbered doors in hotel bedrooms; or dangling from the trees of country churchyards where leaning tombstones like feeble-minded ghosts mop and mow in the long summer grass. The weeds of lonely rivers bind her with clammy skeins; the tides of tropical oceans suck off her shoes; crabs scuttle over her eye sockets. Sheeted and anonymous on rubbered wheels she traverses the interminable bleakness of chloroform-loaded corridors. The sardonic yap of the revolver can be taken as the full stop arbitrarily concluding each ambiguous sentence.

An erratic but steadfast seeking, saraband and stalking of death by violence through the indifferent world. The dance enters upon a movement of weariness, desperation, finale. Just what its form, gesture and detail being variable and in no way permanent. For the occasion may be supposed a town house of a particular type, in an unfashionable, cheap district, a lodging-house possibly. There will be the area, spearheaded railings, crammed dustbins vomiting refuse; the street air stale in the unsweet warm evening; grimy, strident-voiced children, tired and cantankerous, quarrelling at their play. The house door, in need of painting, shabbily formal like a neglected and desecrated altar beneath the fanlight carrying the street number; perhaps a small bed-and-breakfast sign at one side. Inside, the hall, narrow, in gloom, worn linoleum double-tracked towards stairs and basement; a smell here of unappetizing meals, cabbage water and of the mackintosh hooked to the hatrack. A glazed pottery drainpipe, painted with bulrushes, used as umbrella-stand.

The staircase plods upwards, flagging at every flight, the creaking treads sustained by dirt-coloured felt, trampled threadbare. At the top the back bedroom, dismal with furniture discards from many rooms; cluttered with glasses, cups, empty whisky and gin bottles; syringes, scattered tablets, powders spilled from their crumpled papers, needles, empty tubes labelled diamorph., etc., litter the floor. At the sash window, the dingy scum-white lace with the entangled light strangling meanly in it: on the brass bedstead, huddled bedclothes in disorder, beneath which the stiff, frightening shape of some human form can barely, inexorably, be discerned. A wicked black frieze of cowls and chimney-pots beyond the lightly air-sucked curtain, jagged angles of roofs and gables iron-sharp on the sky. The vacant, exhausted sky, like an old shell.

My mother's death made no difference to the house except that she herself was no longer in it. At least her outward presence had gone away. Her sadness and her boredom stayed in the quiet rooms where I lived alone with shadows. As if they felt lonely, these two ghosts attached themselves to me and entered my night-time world. Sometimes I thought they had taken me for my mother, and I felt nearer to her through their nearness. Sometimes it seemed as if her departure had brought her too near. Sometimes her nearness was like a hand on my shoulder; then I felt frightened, and ran and jumped and turned somersaults even, trying to shake off her hand. But the hand always stayed on my shoulder as long as it wished to.

Sometimes, looking out of an upstairs window, I could feel my mother looking out of my eyes. Like people who from a bridge watch fish swimming below them, we saw the outside world as an alien element where we could take no part. Isolated behind the glass of our lonely window we looked down on the daily life which was not for us.

Shouting and singing and hallooing his satellites the gregarious sun comes ranting upon the collective stage. After so many billion repetitions you might expect him to be getting the least bit perfunctory: but not he; no sirree. Like a conscientious actor determined to give the public full value for money, he rampages through his performance as enthusiastically as the first time he put on the act. Of course the rest of the cast plays up to him. The clouds jump to their opening positions, hurriedly snatching the gaudy properties of the co-operative scarf dance. On earth ocean bellows to ocean across the continents like allied commanders exchanging a salute of guns. The mutual greetings of the archipelagos are more *intime*.

As the sunwaves break over the roof of the jungle, flocks of parrots burst upward from the dark teeming mass like an explosion of rockets. The monkey village yawns, fornicates, pinches, scratches, chatters itself awake. In honeycombed caves the glow-worms conglomerate starrily. In linked caves, between clotted stalactites, the bats hang themselves up together. The gentle pandas in their dainty dress indulge in party frolics among the rocks.

At sea it's the same thing: whales, porpoises, dolphins, flying fish, mackerel, sprats, all travelling in schools and shoals; oyster-beds packed to capacity; animalcula and foraminifera swarming in astronomical multitudes.

Higher up the scale there's no difference either. The tribal community rouses itself *en masse*. Everyone begins laughing and talking and praying and crying and cooking and washing and working on top of everyone else. The baskets of the fighting cocks are placed close together for company's sake. Paying the civilized penalty, Mr Whosit awakens flimsily divided from the tens or hundreds of rabbits inhabiting his particular warren. Quick the switch and the dial, then, to bring loud the voices of nations; quick the collar and tie, quick the pants of respectability, the shined shoes to run to the crowded eating-places, the streets, the buses, the trains, cars, planes, offices, parks, night-clubs, theatres, hospitals, churches, graveyards, tombs.

Heaven. The populous scene partly suggests a fairy-tale illustration, partly a picture from an old-fashioned Bible, partly the enchanted cave in a pantomime. Broad brilliant azure sky with cloud cushions on which parties of angels recline. To the left, a landscape of flowery fields where numerous saints and seraphs are strolling about or sitting on the seats placed as if in a park. Fountains playing, birds singing, rivulets rippling. The grass is brilliantly green, the flowers sparkle like jewels, instead of bridges rainbows span the streams, the benches are made out of solid gold.

At the centre, in tiered majestic gradations, there soar, enormously, steps of intense and dazzling white alabaster. Endless streams of angelic figures move in stately procession up and down this colossal stairway which presumably leads to the Throne.

On the right, seen panoramically at a lower level, a sort of huge skating-rink, blastingly bright and surrounded by dense gold-crowned, white-robed crowds. From here rises, very remote, very impressive, words indistinguishable, a vast volume of community hymn-singing with *vox humana* and massed bands accompaniment. When the communal howl dies away there is a sharp prolonged staccato rattle, something like a burst of machine-gun fire, as the saints pitch their crowns on to the glittering surface in front of them.

Now, at the extremities of the stair, appear seraphim whose lifted trumpets discharge notes in crisp upward cadence. The crowds on the right relax after their vocalism, break into groups, laughing and talking, and slowly begin to disperse. They give the impression of lighting up cigarettes, pushing their haloes on to the backs of their heads and then putting their hands in their pockets although of course they don't do these things. While they are strolling away a band of children romp gaily at the foot of the stairs, playing touch-last with the cherubs, whose muslin wings are attached to their shoulders by braces of tinsel braid. The children are all about the same age, twelve or fourteen years old, sexually indeterminate, very china-dollishly pretty, with rosebud mouths and beautiful curly hair.

The little girl B (she is an unobtrusive spectator in the foreground) watches the children admiringly as they dance into the fields and begin making the flowers into chains and posies. (As each flower is picked another immediately springs up in its place.)

B is obviously very much charmed by all that she sees, although slightly overawed. She stands first on one foot and then on the other, looking all round, anxious not to miss anything, but not liking to move away from a bush which partly conceals her and is somewhat ostentatiously decorated with large silver twinkling stars.

The whole scene is humming with holy business, cheerful and social and sanctified at the same time; there is an audible hum too, the articulation of eternal, collectivized, innocent pleasure, a con-fused burble of music and distant singing; laughter, water harps, birds, bells. Suddenly all this is stilled. Silence. A single bell chimes solemnly and with resonance far away.

The smiles fade from the lips of the angels, the saints break off what they are saying and look grave, the children stand quietly with serious faces, the flowers hanging down in their hands. Every head turns in the same direction.

B looks to see what it is they are all looking at. While she has been facing the other way, A has appeared from some unnoted point, and now crosses the foreground, dressed all in black. She walks not slowly and not quickly, but in immense isolation, utterly separate from the shining crowds, at whom, in passing, she glances without envy or interest.

Timidly forsaking the bush which shelters her, B steps forward, starts after her mother.

At the same moment, two executives of the angelic order, severe in their robes, their faces shadowed by long pointed wings, advance, linked by a property arch which they carry between them. The arch, made out of gun-metal-coloured paper (the sort in which silver is sometimes wrapped to keep it from tarnishing), simulates a subway approach and bears a small neon sign in red letters EXIT TO HELL.

Supported by an angel on each side, the arch is set on the ground. The audience looks uneasily from side to side, whispers flying about. A walks under the arch with a strictly impassive face: she seems not to notice where she is going. The seraphim at the foot of the stairs raise their trumpets. The saintly crowds shift, shuffle, whisper, stare, lean forward, expressions of deploring pietude glazing avid curiosity; stare, seasoning sempiternal bright-ness with the zest of distant but contemporaneous shade.

The first notes of the trumpets are blown.

Just as the angels are preparing to carry the arch away B makes a desperate dash at it and dives through.

Everything blacks out – as if in an abrupt dense smoke-screen – as successive curtains of darkness are drawn. The faces of the child-angels last longest, porcelain painted with Os of insipid disparagement. On the obliteration of the last doll face, the hymn singing, very distantly, starts up again and continues, diminishing into final inaudibility, for a few seconds more.

What happens when you start on the downward trip? The elevator doors clang shut, a suffocating infernal wind roars up the shaft, it seems as though you'll never get to the bottom; there's plenty of time to wonder what's coming and to wish yourself somewhere else. Of course there isn't a hope of ever getting out again into the light. Once you're on your way down the machinery takes charge of you, you're caught, trapped, finished for good and all. Certainly there are legends about individuals who have escaped, even after reaching the final platforms. But these are heroes, fabulous figures who perhaps never really existed except as projections of wishful thinking in the minds of ordinary people. At any rate, they are far too dubious and remote to be of any real moral support or to provide any justifiable basis for optimism. You might just as well give in and pluck the cruel thorn of hope out of your heart. It's always less painful to surrender to the stream of events than to turn yourself into a dam to be battered and pounded. It's true that if the worst comes to the worst you'll be drowned: but that's better than being beaten to a jelly; and there's always a slight chance that you may get washed ashore somewhere before the end.

And now, with regard to the drop into the lower regions, things really might be much worse. It's no good pretending that you get the gaiety down here. You don't get the variety or the excitement or the social or cultural life. If those were the things you were after you should have been much more prudent, you should have hung on to your original identity disc, number billion-billion-billion-whatever of the collectivists, instead of losing it somewhere or throwing it away in a fit of bravado. Then you could have trooped along to paradise with the rest and been one of the crowd for ever and a day.

But since it's happened like this, since you've been thrown out on your ear by the celestial party, or thrown yourself out, it makes no difference which way you put it, the only thing left is to adapt yourself as well as you can.

It's lonely? Sure, it's lonely. That's what you asked for, didn't you? After all, if you hadn't been too superior for the gang, you wouldn't be here. And think how much more distinguished it is to be on your own, or with one or two individuals like yourself, than to be an ordinary gregarious animal going about with the herd.

You miss the sun and air? Sure, you do. There are some million miles of solid obstruction between you and the free place where the wind blows and the birds sing in the sunshine. You'll never feel the sun warming you any more. You'll never hear the birds. No bird could live in this atmosphere, this *ersatz* air that eddies here in stale and fetid artificial gusts. But you can breathe in it and like it too. And in the end it will smell sweeter to you than a sea breeze, just as this dim, unvaried and unfresh light will suit your eyes better than the vulgar sun.

You don't like it here? Why didn't you keep out, then, for God's sake, while you had the chance? Anyhow, it's no good moaning and snivelling now. Put a good face on it. Be tough. Show the crowd you can take it. You're an individualist, aren't you? To hell with the crowd. What do you care about them? You're here because you've got no time for the crowd. What do you care about them and their damnfool heaven? To hell with heaven, anyway.

My father thought I ought to be among other children, he sent me to a day school not far away. It was autumn. On windy days when I was walking to school each tree at the roadside stood in its own gold shower. I played a game catching the leaves as they fell. Whenever I caught a specially fine one I put it into my pocket. But next time I looked at it the colours had always faded and I was left with only a crumpled dead thing to throw away.

To begin with, I was quite glad to be going to school. I thought it might be something new and exciting. But it was not exciting, and soon it stopped being even new, and became disappointing and dull. There was a play at the end of term and I had a good part in it. I thought it would be a real excitement to act in a play. But when the day came that was somehow disappointing as well.

After that everything that happened at school seemed unreal and a waste of time, a part of the dull day world which was unimportant. Without understanding the reason, I knew that I had to keep the day unimportant. I had to prevent the day world from becoming real. I waited all through the day for the moment of going home to my night world, the reality which I lived in the secret life of the house.

It's a beautiful spring morning somewhere in the South. This is a
country which later in the year will be burnt brown and harsh, but
now its first ardent response to the sun has flushed it with tender
radiance. Soft sienna villages crown the hills, and in every village
the church bells are ringing. The notes of the different bells drift
and flutter and mingle as if flocks of pigeons with singing reeds in
their wings were wheeling between the hills. From all the villages
streams of gaily dressed peasants are setting out for the town. Some
ride, some travel in carts pulled by lumbering flower-decked oxen,
most of all are on foot. They pass through olive groves where the
scarlet tulips wave wild silken flags in the thin grass. Like *vivas* the
vines brandish new fistfuls of vivid green. The whole landscape
rejoices, the carnival notes of the bells swoop festively through the
brilliant air. The peasants are full of holiday gaiety; it is a celebration for them, a great day. They go along laughing and calling to
one another and singing to the music of their simple flutes and
guitars

towards the town where the great day has also dawned. By
contrast with the traditional idyllic country scene everything here
has a somewhat ominous look. Views, sliding into each other, of the
streets and squares of this town; a medium-sized southern town.
Sunshine illuminates it hard as floodlighting. The streets, hung
with garlands and bunting and unintelligibly sloganed banners, are
all deserted. The main street slopes from a large public building
with marble steps and balustrade down to a frontage on a glass lake.
The lake frontage is planted with flowering magnolias. The boughs
of the trees are black, stiff and shiny as if cut in patent leather, the
flowers dangerously white and upspringing. (Do they recall to the
dreamer another dream?)

From every doorway people can now be seen pouring into the
streets: they come in a steadily advancing spate, filling all available
space and still pouring on. There is a confused throbbing, trampling noise while they are on the move which, as the leading ranks
consolidate into a dense crowd in front of the public building,
becomes shot through with conflicting march tunes, bursts of clapping, singing, cheers; also with boos and shouts; with sharp distant

stabs of shots, breaking glass, screams. The latter sounds are barely audible in the centre of the crowd where enthusiasm is solid.

Certainly the princess doesn't hear them, she hears nothing but cheering voices, as she appears in her crown and state robes at the top of the steps. While she is standing there bowing, a glimpse through a broken window of soldiers entering a room where a man sits reading, paying no attention to what's happening outside. Brief fragmentary flashes of smashed spectacles falling; arm-banded arms wrenching and grinding together thin shirt-sleeved arms; raised rifle-butt; open book on the floor, pages torn and defaced by huge muddy heel-mark. Then the man hanging slack between arm-grips, heaved through a door, slung into the crowd; shirt torn, tie twisted off, blood pouring down his face under limp lock of hair. The people against whom he falls pay no attention, their faces are not seen, they are just trousered or skirted bodies, some with worker's hobnailed boots, some with two-toned suède shoes or natty brogues or patents, some with tennis shoes, pumps, sandals or high-heeled slippers, which automatically trample him as he folds up between them.

The princess does not see this episode (indeed, it hardly lasts as long as a flash of lightning), she is looking in another direction. She is watching a group of villagers, late arrivals from the country, who are hurrying along the now empty waterfront towards the streets lined with soldiers where the crowds are collected. In their eagerness not to miss anything the peasants are almost running: yet they can't help stopping occasionally to admire the wonders of the town with faces of childish and delighted amazement.

Now that the child idea has been introduced it suddenly becomes apparent that they are children, the soldiers are children, the crowds are composed of children, the princess is a schoolgirl in a cardboard crown covered with gold paper.

She stands on the steps, smiling, enjoying to the utmost the acclamation of shrill childish cheers. But only for a moment. Her triumphantly straying eyes are quickly caught by an isolated moving shape, invisible to those facing her, the back view of a familiar dark-wrapped figure walking across the now vacant waterfront and rapidly passing out of sight between the magnolias. Deep in the girl's brain the conflict at once beginning shows in the swift movements of her eyes, back and forth, from the black-branched distant trees to the close shouting faces.

Almost simultaneously with the start of the struggle it's over, her crown tumbles off as she runs down the steps, sheers through the crowd of children, some of whom immediately start scuffling over the crown, which is soon torn and trodden to pieces between them.

At the boarding-school I went to when I was older I felt unhappy, although to begin with I didn't know this. The place was ugly outside and inside. The rooms were noisy and cold and crowded and I was alone in them. Of course, I always had been alone, but this was different. I was alone now in a bad way, alone in a crowded ugliness without respite. There was always winter framed in the frozen windows. The winter light marched along barren hilltops. The metal trees could never have sprouted leaves.

I began remembering things that were far away and forgotten: the way the sun shone in another country. One day when I combed my hair in front of a mirror, my mother looked out at me with her face of an exiled princess. That was the day I knew I was unhappy.

On a large bare round table in vacuum a double-page photographic montage is outspread: the same sort of layout as in an illustrated weekly but scaled up to three or four times the size. Detail of plain white clock-face marking seven-thirty. Jigsaw of school buildings angled in light and shade to sharp abstract design. Very chaotic detail of cloakroom with hockey boots scattered in pure disorder: rows of basins patterned with dirty hand marks, odd ends of grimy soap-cakes; a tap left running, forcing a costive passage through half-choked plug-hole; sodden stained towel twisted and pulled to the extreme end of its roller.

Views of classrooms, high windowed, impersonal: straight plain functional furniture; everything unnecessarily bleak, comfortless, unaesthetic: battered textbooks, atlases, volumes of standard works – some upside down – overflowing from shelves, upon which such things as broken chalks, paintboxes, indian clubs, dumb-bells, skipping ropes, are stacked too in hopelessly overcrowded confusion. Very close detail of grey mottled inkwell with viscous slime of congealed ink dregs coating the bottom. Beside it, on a shallowly grooved wooden desktop, two pens, one with glossy new relief nib and tapered blue holder which terminates in a small heart made of lapis lazuli; the other with wooden holder, splintered and much chewed, nib crossed and encrusted with dried ink.

A funereal black overmantel supporting two bronze rearing horses stiffly tugged at by muscular half-nudes.

Long dining-tables, spotted white cloths; bone, plated, wooden rings clenching unfresh table napkins; huge hacked joint of mutton with gravy congealing; dish of stone-white potatoes; round glass dish cross-glittered with highlights showing glazed fruit-halves like visceral segments.

Detail of a tall highly polished silver cup on its black stand, and of other shapes and sizes of trophies in various positions. Crossed and tangled in a spillikin pile, skates, hockey sticks, tennis rackets (with and without presses), cricket bats. A football-sized ball is shown just about to drop through a circular piece of netting projecting from a goal-post against a sky across which birds are flying. An expanse of grass, very short, flat and arid, girls in tunics and white blouses caught by their shadows in arrested momentum. Girls' arms, legs, torsos, in gymnastic poses with ropes, rings, clubs, parallel bars.

Girls grouped formally on a stage. Girls' hands warming on the coils of radiators.

An isolated radiator, too narrow for its height and by suggestion inadequate, under a curtained window at night; the parsimonious curtains leave a four-inch gap through which a small moon quizzes coldly. Other curtains in dormitories hanging like corrugated fences white in strong moonlight or clumsily bunched behind iron bedrails. Cupboards crowded with identical garments, in drawers, on shelves, on hooks and hangers. Repetitive framed photos of parents on shared dressing-tables. Close-ups of some of these. They are all photographs of the same two people taken in different poses; a stereotyped rather sweet insipid woman's face, slightly faded, with much fluffy hair; a typical pukka could-be-military Britisher vacuously and complacently staring. Beds, or maybe it's one single bed with white honeycomb spread, reflected in mirrors *ad infinitum*.

A rough-grained worker's hand with black broken thumbnail grasping a rope; complementing it, under a glum sky, a bell swung at a steep angle, clapper outlined on sky. A small brass handbell on top of a pile of books, horn-rimmed spectacles and a fountain-pen alongside. The clock-face again. The hands are now rigidly rectangled at nine o'clock. A solitary electric bulb, very isolated and frangible, dangling from white ceiling under a cheap white saucer shade at the end of a dark cord on which two flies have settled.

B looks carefully and seriously at these pictures for quite a long time, leaning her elbows on the round table. She seems to be trying to make up her mind whether she likes what she sees. In the end she apparently makes a negative decision because she turns away from the pages and her eyes slowly defocus.

The uncompromising black-and-white of the dream reproduction now blurs and comes to a minimal pictorial distinctness. The quality of apperception is emotional rather than visual from now on. Everything appears slightly out of focus, as if seen through half-closed eyes: not exactly distorted, but sufficiently out of focus to produce a feeling of great remoteness and unreality.

First a series of calm sensuous impressions; all of a sort to link up with the ideas of warmth, sunshine, security, love; in the background a tranquil rocking, a lullaby, without any threat of discontinuance. The right feeling could be represented here by a deep-South crooning of the 'Do you want the moon to play with and the stars to run away with' variety, provided that the actual black mammy association could be kept out of it.

Gradually materializing pointillist stipple of sunlight sifted through green leaves. Transparencies of huge criss-crossed emerald-green leaves of the sort used by natives as wrappings: frayed fringes of such leaves. Very idealized mild round male oriental face smiling its benign smile; his arms, hands, yellow fingers; his clever fingers drawing birds, flowers, fishes, leaves, on thin rice paper under moving shadows of leaves. Smiling, he lets the pictures drift away on the breeze; one by one they drift off and become real; the birds open their red beaks to chirp as they flutter away; the leaves attach themselves to a bush, the flowers distribute among them their purple and orange wings; the fish float for a moment on the stream's surface before they swerve into the water and disappear. The sun, the sure fountain of warmth and comfort, the man. The smiling yellow face of the sun-man, yellow fingers benevolently juggling the world.

Again the generalized sense-impression of friendly security with its background of peaceful rocking, wordless crooning, augmented this time by the reinforcement of some exclusive and unique support.

A woman with chrysanthemum-curly hair – it is A, of course – approaches from a distance and comes nearer and nearer; slowly and steadily approaches until she stands so close that everything else is shut out. Quietly bending her face neither mournful nor gay, she takes B's hand and walks away with her down a narrow path; receding with her along the private, blind, quiet, inviolate path, the backward-reaching, down-reaching tunnel, as if into the crater of an extinct volcano.

At school the spell I had learnt in my parents' house was no longer sufficient: I had to discover another and stronger magic. At school there was only the day world which I refused to accept and which would not accept me either. I had to find some private place where I could be at home.

A big country estate in the finest old-world tradition. Undulating parkland with plantations of great trees here and there. The trees are all perfect specimens, scientifically nourished and trimmed, there isn't a dead twig or a superfluous branch to be seen. It's the same wherever you look. Everything has been planned, protected and cared for down to the last detail. And you can see at a glance that this has been so for hundreds of years. The lawns which surround the mansion on the hill have been shaved by skilful scythes to the smoothest velvety pile. Huge clusters of grapes hang in the vinery, peaches and nectarines ripen on sunny walls. The flower gardens are awash with colour and scent. In the walled kitchen garden the fat earth overflows like a vegetable cornucopia. Strutting pigeons display their fans on the roofs of stables where splendid blood horses are housed. Sleek hounds drowse at their kennel doors. In sun-speckled shady groves deer daintily roam the preserves they share with the handsome gamebirds. As if suspended in amber, fish hang in the clear streams. Swans steer their stately and immaculate courses upon a lake that with no less exactitude mirrors the passing clouds. Here are no savage rocks, no jungles, no glaciers, no treacherous tropical lagoons, no fantastics of the animal, vegetable or mineral world to startle or cause amazement. Here all is temperate and harmonious; enclosed, perfect, pre-arranged, controlled and known.

A man wearing the uniform of major in one of the better-dressed modern armies steps briskly into the dream foreground, accompanied by an orderly. He has a small dark pointed beard and carries the words Liaison Officer in gold on each shoulder. With stiff one-two military precision the following motions are carried out:

Major removes cap, holds it at rigid arm's length. Orderly takes cap with his left hand: with right hand places halo attached to long trailing flex on major's head: plugs in to point on floor. Halo lights up. Orderly hands dark leather-bound book (the word *Parables* momentarily legible on the spine); in crisp uninflected voice, as if reading orders for the day, reads:

Of course the first essential for a domain of this sort is privacy. It would lose its charm straight away if every Tom, Dick and Harry were allowed to come in and carve his initials on the tree-trunks and litter the grass with cigarette packets and paper bags and all sorts of refuse. There's no getting away from the fact that the general public must be excluded if things are to be kept as they should be.

Certainly it's disappointing from the angle of sightseers who may have come from the city in some hot dusty overcrowded motor coach, to find such an inviting spot hedged round with NO TRES-PASSING notices. One can see the point of view of such people and sympathize with their feelings as they peer through the fence at the cool tempting glades and flowery dells on the other side. What a perfect place for our picnic, they are doubtless saying to one another. And doubtless they feel indignant at the idea of an individual landowner having the exclusive right to enjoy this delightful spot.

But one must look at the other side of the picture as well. Isn't there something to be said for the owner whose whole life is bound up with the property and devoted to maintaining it? Surely he earns the right to his privacy. Especially as he is almost certain to be one of these extremely sensitive people, of an entirely different order from the ordinary run of humans and totally unfitted to live at close quarters with them. Deprive him of his seclusion and you deprive him of everything: perhaps even of life itself; for it's more than doubtful whether his delicate organism would survive such a shock. I don't mean to imply by this that our landowners as a class are particularly asthenic or that their hold on life is specially weak. On the contrary, we have all heard instances of these gentry displaying astonishing fortitude in defence of the things which they consider valuable. They will go to the most extravagant lengths in such circumstances; whether it's on behalf of an ideal or something concrete. But without these value objects – and being private is certainly one of the most important of them – they seem to lose interest in the world and to retreat from it accordingly. It's as if they presented their terms to life, and, the terms being rejected, quietly and proudly withdrew from the scene, preferring non-participation to compromise. Not good enough for me, you can imagine some old squire saying with a half-humorous, half-sardonic inflexion, in face of an ultimatum. And then he will take his departure without any fuss at all, unobtrusively abandoning the stage. For how can he, for so long the sole proprietor of a vast demesne, lower himself to associate with the public in an existence of base competition? No, you can't expect the descendant of a proud race, with centuries of tradition behind him, to tolerate the desecration of vulgarians; and you can't blame him either if, before making his exit, he secretly destroys his dearest possessions rather than have them fall into the hands of the mob.

The trend nowadays is towards more and more collectivism. Of course nobody denies that the good things of the world should be equally accessible to all, and that the owning of property by individuals is in theory deplorable. But it seems to me that careful consideration should be given to the case of the landowners who, far more often than not, are hard-working, abstemious men of high moral principles. Taking a broad view, is it really the best policy to eject them summarily from the positions which they alone are qualified to fill? Qualified, what's more, not only by personal training but by all sorts of hereditary influences, the value and power of which are not yet fully understood. Admittedly, from the collective standpoint, an estate, no matter how perfectly run, is ideologically valueless unless it is accessible to the community. On the other hand, if such an estate is delivered over lock, stock and barrel to incompetent and inexperienced managers, it will soon become factually valueless too. Would it not be possible to evolve some system under which the *status quo* could be maintained – perhaps until the death of the present proprietors – meanwhile raising the educational standard so that the general public will be fitted both to administer the estates efficiently and to appreciate them to the greatest advantage?

The problem, at any rate, seems worthy of study. To my mind, a very real danger exists of irreplaceable treasures being lost to the community through the thoughtless vandalism of uninstructed persons, if all these great places are suddenly thrown open indiscriminately.

What happens when a crowd of holiday makers bursts into such a property? They will uproot plants and damage trees which have taken many decades to reach maturity; they will leave gates open, allowing valuable animals to stray and to ruin the gardens; inside the house no object will be secure. In an hour or so the work of generations of skilled craftsmen will be destroyed.

Don't think that I'm attacking the common people or condemning their high spirits. All I want is to make sure that they don't lose sources of future pleasure through receiving them prematurely before they have had opportunities of learning to appreciate their true worth. That's why I'm entering this plea on behalf of the old landowners.

There has been a tendency lately to speak of these men as dissolute degenerates, given to all sorts of perversions. Let me assure you that in my experience this is by no means the case. In the course of events I have come in contact with a number of them, and they have all been individuals of integrity and moderation, one or two even fanatically ascetic in their personal lives, although naturally their outlook is entirely different from ours. I don't want to appear as a partisan of the landowning class. Indeed, I am aware that I have already pressed their claims beyond the limits of personal prudence. But I would be dishonest to myself if I were to refrain from making a final appeal for serious consideration of the whole difficult problem.

While the Liaison Officer is reading the last few sentences a bell starts to ring, at first distantly, becoming louder and more insistent as the dream grows correspondingly more transparent. Finally he is seen closing his book, preparing to remove his halo, laughing spectrally for an instant, before he dissolves altogether with the disrupted dream.

Now I understood why I had to prevent the day world from getting real. I saw that my instinct about this was a true one. As my eyes grew more discerning, I recognized my enemy's face and I was afraid, seeing there a danger that one day might destroy me.

Because of my fear that the daytime world would become real, I had to establish reality in another place.

Truth, it's everything. The man who said, What is truth? certainly touched on a big subject. The truth of the matter is that there's far too much truth in the world. The world, from whichever point you observe it, is altogether too full of truth. It isn't easy to recognize this truth in the first place, but it's impossible ever to ignore it once it's been grasped.

Every single possibility or impossibility is true somewhere to someone at some time. It's true that the earth is as round as an orange and as flat as a pancake. It's true that the wicked island goddess Rangda is a good goddess when she takes off her mask. Black magic on top, white magic underneath. That proves that black's white, doesn't it?

It's true that the idea of America is a bright and shining thing in the mind. It's true that the idea of America is a crude and brutal land inhabited by adolescents and gangsters.

Defeatism's true; war's true. So's idealism and the hope of a better society. You pay your money and you take your choice. Civilization's gone down the drain. Utopia's just round the corner.

It's true that civilization marches on: atomic energy plus universal war. The Hallelujah Chorus from Handel's *Messiah*; HMV recording. That's a truth, although universal war. There's the truth that you go to bed with and the truth that wakes you up at three o'clock in the morning when the tigers are jumping up and down on the roof and eternity is flapping at the earth like somebody shaking a rug. There's the truth of loving and hating, being an extrovert and an introvert, a success and a failure, travelling all over the world, living your whole life in one place, having security, accepting all risks. Then there's the truth that you find with the dirty glasses stacked in the sink. That's a different sort of truth.

Books continue to be written in one truth and read in another. The radio announces various kinds of truth to suit every listener. Atomic warfare is true and so is the Sermon on the Mount. Truth is everywhere, in everything, all the time. That's why it's true. It's true that all this is obvious and has been said often before. That truth's as true as any other truth too.

The artist paints his picture to suit himself or his client. The artist. Yes, well, let's have a look at him now.

The artist. Traditional with beard, corduroys, big black hat, bohemian scarf. Or, if you prefer it that way, elegantly turned out in a thirty-guinea suit tailored by Simpson, Simpson & Simpson of Savile Row. Anyhow, the artist. As a young man. Full of enthusiasm and theories and alcohol and amours. As an old man. Successful, and respectfully badgered by publishers for autobiography: or nondescript and obscure. Or forty and frustrated and amused-not-so-amused-by-it-all. The artist, anyway.

He turns his back upon Fitzroy Square and walks south down Charlotte Street with his slouching or affected, or jaunty or casual, or alert or pompous, or resigned or aggressive, or indifferent or weary step. Past the art dealers and the window full of rubber devices; past the delicatessen and the tobacconists and the sensational news placards (if not cricket results must be death and destruction tall on the placards); past the cheap restaurants, past the dirty curly-haired kids playing hopscotch. Past the dead tower (dead as all the dead days, Oxford or else Montmartre; dead ones, you who were with us in the ships at Mylae, who had amaranth breath, who had death in the veins, dead living before the world died; dying now no longer); past the fabricators of steel candelabra.

Into Geo. Rowney & Co's. Or Winsor & Newton Ltd., Rathbone Place. It's really quite immaterial which because he can get any material that he wants in the way of material at either of them. Unless of course he prefers the products of M. Lefranc, in which case he may have to walk a little bit farther or maybe not if the truth were known.

As a matter of fact it isn't anything in the paint line that he's after just now. Not water-colour or oil, artist's or student's or decorator's, in any language whatever; so it's simply a waste of breath to offer him deep ultramarine, *outremer foncé, oltremare scuro, ultramar obscuro,* etc.

What interests him today is a good large sheet of Whatman paper with a fairly rough surface and not tinted any colour at all: which he fastens upon the skyline with four drawing pins, *punaises* or thumbtacks, according to the country he's in at the moment: and proceeds to apply a fast wash which runs down in a double-toothed dragon's back of black trees ridging steep foothills, iron-black mountains behind, down to the bottomless cañon of black-green water. A sombre landscape eventuates, worked out in blacks and greys and the very gloomiest shades of viridian. A scowling sky, ominous mountains, water cold, still and solid-looking as ice, trackless fir forests, the fine spray from the gigantic waterfalls fuming slowly like ectoplasm. No sign of life, no living creature visible anywhere. Only the forbidding and desolate silence, deathliness, of this mountainous far-off region. Till suddenly bursting from the high crags, soaring and planing above the highest pinnacles, two great birds, eagles most probably, swoop together into an extraordinary and desperate aerial encounter; plunging down headlong together, and all the time reciprocally involved, diving through a thousand feet of pure frozen emptiness, righting themselves, it seems miraculously, at the very last moment before crashing into the water, to glide interlocked over the surface, without effort, without the faintest perceptible winging, at the culmination of their appalling love flight.

With a *dégagé* flip of the palette knife the paper's off and making way for a clean sheet. This time the artist has changed his style. No more romantic gloom, no more melodramatics. This time it's a street scene that's delineated; or rather, a part of a street scene, a shop window, a toy shop window to be precise, with a Noah's ark in the middle. Up the gangway the animals troop, there isn't an odd one among them, everything's in perfect order, not a single mistake, no two of the same sex, not even the earthworms, though heaven knows one might easily make a slip. Last of all Mr and Mrs Noah shoulder to shoulder and carrying between them a pair of huge indecent shells stuck together like jujubes. In they go, the doors slam, Gabriel sounds his horn, the lady evangelist with gold voice and armour-plated bosom breaks a bottle of champagne over the bows to complete the launching. Don't deplore the extravagance, friends. Replenishing the earth is no picnic, and it wasn't the best champagne anyway.

Not the incomparable Moët & Chandon Dom Pérignon Cuvée of 1921; or the great Lanson of that same year; or the magnificent Moët & Chandon Imperial Crown English Market. Not even one of the 1928s; such as a Perrier Jouet, or a Pommery & Greno, or a Bollinger, or a Krug, or an Ernest Irroy, or a Pol Roger, or a Clicquot Dry England, or a Heidsieck Monopole.

Don't worry, folks, there's plenty more where that came from, could be magnums, could be jeroboams. The fashionable wedding breakfast's overflowing with gold-necked bottles in coolers, with orchids and caviare and diamonds and pearls and the creations of the most exclusive-expensive couturiers and the perfumes of a royal prince. Don't ask awkward questions, comrades. Don't bring all that up again now. We've got to increase the population somehow, haven't we? Otherwise how are we going to keep on fighting everyone everywhere all the time?

Under striped awnings the wedding guests depart; in cars, in bars, they re-shuffle, re-sort themselves for the night. The old act is on: Boy meets Girl, at smoky parties, in public conveyances, in the best hotels, in the lowest boozers, in suburban parlours, on park benches, under viaducts. And steady trains of midgets march behind.

Off comes the paper again. And now the artist seems to be impatient. It isn't enough just to rip off the sheet and leave it wherever it happens to fall. This time he has to tear it into very small pieces, crumple the scraps in his hand, and throw them peevishly into the grate along with the cigarette ends and the empty cigarette packets, the spent matches, the paint rags, the flattened and finished tubes. Perhaps he's a trifle hung-over this morning. Perhaps the breakfast coffee wasn't strong enough; perhaps he really needed a couple of doubles to start the day with; perhaps there were too many bills in the morning mail; perhaps his wife walked out on him yesterday; perhaps he's just happened to catch the eternally calm clear eye of one of the Heaven-Born. Or perhaps it's one of a million other possible trials which accounts for the dissatisfaction he feels with his own efforts.

After all, they do these things much better on the moving pictures. So let's turn to the dream screen, which displays simultaneously three superimposed themes.

The most remote of these presumably should be the one used as background, very frail, very underemphasized, ranks of uniformed figures marching on a diagonal slant from upper right to lower left. These figures are exactly similar, featureless, diminutive, uncoloured, like the outline drawings used in demonstrating statistics. The ranks are evenly spaced, extending across the whole screen; they march throughout at a regular medium pace, raising their legs in a modified goose step. The effect on the eye of this transient army is no more disturbing than a background of falling snow or continuous heavy rain. The background does not fade or solidify: it is not modified in any way by the development of the other two themes; nor is it ever extinguished by them.

Against the basic motif, moving roughly horizontally, but in a fluid, swerving, weaving band, a stream of dancers, men and women in couples, appearing small at left, gradually enlarging centre (certain couples enormously), diminishing again as they move towards right. As the dancers individualize they are seen to be of all ages, classes and nationalities, stepping their various rhythms to a jumble of distant dance tunes further confused with intermittent far-off blaring of martial music. No face remains prominent long enough for complete apperception, but continually changing details emerge. A schoolboy in Eton jacket partnering a heavy fly-blown woman of fifty with bull neck and sparse blue marcelled hair. A hard, judge-like man of about sixty-five, personifying the more hidebound and sadistic type of disciplinarian, woodenly placing his feet in bright patent leather shoes. Simpering over his stiffly encircling arm, a horribly travestied sweet young girl of sixteen in perfectly transparent white muslin; the rouged points of her breasts stand out through the white like the red spot on a tarantula. A poet-like, precious young intellectual, spectacled, wearing a silk shirt and otherwise a baby's napkin, is dancing with a big black negress whose far-too-tight satin dress is bursting at every seam. His twin brother, identical except that his face is redder and that he wears an eyeshade instead of glasses: in his case a striped and monogrammed blazer goes with the napkin. His partner a Peter Arno blonde with the usual trimmings. A dear old lady in white fichu and cap; her swollen ankles teeter dangerously over three-inch pinpoint heels studded with brilliants. An overalled surgeon, sinisterly grotesque with his gauze mask and rubber gloves. A yellow gentleman flashing yellow diamonds. A bus-driver in uniform. A very dignified, polished, bearded member of the Académie Française attired in full *tenue de soir* with the Legion of Honour in his buttonhole. Fliers, bellboys, witch-doctors, scientists, typists, waiters, beauty queens, parsons, racing cyclists, whores, sandwichmen, cooks, schoolmasters, prizefighters, Chinamen, kings. These people can be rearranged indefinitely to include any combination, as they waltz or shuffle or glide or rumba or tango or walk or whirl or whatever across the screen.

The third theme has as its accompaniment sentimental song-hits of the most saccharine variety, which fragmentarily make themselves heard cross-jangling the other tunes. Equating pictorially, numerous quick flashes flicking about the screen with glimpses of conventional love scenes in gardens, conservatories; a girl and boy on a staircase embracing; an enlaced couple leaning over a steamer rail and watching the moon rise (moon is searchlight); mouths searching, clinging; hands (male and female) fumbling, stroking, clutching, questing, trembling, gripping other hands, bodies, slipping straps from shoulders, unfastening buttons; shot, from above, of a man and girl in bathing-suits pressed together in a tight clinch on a beach; close-up of the girl's up-turned, imbecilic, nympholeptic face. Various erotic flashes, in boats, cars, bedrooms, parks, dance-halls, etc. None of the shots, which break out at random all over the screen, lasts for more than a second. The effect is rather that of looking at a high building in various parts of which windows are lit up one after another as lights are switched on and off in the different rooms.

Music increases to utmost confusion of dance bands, military bands, crooners, as something whitish, roundish, rises from centre base and slowly travels straight up like a balloon, like a bubble, traversing the whole height of the screen. Maybe it's an igloo; maybe it's an egg. Up it goes, steady and sedate, and inside it B is sitting cross-legged, reading a book. Just as the bubble, the balloon, the igloo, the egg, or whatever it may be, reaches the top of the screen it explodes quietly with a smothered genteel belch.

The bubble-plop signals disruption of the combined themes. The dancers and lovers blow madly in all directions; fly apart; disintegrate: they and the music vanish together.

The ranked figures continue their unassertive march for a few seconds, until it becomes clear that they are quite young boys in some sort of uniform, Boy Scouts perhaps, or members of some other youth organization.

The troop of about twenty boys marches along a dusty road in full summer sun. The marching is not at all smart, several boys are out of step and others have broken rank and are lagging behind. They are all hot and tired and quite considerably bored. One who has a blistered heel scuffs along barefoot with his shoes in his hand.

At right, parallel to the road, from which it is separated by a wire fence bearing NO TRESPASSING notices, a cool, shimmering lake with flowering flags growing to the edge of the water. A freshly painted rowing-boat is moored to a miniature jetty. Opposite this the march falters, breaks down completely, the boys straggle up to the fence, bunch together there like young cattle, eyes focused enviously on the boat and the water. Simultaneously with the break-up of the march, from behind some willows on the other side of the fence, two smiling girls (one is unmistakably B – could the other be A in her younger days? It's impossible to tell really, they're so much alike) appear on the sunlit slope. Smiling into one another's faces, oblivious, self-contained, they walk hand in hand to the jetty, unfasten the boat, get in and row out and away, towards the centre of the lake.

From the level of the boys' eyes, through the thick wire mesh, as if looking into a cage, the boat shown withdrawing swiftly, with extreme effect of solitariness, inaccessibility; diminishing into a toy, a waterbird, a floating leaf in the distance; vanishing.

Out of my urgent need I found the way of working a new night magic. Out of the night-time magic I built in my head a small room as a sanctuary from the day. Phantoms might be my guests there, but no human could enter. Human beings were dangerous to me, like tigers prowling at large in the daytime world. Inside my secluded room I felt safe from the tigers I sometimes envied. Sometimes a savage beauty lured me into the sun and I would start to love the danger a little. On these occasions I felt the reluctant love drained painfully from me as blood drains from a deep wound. The tigers lapped my love's blood and remained enemies. The inhabitants of the day laughed at the gift I wanted to bring them, and I shut myself in my inner room to escape the betrayal of their arrogant mouths.

Someone is running madly up and down stairs. What devilish torment can hunt the poor fellow like this? No sooner does he reach the foot of the staircase (it's short, mercifully, but quite steep), than he turns and is off to the top as fast as he can go. Then down he rushes at once, almost tripping over his own feet in his crazy haste to get to the bottom and start climbing again.

So he keeps on, up and down, up and down, up and down, like a caged squirrel or a mouse caught in a treadmill. Such agitation is horribly painful to watch. One holds one's breath in suspense, waiting for him to fall badly and break an arm or a leg: or else his heart must surely give out and he will have a collapse of that kind. Already he's worn to a shadow, a wraith, whose features are too ghostly to be recognizable.

Each moment he grows more shadowy, more transparent. He's getting smaller and smaller too, as the altering dream perspective banishes him to the distance where, finally, his frantic restlessness is no more disturbing than the activity of a spider within its web.

Are these clouds or mountains which now blossom like huge flowers in the glowing light of the sky? They might even be figures, solemn supernatural beings, archangels or gods, with faces masked in their own radiance. Light steadily fills the whole dream until there's no room for anything else. Even the disembodied voice of the Liaison Officer can barely squeeze itself in, so that only fragments are heard of the lines he is reading about

the Blessed Genii   who walk above in the light, gazing with blissful eyes of still, eternal clearness

The perennially clear eye of the Heaven-Born opens to a stare of shockingly bright moonlight. The eye is located at presumptive God height so that the terrestrial globe is seen as if from an aeroplane cruising over it at about three thousand feet.

A cold, steady review of night, moonlight, vastness, emptiness, loneliness, desolation, by the celestial eye. The bleak and enormous reaches of its vision swoop occasionally to focus detail at close range but never linger on anything. The eye is checking a record of silence, space; a nightmare, every horror of this world in its frigid and blank neutrality. The actual scope of its orbit depends on the individual concept of desolation, but approximate symbols are suggested in long roving perspectives of ocean, black swelled, in slow undulation, each whaleback swell plated in armour-hard brilliance with the moonlight clanking along it; the endless, aimless, nameless shoreline, flat, bald-white sand, unbroken black-tree palisade; the heavy and horrid eternal onrush of breakers sullenly exploding their madness of futile power, millions of mad tons piling, booming, collapsing, swirling in chain-mail mosaic of mad moon splinters; blanched mountain range a ridge of clenched knucklebones.

The eye sinks slowly to travel at tree height past clattering black slats of palm leaves knife-edged on steel;

and looks at a hideous fanged stone idol in front of which lies a hyena, gnawing away at a lump of half-rotted flesh; dips lower to inspect three strung human skulls dully ululating in wind; rises again to medium altitude and directs its impassive scrutiny towards death-white ice-caps; towards hopeless vastness of dreary continents crawling with pestilential rivers, scabbed with plains in the corners of which perpetual dust-storms are festering; towards blasted battlefields and ruined cities running with seared putrescence; over dead village roofs and poisoned gardens, broken walls bitter in snow or moon, blank windows black with nothing.

And so on, in regular and perfectly unflinching survey

which non-dimensional B from deep within its pupil coincidentally shares

until a fresh manifestation gathers itself together, and forces interest on:

the castle   the sun

The sun is, in fact, just on the point of rising over the town. This is the precise moment when Day and Night are balanced before exchanging their spheres of influence. Low in the left segment of sky the full moon still shines white on steep gables and eaves, and glazes window panes behind which people are still fast asleep in their beds.

People are in bed too in the houses at the opposite end of the town where a faint preliminary pink is spreading fanwise out of the east. But it's noticeable that the sleepers here are restlessly stirring, already beginning to break away from their dreams. The moon retires with graceful prudence, her blue train trailing behind, switching slickly over the horizon before the roguish rosy-fingered retinue has time to twitch at it. Up swaggers his majesty in the spotlight, adjusting the gilded curls of his peruke, tossing his daily largesse with elegant gestures of careless munificence, flicking the golden flakes from his laces like snuff.

As the first gold strikes the weathercock on the castle tower the sleepers waken, throw off the bedcovers, jump into their clothes. All in an instant the life of the morning's begun: white smoke puffs briskly out of the chimneys beside which storks are tidying up their nests; eggs and bacon sizzle in frying pans; steaming coffee pours into over-sized flower-patterned cups; the cheerful clatter of break-fast things all over the town is punctuated by the double knocks of postmen going their rounds. In next to no time all these things happen: and then the school bells start ringing, children with satchels and apples come tumbling and chattering out of the many doors, crowding the narrow streets which are crowded already with people going to work, with market carts, with street-sellers putting up stalls, washerwomen carrying bundles of linen, dogs pulling handcarts, priests hurrying along with rosaries or small black books in their hands. The day's well established before you can turn round. And now all the workers are busily employed: a drone of voices comes from the schoolhouse windows; housewives are know-ingly prodding the provisions set out in the market or haggling with stallholders; in steamy washhouses, women up to their elbows in suds shout jokingly or crossly to one another; the dogs are panting in the shade of their little carts at the end of their task; the priests are closeted and anonymous in solemn confessionals.

From high up in the castle dominating the town B watches these activities somewhat dubiously. There's a section of flat roof which forms a sort of terrace between two turrets, and it's here that she's standing looking over the parapet beside a clawed gargoyle which has melancholy human eyes in its pig's face. It seems to be a whimsical, jolly, busy, toyshop scene that she's looking at: except that, like all horror-dream backgrounds, it's a bit too harmless to be truly disarming. Its very innocence gives it away. Such emphatic innocuousness is bound to contain a submerged threat. The threat never comes completely into the open, but is concealed in isolated glimpses and incidents, trivial in themselves, yet generating a growing sense of tension, anxiety, apprehension.

For instance:

An open window behind which, in the shadowed room, indeterminate worrying movements are faintly discernible; a hand suddenly comes out, grabs the window shut and snaps down the blind.

In a small public garden, watched by a few idlers, men with besoms and long-handled rakes are making a bonfire of leaves; and this is only remarkable because it's summertime and the leaves haven't started to fall yet.

A neatly dressed man with a bag in his hand is hurrying along the street to the station. His arrival is timed very well as the smoke of the train can be seen in the distance just as he gets to the booking office. But then, instead of buying a ticket, he suddenly walks out of the station again, takes a piece of chalk out of his pocket, marks something on the door of one of the neighbouring houses, and hurries off in quite another direction.

B isn't looking out for incidents of this sort: in fact, she's hardly aware of having observed them at all, being consciously preoccupied with the general pattern of which they are only insignificant details. Nevertheless, she is influenced by them without knowing it, they are responsible for the vaguely disturbing background of uncertainty in her mind.

Presently there's a new sound, a noise of cheers and clapping, approaching the castle. A famous ballerina is driving through the town in her open carriage, the people in the streets recognize her and acclaim her as she goes by. B leans over the parapet to look. She has an excellent view, the carriage is driving right up to the castle entrance. It's a fine carriage, polished like jet. The horses are beautiful, glossy, spirited creatures. They slow down as the coachman tightens the reins. Yes, they are actually stopping just below the place where B stands. A flock of pigeons which has been circling around the turret simultaneously alights in the street. As if for some prearranged purpose, the birds assemble all round the carriage and the prancing horses.

The fair-haired ballerina looks up and waves her hand. Come down here, she is calling to B. Come for a drive in my carriage and I'll show you the town. Her voice carries like the sound of a bell.

B does not move. There's a violent conflict inside her. She longs to go down to the famous dancer, she's longing to see the sights of the town at close quarters instead of looking on distantly from her tower. And yet something is holding her back, warning her not to venture out of the castle.

Come down, come down, the ballerina calls again and again.

All right, I'll come, B answers finally, overcoming her hesitation. Wait for me. I'm coming immediately. Please don't go on without me. I'll be down in a moment.

The pigeons fly up to her as she hurries away, they flutter about her, filling the air with their wings so that she can hardly see where she is going. A sound something like a groan comes from the gargoyle, which laboriously raises its claw in a gesture of restraint or appeal. B is far out of reach already: she does not see the movement or the stone tear which slowly and painfully extrudes from the gargoyle's eye and rolls down the length of its pig's snout.

Soon she's climbing into the carriage. And how glorious it is to be careering along behind those spirited horses at the side of the ballerina. It's all wonderful, like a new world; the speed, the excitement, the applause, the hat-raising, the salutes of the passers-by, the privilege of being the envied companion of the subject of such universal admiration. The town, too, takes on a new aspect from this angle. The streets, which B is accustomed to viewing in foreshortened perspective, seem much finer than she had supposed them to be. Even the crooked lanes leading to the poorer quarters promise adventure and mysterious revelations.

The ballerina points out new wonders at every corner. Look, look, she cries, and when she raises her arm the sleeve falls back like a calyx and new marvels reveal themselves. A girl has come to the fountain to fill her bucket with water; but as the carriage rolls by diamonds, emeralds, sapphires spout from the dolphin's mouth, in a second her pail is full up with precious gems, a whole fortune flashes into the bucket in one beam of light. The ballerina laughs. The sound of her laughter is like bells ringing out from the hilltop. B seems to have heard that sound of bells in another place.

Look, look, says the dancer again. In every window-box of the house they are passing the flowers come out with a rush and fling their bright petals down, showering the carriage and its occupants with scented confetti.

Things like that keep happening continually. But now the horses are racing so fast that B doesn't have time to catch more than confused glimpses of what's going on. The speed at which the carriage is travelling makes her quite giddy and she has to cling to the edge of the seat to keep from overbalancing as they swing round the corners. Far, far overhead in the burning blue sky the pigeons are flying, keeping pace with the horses whose wild hooves clatter frantically on the paved street.

Too fast, B calls out, I'm missing everything. Can't we go a bit slower?

She's really a little nervous. Supposing one of the horses should slip and fall, or the carriage upset or run over somebody? It seems only too likely to happen.

The dancer just laughs. Probably she didn't hear what B said in the rush and noise of their progress. She at any rate doesn't seem in the least anxious. Her yellow hair blows out in the wind as if a fire lighted her laughing face brilliant with power and joy.

Suddenly the astonishing drive is over. Rearing and slithering, the horses are pulled to a standstill. The carriage rocks dangerously; and before it has become steady, the ballerina darts out like a bird, her feet in their green slippers fly up the steps of a magnificent building outside which an equestrian statue threateningly brandishes his great sword.

Where are you going? Wait for me, B shouts, getting out of the carriage as fast as she can. The dancer doesn't answer or look round. Perhaps she doesn't realize that B has been left behind. Perhaps she has suddenly forgotten about her.

In desperate haste B starts climbing the steps in pursuit. It's no good, though. These steps up which the green shoes flew like birds B's feet can only scale slowly and with infinite labour and pain. Each single step towers in front of her like a wall and she can only drag herself to the top of it by putting out all her strength. Her feet too feel hopelessly heavy and out of control, seeming, as they do sometimes in fevers, to belong to somebody else or to be weighted with heavy stones. Once or twice more she calls out to the ballerina. But already she's lost hope, she knows there won't be any response;

the dancer has vanished behind the huge mounted knight who looms in between them.

Besides, B is really too exhausted for shouting. It's as much as she can do to draw breath at all. She stands quite alone now among the hostile faces that have collected around her. The crowd which previously waved and cheered with such enthusiasm has all at once become angry, threatening, morose. These people in their dark clothes watch her silently, like a herd of dangerous beasts, occasionally shifting their positions, or muttering, or exchanging ugly glances between themselves. They do not make any overt accusation, but B understands they resent her presence in that place, she has no business to be there and will be made to pay severely for her trespassing. What the penalty will be she hasn't the faintest idea. But it's only necessary to look at those heavy, lowering faces, at the same time stupid and vicious, like the heads of treacherous animals, to know that no brutality is out of the question.

Very slowly the crowd is closing in on her, edging forward almost imperceptibly, but always decreasing the space which is her precarious safeguard. Panic-stricken, B's eyes search wildly in every direction, without discovering a solitary sign of hope. Above her, sheer as a cliff, the blank façade blots out the sky. Like an implacable and denunciatory finger the long black shadow of the knight's sword points to her over the heads of the crowd. The carriage has silently disappeared from the street below.

A rumble such as might herald a natural catastrophe, a tidal wave or an earthquake, comes from the onlookers who are all together murmuring the same fatal indictment, as, with obvious intent now, they draw in their constricting circle. B is like a mouse in a trap. She spins round, first one way and then the other, hardly knowing what she is doing. In one place, the ranks of bodies seem less compact, she imagines that it might be possible to force a way through at this point, and dashes towards it. At the same moment she feels herself falling, the whole vast stairway collapses disastrously beneath her. With a great rush of wind the pigeons whirl down and beat all about her with their strong wings, bearing her along between them

into a small room with no windows or doors visible. The walls are scrawled over with dimly seen occult symbols, pentacles, wands, swords, etc. There are shelves of books; and a few phantom-glimmering shapes of vases, or urns. B sits on what might or might not be a narrow bed, reading by the light of four candles in a cross-shaped holder. It's very dark. The candles shed a flickering, limited ring of light over B and the open book and a part of the dusty stone floor, leaving everything else in shadow deepening to blackness in the corners. Here and there round the walls faint traceries of signs or letters come and go as the four flames waver. Absolute stillness. Hush. At approximately regular intervals B's hand moves to turn over a page.

After a time a vague stirring, thickening, in one of the dark corners: nothing so definite as movement at first: it's more a sort of concentration of tension in that corner. From which tenuous chrysalis presently emerges a second B, B's *doppelgänger*, materializing out of the shadows; coming nearer the light although very similar, with similar fair curled hair, discernibly older, wearier, more assured, more disillusioned; in fact, of course, A. Who, standing behind B, looking over her shoulder (B is unaware), remains for a while apparently reading what she is reading. Then, moving across the room, gradually departs from the scene in a reversal of the procedure by which she lately arrived.

Simultaneously with her dissolution, a faint sibilance starting, not from any special point, but emanating from all over the room, very subdued, seeming as if it might be voiced by the four walls or by the ceiling and floor. A rustling, a susurration, like blown leaves, in which now and then some reference to danger becomes incompletely distinguishable. This sound continues from now on, principally as an indeterminate rustle as of water, leaves, wind, occasionally clarifying itself into the actual word Danger or one of its synonyms. B, without actually hearing, is not oblivious, because whenever the word becomes recognizable, she looks up or makes an unquiet movement. Finally she jumps up, glancing nervously round the room, pushing her book away so that it strikes the candle-holder, rocking the candles and sending waves of light alternating with shadow in confusing sequence, like pages turned rapidly back and forth.

At the same time the whispering loudens to ordinary speaking pitch, to clamour, to shouting, to utmost volume, as near deafening as possible, of voices chaotically shrieking, together, separately, interrupting, competing, with increasing speed and intensity, such phrases as: Danger, Keep Out; It is Dangerous To Open The Window; Danger de Mort. And so on.

The earsplitting pandemonium is suddenly shattered; into long dry grumble and growl and intermittent snapping and cracking of bursting timbers, crumbling masonry, as the whole structure of the room collapses inwards, obliterating B in a heap of amorphous wreckage, rubble, from which thick clouds of dust are seen blowing upwards like spray. This, under blank moon as before, the celestial eye transiently takes stock of, passes on.

Was my mother afraid of the tiger? Was that the theme of the music she danced to with death in our quiet house?

When I went home between the school terms I was still alone in those rooms where nothing had altered. It was the same then as if I'd never been away. My mother's sadness and boredom still lived in the house with the shadows and the grey rain on the windows. Their presence accompanied me as I took my unspoken questions from room to room.

Sometimes I had an impulse to ask my father about the things which perplexed me: I watched him and waited for the right time which never came. My father always seemed to be in a hurry. He was like an important stranger with no time to spare. He made decisions for me about practical things, he directed my life, and when he had done what was suitable he forgot me.

At school and at home it was the same; I was alone. This I accepted and knew it would always be so, wherever I went, and whatever happened to me. There was no place for me in the day world. My home was in darkness and my companions were shadows beckoning from a glass.

This time it's not just the voice but the visible presence of the Liaison Officer which opens the dreaming eye. He's reading again from what looks like the same book (although one can't see the title), but the details of his appearance have altered, he is bare-headed and wears a white garment – a smock or an overall – on top of his uniform. The chief alteration is in his manner. He's no longer sure of himself, his voice sounds uneasy, his expression is puzzled, and he keeps glancing anxiously out of the window where there's a distant view of a castle floating mirage-like in the mists. Except for the window and the major himself, there's nothing much to be seen in this great gloomy old hall. Everything's ghostly and grim and dark, and though there are people present, they seem to be in another dimension. All that's perceptible is a continuous vague stir, as if a crowd of transparent onlookers were seated in thin air, fidgeting and whispering, rustling their spectral papers and shuffling their unseen feet.

It's enough to make anyone reading aloud feel nervous: especially as the atmosphere generated by these invisible spectators is far from friendly. There's a sort of malicious tittering in the background: a nightmare Alice-in-Wonderland inconsequence, which is most disturbing. The inconsequential element is manifest too in certain architectural caprices and light shifts, whereby the building is given a fluctuating resemblance to a church, a law court, a prison, an operating theatre, a torture chamber, a vault. That the major is more and more affected by these metaphysical stresses, is evident from the increasing tension of his manner and voice as he reads:

An instance of how misunderstandings and estrangements can occur between relatives:

B wants to talk over some obscure point with her father. She has probably made several efforts to approach him already, but without success. Her attempts have up to now been always inopportune; perhaps made at a time when he was on the point of leaving for his office and, already a few minutes late, could not possibly delay his departure any longer. Or perhaps she spoke to him when he had just come home after a hard day's work on some specially intricate and abstruse official problem and was too tired for talk. Or else, when other circumstances were propitious, an important message to which he was obliged to attend may have been telephoned through from the department by one of the under-secretaries.

Today she makes up her mind to ask him at breakfast to fix a time for the conversation. At the regular hour she goes into the dining-room only to be told that her father ordered his breakfast earlier than usual and has left the house.

B decides to follow him to his office, a journey which, travelling on the suburban train, normally takes about forty minutes. This morning, although no warning is given of any alteration in schedule, the train not only takes over two hours on the way, but finally deposits its passengers at a terminus in quite a different part of the city, from which she is obliged to make a complicated bus trip, involving several changes, to reach her destination.

When she gets there, in a state of nervous anxiety after all these delays, a secretary informs her that her father has gone to lunch at a certain restaurant which she knows quite well. The man is friendly and sympathetic, he is anxious to help her, he is certain that if she goes at once she will catch her father before he has finished his meal. B thanks him and hurries off as fast as she can. But in spite of the fact that she's perfectly familiar with this restaurant, has herself been taken there several times, she is unable to find it. Various passers-by of whom she enquires the way give her conflicting directions. In the end, a policeman tells her that demolition work was started some days ago on the building which had recently been classified as unsafe.

Rushing back to the office, B arrives there just in time to see her father getting out of a car in front of the entrance. He pauses to say something to the driver. B calls out and starts running towards him. Her voice is drowned by the noise of the traffic; and, at that instant, by the sheerest bad luck, a whole lot of people, jostling one another in their anxiety to board an approaching bus, come crowding along, getting between B and her father who crosses the pavement quickly in front of them. B has no time to catch him before he disappears through the door which a saluting porter swings open and through which she is never allowed to pass. She sees the car glide away. She sees the door close. The situation is hopeless. The only thing left for her to do is to go home again.

This time the journey takes no longer than usual. But at the house it transpires that her father has already been and gone; he must have driven home in his fast car immediately after she saw him, having found that he would be obliged to undertake a business trip to another city and wishing, since they had not had many opportunities lately of being together, to see B before he left. She hears that, having made the long drive, for which he could barely manage to find time, on purpose to say goodbye to her, he was naturally rather put out to find that she was not in the house and that his time had been wasted. He had actually waited half an hour, expecting her to return. At last, as there was no way of knowing how long it would be before she put in an appearance, and as his own business was urgent, he had gone off looking cross and aggrieved. In fact he had left a message to say that he was most disappointed and upset about the whole matter.

Very distressed at the way her good intentions have gone wrong, B consoles herself with the prospect of getting the entire complex straightened out as soon as he comes back. But then she remembers that he will not be returning until the following week, and that by that time she herself will probably be away from home.

Once more the suburban house THE ELMS, the desirable residence. The trees have grown slightly taller. It's raining. Saturated soft lawn, like a green sponge; black tree-trunks glistening with rain. The wet brick walls of the house: the paint on the doors and window frames is less fresh than it used to be; but this would hardly be noticeable.

A general view of the house in its trees, roofs of adjacent houses appearing on all sides through the trees. Tree-tops are doleful in grey and cold douche and drench of rain; leaves are bent under weight of raindrops, tipped, freed and weighted again; the roof, the whole slant of tiles, swims under a thin film of water, rain slithers thinly to gutters, gurgles in pipes and gutters, trickles from vent-pipes, seeps into sodden earth. Raindrops spatter a puddle beside the porch. A blind taps on a half-open window its untranslatable message.

Now inside. It's no particular season or time of day. The rooms are chilly, somewhat dark because of the dark sky reflected in windows steadily blurring with rain. The recent thud of the front door perpetually hangs suspended in feeble blind-tapping, rain noise. Most of the rooms are unoccupied. Outmoded and unloved knick-knacks haunt the dusted drawing-room with desolate derelict neatness; the oriental boxes empty, the fretted sandalwood fan folded in exile. Encamped behind the closed kitchen doors two women servants, shut off with cups of tea, gossip and sip; they seem unconnected with the rest of the house; nor is the house affected by their presence there.

Solitary B wanders aimlessly from room to room. She is making a tour of boredom, loneliness, monotony, dullness, although she's not conscious of it. In room after room the rain filming on all grey windows; gloss-hard or padded gentility of heavy furnishings; genteel formal masculine room, smell of telephone, leather, tobacco; aloof genteel dining-room glinting of silver.

B finally goes to her own room, stands for a minute fingers drumming the window-pane swimming in rain, then sits down on the bed, opens a book.

The book opens with a thud of the front door. Contemporaneous with this sound, the hurried suggestion of a man dressed in dark business suit and carrying a dispatch case, leaving the house, getting into his car, driving away. The empty rooms of the house filled with rain noises, dullness, nullity, the morse-tap of the blind; closed in the kitchen, the two prim-faced servants, apart in their closed world of picture papers and tea.

B turns the pages. Each one is exactly the same as the one before. She turns them faster and faster, running them over between her thumb and first finger, speeding them up into a bioscope blur, the door thuds spraying out quick like gunshot pellets. When she comes to the end she closes the book

and puts it down on the seat of the railway carriage. The train is just roaring into a tunnel. B looks back, through the transparent coaches and baggage car of the train. Far behind, very small, framed in black circular tunnel mouth, diminishing at great speed as the train rushes the opposite way, the suburban house wet in its trees, rain still greyly slanting.

At the terminus all is noise and confusion. It's a great cold dingy place full of bewildering hustle and shouting, escaping steam-hiss, whistles and clanging bells. Everyone is in a terrific hurry: gangs of people dash wildly in different directions, loaded with all sorts of impedimenta, piles of books, bags, overcoats, boots and shoes, food, mascots, pictures, pets, awkwardly shaped wooden objects, bats and rackets, boards and unwieldy globes, which they hurriedly deposit in various places. But no sooner does one of the groups succeed in getting all these things arranged in some semblance of order than, in obedience to whistles, bells, shouts, the whole collection of articles is snatched up again to be bundled off to some other position where the process has to be gone through afresh. To add to the general confusion, loudspeakers are continually bawling out orders or directions of some kind, while, only slightly less loud, other unamplified voices seem to be reciting or chanting, and still others are carrying on shouted conversations with friends. And as if the jumbled parties helter-skeltering this way and that didn't create sufficient disorder, isolated individuals keep scurrying among them, forcing their way in the opposite direction to their neighbours, leaping down from the tops of piles of boxes or scrambling to precarious perches on high window-ledges, perhaps in search of a missing companion or a piece of lost property, the subject of their incomprehensible shrill enquiries.

In the midst of all this turmoil B is quite at a loss. Someone who seems to be in authority has called out to her to join a certain group, which group she doesn't hear, and before she can ask for more information the person who gave the order has disappeared. B looks round hopelessly. How in the world is she ever going to find her right place in this beargarden? Nobody seems in the least interested in her. Nobody seems to care what she does, where she goes, what becomes of her. It doesn't seem to matter to anyone whether she moves or stays where she is all day long. People are constantly bumping into her and pushing against her with their clumsy paraphernalia, but not one of them can spare a moment to stop and answer her questions. Occasionally an individual, better natured than the rest, will call back before vanishing some muddled instructions, of which B cannot make head or tail – particularly since only a word or two is audible in the tumult.

She really begins to feel desperate. The people here are all so rowdy, so scatterbrained, so intent on their own higgledy-piggledy affairs, that it's useless to try to catch their attention. And then the place is so huge and dreary, and every part of it is so much like every other part, that to find one's way about in it seems an impossibility; to move in any direction is almost certainly to get lost among the hurrying crowds, the stacks of indiscriminate objects which are for ever collapsing as something is dragged out from the bottom, and then being chaotically heaped up anew.

Still, she can't stand in one place indefinitely, to be jostled and pushed from one side to another. Without any aim in view, simply because there's less of an uproar this way, B moves in a certain direction. For some reason or other there are far fewer people here, the main throng suddenly seems to be concentrated elsewhere.

Soon she's in a quiet space, by herself, in front of a door which is evidently not meant to be opened, or even to be seen, because it is painted exactly as if it were part of the wall. However, it does open quite easily when B turns the handle, and she goes through it on to a narrow platform above a stage

where a ballet of the Graduation Ball type is in progress. The platform is flimsy and small, balanced on scaffolding up there in the wings as if perched on enormous stilts. B advances timidly to the edge of it and looks down.

Level brilliant light on the stage, warm coloured; from the footlights and a strong generalized flood (not spotlights) from high up above. The auditorium is merely suggested by a receding tide of shadow beyond the footlights. No orchestra visible. The ballet music is stimulating: it has much gaiety, freshness, without sugariness; it has 'a curious perfume and a most melodious twang'.

The dancing master in black satin knee-breeches and buckled shoes leads his class, which consists of about twenty boys and girls in equal numbers. The boys are dressed in fancified cadets' uniforms; strapped long white trousers, gloves, coloured monkey jackets with silver or gold buttons and touches of lace. The girls' costumes are more varied. Some wear full muslins, just over knee-length, a cross between ballet skirts and the usual young girl's white party frock; these have wide sashes made of stiff silk with fringed ends in sharp naïve colours tied in large bows behind. One or two are in period dresses, bustles or crinolines with display of lace pantalettes. Others wear fantastic versions of conventional school clothes, lustrous velvet jibbahs, candy-striped guimpes. Accessories, such as gold corkscrew-curled wigs: ropy gretchen plaits held by flat ribbons; demure chenille snoods; fans; openwork elbow-length lace mittens, black, white or coloured; bronze or black dancing sandals, crossed ankle elastics; block-toed ballet shoes in different satins.

Across the stage, to lively four- and eight-bar strains, the pupils dance in double line, girls ahead, following the master who is leading them with brisk yet dignified steps. Then pirouette and back with the boys leading and the master an agile black grasshopper in the rear. He waves his brittle arms like antennae, tattoos his buckled shoes in dry rataplan on the boards.

Now to different rhythm, in spaced mock-formal advancements, uneven numbers, one, pause, two three, pause, and so on, the girls sedately skip into the centre, take places on frail spindle-legged gilt chairs set by powdered and liveried menservants for each one as she approaches.

All sit, feet crossed, hands folded, in identical poses of mimed modesty.

Then the boys, all together in tin-soldier military formation, march up, left right, crisp rap-tapping metre, halt, click heels, stiff toy-soldier salute, each in front of a chair.

Girls rise.

Footmen swiftly and silently remove all chairs except one, which is left standing in the exact middle of the stage.

After prim exchange of bows, curtsies, partners dance off together, steps and deportment very hypocritically *comme il faut*, under the stern supervision of the master who mounts the chair and from this eminence critically watches the class, scrutinizing each couple in turn, occasionally giving a defaulter's shoulder a smart rap with the baton which he uses to beat time to the music.

The dance, which starts off with so much decorum, gradually begins to lose its formality as the tempo quickens. Covert smiles and whispers, arch looks, spread from one pair to the next, relax into more and more open mischievousness, frivolousness, flirtatiousness. The dancing master scolds, reprimands, works himself into a frenzy, hitting out left and right with his baton, all to no purpose. He rapidly loses his dignity, loses control over the class which will not pay attention to him any longer. He becomes a figure of fun. The pupils, girls and boys, laugh and mimic him, dodging his baton as they pass by. Finally a boy snatches the baton away, dances off brandishing it mockingly. Another boy tilts the chair, tips the master on to the ground. Now more than ever like an irate grasshopper he hops among the revolving couples, chattering with rage, ineffectually trying to recover his precious baton, his symbol of authority, impotently striking promiscuous fist blows which are warded off with derision.

Feet fly faster and faster. Skirts spin faster and faster. The dance develops into a kind of age-of-innocence orgy in the midst of which dervishes the black insect-like maestro, frantically flinging in all directions his stick-dry limbs that appear to be on the point of snapping off from his body.

Down into the midst of this comes B, her green slippers seeking in time to the music the rungs of the ladder leading down to the stage. The music has gone to her head as well as her feet. Without any reserve she darts in among all those twirling dresses, those flying curls, those slapping braids, on eager toe-tips shuttling between them, soliciting every couple in turn. But no one surrenders a partner to her: and she is obliged to perform with the dancing master a feverish *pas de deux*, the pair of them oscillating vertiginously, caracoling, glissading: she in search of a partner, he pursuing his puissant baton which is passed by the dancers from hand to hand, tantalizingly flourished before his face, tauntingly tossed away.

At last, to crashing tumultuous chords, the fantasia terminates. But music immediately takes up again on a delicate down motif, very limpid, young, pure; an aubade.

With dainty tripping rustle of petticoats, brisk scissor-criss-crossing of white trouser legs, the dancers retire to the back of the stage where chairs are now arranged in a wide crescent; girls settling themselves with bird-like preening, flirt and flutter of hair, skirts, fans; boys sitting on the floor or leaning on the backs of the chairs.

Out in the centre the master, B and one danseuse who did not withdraw with the rest of the class, are dancing the tentative opening phrase of a new movement which develops the rapprochement of the two girls under the maestro's aegis.

The dancing master has unobtrusively regained his baton and with it his dominance. Depended from his thin fingers, the baton swerves delicately in time to the music as he dances, inspiring the dance of the girls. Their four green shoes move complementarily about three feet apart. Up to now the quality of the music has been predominantly ethereal, and this feeling the dancing girls, in their spacing apart and traditional formalized posturing of head and body, also convey. It is still aloof and airy as possible, but now superimposed on the initial morning simplicity of the theme are certain elusive suggestions of provocativeness, ambiguity, as the girls approach one another more closely, touch hands, finally become linked together in their gossamer intrication.

They glide hand in hand in front of the master. While he grows steadily taller they both lift their identical pairs of eyes slowly and seriously towards his face, into which they look questioningly for a moment, heads tilting back to focus him as he towers upwards: then their eyes lower, sliding without dubiousness sidelong to meet each other; they look into each other's eyes for a moment; simultaneously and very slightly and briefly they smile, and circle dreamily in exact imponderous harmony, and, with a lacing of buoyant arms, embrace one another's waists.

The master's head has reached up to the roof. His hair is the roof, the illumination of the stage pours out of his eyes, his thighs are gigantic buttresses shoring the building. From his fingers dangle the puppet strings. For a few seconds longer he manipulates them, jerking the green feet back and forth, propelling and twitching the rigid arms. On gilt chairs the abandoned puppets (they are like bright scraps hoarded for a patchwork quilt that have been carelessly turned out of a workbag and left in disorder) have fallen this way and that; backwards with legs in air, sideways across one another, forward with heads on knees, heads on to floor. The puppet master drops the remaining strings; the last two dolls, collapsing, droop over each other's shoulders with stiff arms outstretched; a monstrous, dry, horny hand descends on them, pinches one negligently between thumb and first finger, lifts it up out of sight. The lights go out. And though 'There's nothing more' remains unsaid, grey draughts of emptiness drift from the stage.

Things at school began going wrong. I broke rules and was often in the detention room. People started saying how difficult I'd become. Generally they were angry with me, but occasionally one of them spoke kindly and asked questions which I wouldn't answer because I distrusted kindness. Once a doctor wanted me to tell him what went on inside my head, but I didn't trust him either. I wouldn't talk to him in case he was on the enemy side. How could I know that he wasn't one of the tigers?

How could I explain that school was a machine running by clockwork, and that it was because I didn't fit the machine that I was always in trouble? At the start I had tried to fit in. Now I'd stopped trying because I knew it was hopeless. I knew there was no place for me in the day unless I gave in altogether, and this I was determined I wouldn't do. The daylight world was my enemy, and to the authorities of that world who had rejected me I would not submit. They had insulted and damaged me and I would never surrender to them.

A much enlarged presentation of a pile of forms on a flat surface under a window. The pile is seen from the side, very monumental in the strong light, as if made of stone. The effect is somewhat like that of a model cenotaph squarely set on the dark featureless plane. The top of the pile is in full blank-white, flat-white daylight. Cold white light edges the edges of certain projecting forms, striating the black-shadowed perpendicularity in a way suggestive of steps or of sharply jutting relief.

A very clean large ringless hand approaches the pile. It could be either a male or a female hand. The practical fingers have squarish shortish neatly trimmed nails. The flesh of the hand shows tallow-white against ice-white paper.

The hand hovers momentarily; sinks; the thumb moving *glissando* along the edge of the topmost form, fingers curving above, till it reaches the corner; first finger smoothly descends and in co-operation with thumb raises the paper slowly upwards: holds it vertical for a moment (the words EXAMINATION RESULTS, and CASE NOTES, come alternately and fugitively into focus heading the form): lowers it to horizontal position on smooth dark surface.

The paper now seen laid out flat on the surface, of which only a narrow border appears framing it, with the mass of piled forms rising steeply behind, top of the pile is out of sight. A huge highly polished black fountain-pen like a gun-barrel is trained on the paper; the glittering nib over the black ink-feed carries a dazzlingly brilliant bolus of light on its rounded tip.

Discharging brisk light-volleys, the nib travels judicially down the left side of the paper where a sequence of printed categories is set out with appropriate sections for comments: halts opposite CON-DUCT near the top of the form; after hesitation proceeds at reduced pace downwards to SYMPTOMS; pauses again.

The fountain-pen poised like a gun taking aim. This position is held while, very distantly, a bell begins ringing. On the last stroke of the bell, nib, jabbing brilliance, is sharply directed to paper which it contacts with a short crackling explosion.

Immediately, light and sound condensing, concentrating into, respectively, the voice and nimbus of the Liaison Officer (restored now to his original smart dress and assurance), who reads from the original spine-titled black volume, in his original dry, precise, ex-pressionless, military tone

The Terminus Clock

Choosing a clock for an important terminus is a serious matter. It's not a question that can be settled offhand, like buying an alarm-clock or a wrist-watch, in the course of a brief visit to the *horlogerie* round the corner. No indeed: this is a totally different affair, and one which may easily require years of research and consideration. Just glance for a moment at the various aspects of the problem. Let's start off by asking ourselves what are the essential qualities that such a clock must possess. First and foremost I imagine everyone will agree that it must be an accurate timekeeper. When it is remembered how many urgent matters – matters literally of life and death, to say nothing of vast business transactions and state operations – depend on it, there can be no doubt that everything else must be secondary. As long as there is any integrity left in the human race there will be also the desire for an impartial standard of accuracy. That being decided, however, we are only at the start of our difficulties. The concept of accuracy is not static; it is, on the contrary, constantly fluctuating; a clock which keeps perfectly good time for us may be quite unreliable for our neighbour, and indeed for us too on another occasion. So in whose hands are we to place the decision? It might be best (if we could establish a majority) to trust to a majority judgement. But that is not feasible. The probability is that the very people who are most unanimous today in their opinion will tomorrow be all at loggerheads, and each come hurrying with some new recommendation of his own to supersede the previous common agreement.

Such obstacles paralyse one from the beginning, and so it may be advisable to pass on and to think less about the mechanism of the clock than of its design. Here again every section of the community will want something different: practical people being most likely in favour of functional plainness, while the aesthetes will demand an artistic presentation. And these conflicts will be further subdivided among themselves into minor clashes; as, for instance, in the case of the artists, between the so-called moderns and the academicians, and then into still finer distinctions, impressionists versus pointillists, symbolists versus surrealists, *etc. etc. ad infinitum.*

Even supposing that by some arbitrary move the clock has actually been installed in the terminus, this, unfortunately, will only lead to fresh strife and fresh complications. Factions are sure to complain that the wrong site has been chosen, the clock-face, besides being of an unsatisfactory shape and size, is either too high or too low, or else is improperly illuminated; that it can only be seen with difficulty from the waiting-room, and not at all from behind the bookstall, and so on. On top of this comes the technical problem of servicing the clock and maintaining it in first-class running order without in any way interrupting or interfering with the general routine functioning of the terminus as a whole.

When all these things are added together one begins to recognize the probably insuperable difficulties of the undertaking, which all the same can't possibly be abandoned. The long patient hours of thought and study which serious-minded people have devoted to it all culminate in a longing for the time when the thankless task can be concluded and put away, like a difficult book the contents of which have been mastered. And for that reason the terminus clock is represented by students as being composed of sixty metal sheets, one for every minute of the hour, which fall and cover each other successively like turned book pages.

The Liaison Officer is seen for a second beneath a huge station time-indicator, closing his book, in the act of turning away, as the dream changes.

A harsh metronome clicking, getting gradually louder until it reaches the loudness of the snap of a medium-sized dry branch repeated at three-second intervals. Now with each crack a rectangular plane, describing an arc, rising, falling, horizontal, in the fashion of a series of loose leaves held together at their bases, or of the type of clock that marks each minute after the hour on changing indicators. All ephemerally exhibiting pictures of doctors, civil servants, professors, government officials; making reports bent over desks or tables. The high-heeled shoes of a typist and her rayon ankles twined round a chair leg; a group of white-coated workers comparing case notes.

With abrupt speed-up of clicks to one-second spacing the

turning leaves distinguishable as college, hospital, government forms snowing into a pile. It is not possible to read what is on the forms (most of the printing is just a blur), but on one or two of them B's name is legible, on others single printed nouns appear as: AGE; QUALIFICATIONS; CLASS; DESTINATION; ATTITUDE TOWARDS; RESULT: with the beginning (indecipherable) of a written comment.

Suddenly a precise disembodied voice asking coldly: Have you any statement to make at this stage? Followed, after slight hesitation, by the voice of invisible B; at first stammering, scarcely audible; gaining gradually force and tension until it breaks on an overtone of hysteria.

By what judgement am I judged? What is the accusation against me? Am I to be accused of my own betrayal?

Am I to blame because you are my enemies? Yours is the responsibility, the knowledge, the power. I trusted you, you played with me as a cat plays with a mouse, and now you accuse me. I had no weapon against you, not realizing that there was need for weapons until too late.

This is your place; you are at home here. I came as a stranger, alone, without a gun in my hand, bringing only a present that I wanted to give you. Am I to blame because the gift was unwelcome?

Am I accused of the untranslated indictment against myself? Is it my fault that a charge has been laid secretly against me in a different language?

Is my offence that I stood too long on your threshold, holding a present that was unsuitable? Am I accused because you, wanting a victim and not a friend, threw away the only thing which I had to give?

Immediately after B's voice fading, the metronome click speeding up to crazy haste, papers storming down in frantic acceleration; men's, women's voices (some with foreign accents), pedantic voices, affected, bourgeois, professional, authoritarian, etc., voices; speaking all together, from all sides, in confused unrelated comment, all with somewhat derogatory tendency, from which only a few phrases emerge with any comprehensibility or consecutiveness. As

   B does not concentrate .... Does not adapt .... Does not co-operate .... Does not compromise .... Not satisfactory ... unsatisfactory ... Does not ... Un ... Dis ... Does not ... Non ... Un ... Not ... Non ... No ...

By the time I went to the university I had become more skilful in my dealings with day. The secret the rain had whispered to me years before, the secret of living apart from the daylight world, had now taught me to avoid conflicts without endangering my seclusion. Working from my hidden base in the dark, I warily reconnoitred the territory of the light, and described what I found there.

In all the chaotic violence under the sun, I saw only more cause for distrust and withdrawal. But now I was stimulated by danger, changing my anxiety into written words. I relied on what I wrote to build a bridge which could not be cut down. It was my own self in which I trusted, not seeing self as that last cell from which escape can only come too late.

Has the blissful eye lost its clearness for once? Can it be suffering from an attack of migraine, or what? The outer fields of its vision still remain fairly clear, but the centre, where attention would normally tend to focus, is occupied by a dead spot, a blur of no special colour or shape. Extending and underlying the pathological suggestion, the outlying images are all of a nature to accent the ideas of confusion, danger, violence, chaos, strife.

The extreme periphery concerned with colossal cosmic disturbances, fiery birth-throes of planets and the cataractic dissolution of globed systems on a scale too shattering to be more than hinted. An angry pulsating miasma of bloody red suffuses all this as though the capillaries of the eye were deeply inflamed.

Drawing in somewhat, the scenes moderating to terrestrial proportions, but still uniformly disastrous, world wars, ruinous sieges, plagues, famines, appalling contests of atomic weapons, vaporized and dissolving cities, whole continents exploding in flame, universal torture, destruction, death.

Contracting again, approaching the fringe of the central blur, certain pictures emerging in much greater detail. First, details of cracking, toppling masonry and structural damage so close as to resemble earthquake fissures; leading with more distant and now unequivocal view to the disintegration of a city after atomic bomb hit and to the presentation of the ultimate vaporizing preceded by its upflinging a strange and fancy mushroom in the sky. Also establishing, beyond human destructiveness, the appalling blankness and the intense oppositional indifference of the cosmos.

Followed by glimpses of one and then several abandoned cages of a travelling circus, and the stretched jaws and skeletal midriff of a starved tiger fighting the bars of the cage, the landscape behind rainswept, a road crammed with panic-stricken refugees, vehicles stogged in mud, overflowing the bounds of the road.

A sudden spuming oil well, ignited, horrific flame fountain; another one blazes up; a mammoth warplane; a mischievous boy's face grinning as he releases death; the smashed city; the current familiar pathos (whatever its up-to-minute form happens to be); domestic ruin, broken-up homes, toys, etc. A beautifully delicate and pure fan of water from a burst main spraying a bloodied arm-stump among avalanched paving blocks.

A few more eye views: they are conceptual rather than actual, symbols of global violence in the opening mind.

A high wicked barbed-wire fence in hard sunlight, the small mad eyes of the barbs glinting with murderous brightness. Close behind the fence, an undersized, emaciated, intellectual type man, no special race or persuasion, peering through the powerful elaboration of wire in which he is caged. He wears a ragged, collarless shirt and torn trousers; stands with the somewhat irritating pathos, the masochistic, slightly stupid, sadism-provoking nervous defiance of the predestined victim, myopically peering through the inevitable badly cracked, clumsily mended spectacles. There is the inevitable large bruise on his jaw. The inevitable shout cracks out and he jumps violently, drops his defiance as a handkerchief drops, spins round, and shambles off at an awkward trot.

From far away down the centre of a dark street-crevice between huge skyscrapers, a small group of men and women appear unevenly, wearily marching: they are slight, poorly dressed, insignificant, utterly dwarfed by the monstrous size of the buildings. Rows of indignant, indifferent, glum or frightened faces watch them from the kerb; but these hastily fade out before the arrival of a troop of giant policemen. A thin batlike whimper flitters between the enormous walls as the demonstrators are clubbed off the street.

Now an elderly middle-class couple pottering along the pavement arm in arm. Both are neat, frail, not well-to-do, intensely respectable. The old lady carries a shopping basket, the old man is using his umbrella as a stick in his free hand. They look like two old people up from the country as they advance, glancing timidly at the buildings and the crowds who hurry past without noticing them. Finally they come to a halt in front of tall ornate closed double doors where the word BANK is visible on the scrolled ironwork. The old man approaches and reads a small placard which hangs in the middle of the shut doors; his mouth slowly drops open; he stands staring at the notice for a minute, not believing, not taking it in; then comes back bewildered with unsteady gait to confer with the old woman. The inevitable brutish-faced armed policeman beside the door watches them in scornful aloofness, swinging his truncheon. After a while the old man pulls himself together, steps up and says something to the policeman who, cynically narrowing his eyes, dribbles a few words out of the corner of his mouth almost without lip movement. The old fellow lingers in dazed appeal until the other's callous attitude dawns on him; drifts forlornly back to his companion. They stand side by side, dumb, as if lost or stunned, while rain starts to fall and the policeman looks on, leaning against the doorjamb. The old man becomes aware of the umbrella he is holding; then of its use; his hands twitch at it paralytically; he unfurls it at last and automatically raises it over the old lady's head; takes her arm again; vaguely leads her off through the rain. The policeman looks after them, swings his truncheon, moves farther back under shelter of the portico; yawns.

Immediately after the departure of the old people, a few yards up the street, a girl hurries out of a doorway. Turning to wave goodbye to someone behind her, she runs towards a bus which is approaching the stopping-place, slips, loses her balance, trips over the edge of the wet kerb into the road. A cruising taxi squeals into a ghastly skid just as it is upon her, the driver pounding a frantic yowl out of his horn. A high shrilling momentarily punctures the traffic roar, cuts off sharply. One or two people start running; others shove and crane between their umbrellas to see what has happened. The policeman saunters up heavily, scattering everyone with the swing of his huge bruise-blue shoulders, swinging his truncheon.

The dream closes into the central dead spot.

With delayed, lingering uncertainty this is disclosed as perhaps a web spun with grey mist-fibres of involution; perhaps a carcinoma; perhaps some sort of transparent maze. As uncertainty concentrates, involution honeycombs into greatest possible number of hexagonal cells on pyramidal base. As the honeycomb crystallizes, the cells quickly expand, differentiate; involution, now occupying the entire visual field, defines into ... catacombs ... ? hospital ... ? prison ... ? town with antique northern buildings.

Narrow streets, spires, quadrangles, stabilize cool in still grey light; so peaceful and so extremely quiet, remote, that they seem suspended in crystal. Calm in soft pigeon-coloured stone, overlooking a lawn formal with spaced mulberry trees, a gothic façade pierced by slender windows, old, secure, rigorously remote. Figures stroll in and out of doorways, cloisters, with very faint droning accompaniment of academic discourse, distant sporadic chimings of clocks and bells. The speakers' voices are subdued, their tones unhurried, unheated, their cadences falling. Brief snatches of talk; such topics as the abstract entities, Wren's interiors, the migration of wild geese to Spitsbergen. Presently a more sustained ringing, bell-sounding from the high towers, reverberates with gentleness and solemnity. The figures continue to move up and down for perhaps half a minute longer: then quietly drift away.

The secluded scene is disintegrating, is blurred out, it reverts to the dead spot: the town is dissolving, it amalgamates with the dead spot (so that there is here, suddenly, the blank central eye-blur again): only the perimetral area is pulsing now at ominous speed and with the ominous growing tension of tom-tom beats steadily increasing in tempo though not in loudness.

This the dream college points with the man behind the barbed wire hunted by more and more panic, running more and more awkwardly, undirectedly, his glasses falling, his eyes screaming out of the horror of his foredoomed and sweating face.

Glued to his face, biting it to bloody bits, now presses the turgid mouth of a great thick black salivary-shiny gun: the megrimed retina pulps and gushes into the dead spot spattered with brains and buttons and the grey blur still pumping.

Clear but very diminutive vision across the convulsing of this man-spattered superopticity, a quadrangle, empty, under watery cool clean evening sky. Lighted windows appear one after the other.

Which is being stored up? Which is being selected? Is it a quiet précis of monastic routine unwinding its neutral and satin-smooth spool of days snarled by nothing more serious than the easily unravelled knot of an examination?

Perhaps one could find out in some textbook   ?
perhaps the Herr Professor would be able to tell us   ?

Does the brain choose the images to be retained   ?
Or does the memory rest on a psychological trestle that can be pushed in any direction   ?

At the instant of balance, when the scale trembles between the polarities of night and day; what is it that returns?

The light rain showering in sunlight while we sheltered under the archway; and went on over green velvet grass, between mulberry trees: and strapped books on the carriers of bicycles or piled them in baskets fixed to the handlebars, on our way to the evening, to drink coffee, and to talk for hours.

And when we were sentimental, standing in front of the house where he used to live, the poet, the tears came in our eyes, and we were uplifted. We said to one another, We too will write beautiful words, we will be remembered. And we felt uplifted. While you are young you have splendid pure feelings. Afterwards it's different, there are various euphonic substitutes.

Which are the prints to be pasted into the album out of the jumbled snapshots?

Traveller on the world's oceans, in waking do you know the sea which rocks your temporary bed, or whether the shadow of the tropic bird or of the stormy petrel sidles across the deck?
There are certain pictures which did not fade or get thrown away
          Look at the pictures quickly   And you will catch your morning bird soaring above the towers, you will see your shadows fly over choristers and midsummer morning bells from the tower at the bridgehead.

There was a poem written for me on my comb; written very small with the nib of a pen used for mapping. And when we drifted in the punt, late, in the backwater, I combed my hair, and I was Orlando, I was not man nor girl, and I was Ariel, drifting between the worlds and a poem in my hair.

I do not know why I must keep these pictures   small eyes, mad eyes that should have been starry   the lovely danger waiting beneath the lime tree   or faces cheating as they pass by, frozen for ever in their fraudulent smiles with the clocks striking an uncounted hour   masks
     Why this one   ? Or that   ? How chosen   ?
Inexorable self, carried like the superfluous and tiresome piece of luggage which it is impossible to lose; franked with the customs' stamp of every frontier, retrieved exasperatingly from the disaster where everything else is lost, companion of the dislocation of cancelled sailings and missed connections, witness of every catastrophe, survivor of all voyages and situations I

Feeling more confidence in myself I was able to feel almost at home. At the university I met for the first time people who seemed to be of my own sort because their interests were like mine. These people could not be tigers, surely? They smiled at me, they wanted me for a friend; how could they be on the enemy side? I almost trusted them. But a barrier always stood between us, preventing friendship. I didn't know what this barrier was. Sometimes I thought my mother's shadow divided me from everything that went on in sunshine. I had only learnt how to be friends with shadows; it might be too late to learn the way of friendship in the sun.

Later I was thankful the barrier had not fallen. I found out that these people were not what they appeared; they were different from myself although they spoke a similar language. They were traitors who had betrayed their dark and magical origin for a cheap citizenship of the day. When I discovered this my confidence vanished, I felt afraid and ashamed. It was a terrible disappointment, a dreadful humiliation. When I saw how nearly I had been tricked into an alliance with traitors, I hid myself away in my secret room where no treacherous sight or sound could deceive me again.

How lovely the summer country is with flowers. The simple country flowers, pure coloured and innocent, fill the air with their sweet freshness that is like a message telling everybody to be happy and good. Whether you go up on to the hills or down to the plain the fragrant message breathes all around you. Between the thymy aromatic cushions on the hillside, peals of harebells are soundlessly chiming. Under the burning green of the young beeches, bluebells spread a coolly translucent tide, and the wood anemones hold up their airy cups on stems as frail as the antennae of moths. In the disused chalkpit at the foot of the hill the last primroses are lost in the long grass, together with wild white violets, themselves the colour of chalk. A small confetti of many-coloured stars trims the deserted track leading to the marshy fields where the plovers nest and fritillaries and kingcups stand up among the reeds. Milkmaids and cowslips share the meadows with daisies and buttercups; in the lanes, the hedges are spangled with dogroses slowly turning pale in the sun.

As if to make sure that no one misses the goodwill that the flowers are everywhere distilling into the air, the birds have taken over responsibility for making their message vocal. Surely nobody could be impervious to the gay fountains of song that hundreds of invisible larks are spraying towards the sky? To say nothing of the music which comes from the thrush ambushed in lilacs, or the unearthly treble thread of the willow-wren.

The flowers and the birds between them, helped by the sun and the pleasant light breeze, have made a natural paradise which it is impossible to imagine as being invaded by anything evil or cruel or frightening or even sad. And to crown all this it must be a fête day as well. The low grey tower of the church, so old that it seems to have sunk into itself under the weight of the centuries, is now enlivened by the gaudy brightness of flags. Flags are fluttering over the vicarage and the manor and the school and the post office and out of the cottage windows.

The inn at the foot of the hill has other decorations besides the large flag the shadow of which dances over the grass outside. Wreaths and garlands of flowers, as well as fresh branches and coloured streamers, are fastened above and around the two open doors and the porch and the squat bow windows. Some agile person has even climbed up the pole of the inn sign and fastened a great loose bundle of honeysuckle to the iron scrolls supporting the board upon which a nameless rural artist has painted the likeness of some heraldic beast. The inn itself is a long low mellow building that seems to smile. And it's quite right that it should have this smiling look because it's the centre of all the gaiety, the headquarters, so to speak, of the message which the flowers and the birds have been spreading so diligently ever since the sun rose on this happy morning. Inside, a lively bustle of preparation is going on. Just now the doors set invitingly open don't reveal much except high-backed settles and white sanded floors: but from time to time one catches a glimpse in the background of a figure hurrying past with a tray of good things, hams, cheeses, fruit, or a basket of crusty loaves hot from the oven, indications of the feast to be served later in the day.

At present all the activity centres out of doors, where a sort of impromptu pageant seems to be going on. Under the chestnut tree on the green a number of benches and tables have been set out, and here people are sitting with tankards of cider and ale, an audience for the panting, beaming maypole dancers with their whirling smocks and ribbons, and for the group of children who are singing a folksong in reedily cheerful disunison.

The black-coated clergyman, like an approving sheepdog, smiles at the innocent antics. And a party of local gentry also looks on from the platform festooned with meadowsweet and with white, pink and scarlet may.

To the left of the platform, among other young people, a girl in green shoes is holding a great dog on a leash plaited with vivid cords. It looks as if she and her companions, with whom she is laughing and talking, will have some part to play later on. They stand there together with faces of excited expectancy; and the dog seems to share their pleasure, as he flourishes his whiplike tail and prances in anticipation.

The children's chorus falters unevenly to a close. Flushed and gasping, with a jingling of little bells at their ankles and wrists, the dancers laughingly troop away from the pole around which their variegated ribbons are left tightly twined. The audience claps, mugs are banged on tables, a waitress in a check apron comes out carrying in both hands a huge foaming jug, the clergyman hurries here and there with directions and praise. For a minute or two the green is in confusion, before what must surely be the turn of the girl with the dog and her friends.

But she, all at once, at this critical moment becomes *distrait*. Her eyes wander. She is not looking any more at what's taking place, but at something everyone else is too preoccupied to observe, a woman in black who is slowly coming towards the inn from the direction of the churchyard. Slowly but steadily the stranger comes on, unnoticed, and taking no notice of anything. She does not look right or left and her face is not seen. She walks as if meditating, with bowed head, and with hands loosely linked at the ends of her long black sleeves. In the sun a sapphire flashes blue on her finger: it is the only colour she wears anywhere about her. She slowly passes the green, making for the road that leads upwards into the hills

followed at a little distance by B, who lets the dog's lead fall and, unobserved by her companions, slips away through the crowd, in the wake of that dark and impassive form.

Come, they said, the co-operators, the false ones. Come and sit with us tonight, we are having a friendly discussion (to fit the universe into pigeon-holes), quite informal of course, and a nice warm kiss, at sunrise, to finish the party. There will be a place waiting for you. And this sweet brew which contains soothing syrup is something to warm the cockles and to make you cosy. Let's be cosy together. Draw the curtains. Make up the fire. Don't look out of the window. Why do you want to look out? It's dark and cold out there, so let's settle down to be comfy and to discuss the shadow of Emerson's Man.

Night time: a spirit of festivity is again in the air. And though it is not the idyllic Arcadian gaiety of the pastorale but something more sophisticated, more artificial, still there's an atmosphere of expectancy and joyous excitement gleaming from the eyes of street lamps and lighted windows. In fact it is a city of lights, the whole dream is ablaze with light, the whole sky is one vast shimmering aurora borealis of reflected brilliance. It's impossible to tell whether the stars are out or whether the moon is shining. All one sees in looking over the housetops is a diaphanous aerial curtain of wonderfully blended hues, red, orange, yellow, green, blue, indigo, violet, the whole spectrum extended and repeated from horizon to horizon like an endless series of rainbows in tremendous array. And on top of this, as if such a display wasn't dazzling enough, over the glimmering folds of the resplendent light-curtain, strange wavering bands of pure white luminosity flicker and weave strands so incandescent that they appear to be glowing with limpid fire.

It's really too much of a strain on the eyes, one can't look upwards for long. Not that there is any contrasting dimness below. The streets are as bright as day, for the numerous street lights on normal duty are for this special night reinforced by countless additional flares, torches, links, blazing braziers, relics of ancient times which have perhaps been preserved and stored for the purpose of being resurrected on occasions of this sort. Nearly every window, too, seems to be pointing its burning finger into the night; for few people have thought of drawing the curtains.

At the palace a state ball is in full swing. The great building, with every window aflame, rides the night like an enormous ship, isolated as it is from the glaring streets in a dim sea of encircling gardens where only the fairy-lights show a pale luminous phosphorescence among the trees and the sleeping roses. It is tempting to linger in these cool shadowed walks drowsy with the heavy scent of nightstocks and tobacco flowers. Hidden away at the edge of a lily pool is an arbour where the glow-worm globe silvers the cheek of a gardenia and the folds of a lady's gown. Accompanied by the faintest rustle of silk, a pair of lovers drifts past the little statue who holds up his cornucopia full of a pretty paleness of flowers or snow.

But here is the wide sweep, deserted now, where recently arriving guests thronged beneath tasselled awnings; where still the guards stand frozen in their grand uniforms, the powdered lackeys no less immobilized beyond.

There's no need to describe the splendours of the palace; the statues, the winging staircases, the columns, the balustrades of marble and onyx and agate and porphyry. What's the use of talking about the grandeur of the ballroom, the elegance of the dancers, the skill of the orchestra? Such things are better left to the imagination so that everyone can fill in for himself such details as he finds most satisfactory. Just as we can all picture the magnificent banquet overflowing with the choicest wines, fruits, rare dishes of all descriptions, *sanglier*, sturgeon's roe, peacocks stuffed with peaches, or whatever seems most delectable and exotic.

Only as regards the ballroom it is necessary to mention the elaborate chandeliers (if that is the right term with which to describe these sparkling crystal confections of ice-bright lights, fantastically crown-shaped, and pouring an absolute flood of brilliance upon the scene). It is these amazing illuminations which give the ballroom such a unique distinction; for they are quite unforgettable; and a person who has once seen them is not likely to be much impressed by any other wonder encountered in his travels about the world

which makes all the more surprising the potency of the attraction
that draws the girl with the glistening green glass slippers to leave her partner standing thunderstruck immediately under one of the radiant crowns   in order to follow a silhouette darkly beckoning and window-framed in the sapphire recessive night.

And so on: in considerable repetition, with varying details, of the basic situation; the central theme itself being subject to variation in so far as the attraction is not inevitably to darkness from light.

For instance; the dream travels, quite briefly, through a picture sequence in which each view lasts only just long enough for apperception before it is superseded.

At first there is seen, from some distance away, a small one-storey house near the edge of a forty-foot cliff, at night; it is not very dark. The shut box of the house, with snaky convolutions of surrounding tree-trunks, is at the top of this picture: the rocky cliff face (below it the tarry water) is the crucial centre. Next a glimpse of the interior in which (in bedroom with drawn blinds) an indication is made of someone asleep in bed: the indication further extended to suggest B. Quick shift outside again to the night sky pricked with a few stars. Huge storm-clouds gathering, expanding, immediately eat up the sky and its stars. The sea rising: the heaving sea-mass bursts into white horses; the wind lets fly; the wind pitched so that its noise is too the hissing spray blown from the breakers which now are filling the dream picture. The cliff is black shadow. A wave crashes; against the rocks the waves hurling a deadwhaledeadweight of water; the spray unfurls its enormous fan; the rocks quake among rush and lather and foam of retreating water; their stubborn, drowned, again battered, not yet quite smothered heads (did they really tremble?); upthrusting spray jets higher and higher from the successive breakers. Terrific waves swelling; huger, fiercer waves accumulating and exploding: a wave pounds on a balanced rock; the rock lurches with thunder-thud into the seething sea trough: another pounding thunder-roar, and the cliff quivers with tremor of walls in bombardment.

A lightning flash is stabbed into the sky and jabbed at by other flashes, their crazy neons jittering into word shapes, WHAT IS LOST NOW IS OUR HOME IN THIS WORLD . Immediate glimpse of monstrous vicious crocodile snouts thrusting out of the waves and flaming, fire-belching with deafening shattering booming reverberation and blinding eye-thunder (black and fire everywhere); could be warships, submarines, could be leviathans in their death-throes.

Now the cliff, in black-and-white flaps of fire and thunder, bashed and battered by waves and beaten to breaking point; rocks, a whole buttress, loosen with earthquake rumble, start to slither; a whole segment of the cliff crumbles and falls away, bearing with it a tree, torn-up roots wildly writhing; the house hanging suspended, projecting over the now concave cliff verge, overhanging nothing.

Inside the bedroom, the sleeper has woken. In this dark room a stirring movement, the door opening, someone entering. Hands, fraily phosphorescent, extended, groping, delicately contacting the edges of furniture, feeling their way like blind hands. A blue ring flashes; two hands are joined, one leading the other, and flashing its bright ring; the hands moving through the dark house together, in darkness, out of the house; leaving it:

outside the tumult speeds up, the storm noise getting steadily madder; the flaming monsters vomiting more and more frenziedly, blasting each other; finally wrecked and ruined and sinking, sizzling in sparks and white-hot seethe of lightning and steaming sea:

with deafening roar the entire cliff crumbles, collapses; the house curtseys, sinking forward slowly, turns over, slowly and gracefully disintegrates (walls fall outwards like sides of cardhouse), disappears.

The pandemonium is dimmed quickly into sound of rushing wind; dull, heavy and broken thumping of waves subsiding; then silence.

Two vague figures, one leading the other by the hand, seen receding far off under the quiet night sky where a few watery stars are starting to reappear.

A most remote, primordial scene. A large expanse of mountainous country, no trees, no water, no habitations. Although there are no really high peaks in sight one gets somehow the impression of being at a high altitude, on a plateau among the tops of the mountains. The rock formations are flattish, truncated, the higher tors assuming the shapes of miniature Table Mountains. The colouring a uniform cool lichen grey.

The sun has just set and the sky is still faintly pink in the west behind a low blurring dust haze; elsewhere it is a very limpid and unimpassioned shade of delicate lime green. In the segment of sky opposite the sunset, above the crenellated horizon, a star, at first only just visible, growing momentarily brighter, assumes an elongated shape like a candle-flame. It is at first the only star to be seen: but very soon another, another, and then another, make their appearance. Towards this cross-shaped constellation, across the plateau in the fading light, a procession of vaguely feminine forms moves slowly on foot. The leader raises her hand in encouragement or in exhortation, points to the four stars. So swift is the passing of the subsequent flash that it is impossible to say whether ring or stars originated the light.

The pilgrimage continues to follow the stars which grow larger and brighter, more strangely shaped

until they reveal themselves as candle-flames in a small dark room with no windows or doors visible. The walls are scrawled over with dimly seen symbols, pentacles, wands, swords, etc. There are shelves of books: a few phantom-glimmering shapes of vases or urns. B sits on the floor, reading by the light of the four candles set in their cross-shaped holder.

The Liaison Officer in his smart uniform is preparing to read out of his book again. There is the impression hanging about the dream that he has just finished a part of his lecture or sermon or whatever it is, and is about to start on something new. This he does, by reading in a clear cold voice which has perhaps grown somewhat more authoritarian in its inflexion.

Many people have said that retreats are undesirable and that they should be abolished because their existence constitutes a threat to the supremacy of the authorities whose powers ought to be absolute. But when a man says that he is going into retreat it does not mean he is evading the law, which is an impossibility anyhow: it means that he is effecting a change of authority, a transfer from one set of laws to another set at least equally mysterious and severe – so that he is certainly not making an escape of any sort. All that these retreats do is afford an alternative code, no less exacting and quite as incomprehensible as the one held in more general observance. But when it comes to the attitude of the authorities towards such institutions – here, I think, we are getting out of our depth.

In this connection it could be argued: if the authorities really are supreme, why should they permit the continued existence of a system which competes with their own? Is it not much more likely that the retreats are licensed by the authorities because, in some inscrutable way, they play their part in the established order?

There is even the possibility that the regime of the retreats, although it appears (superficially at least) totally different, is nothing but a disguised version of the regulations in force outside. This theory, improbable as it sounds, is supported by the fact that in certain contingencies the two spheres of authority indubitably converge, and perhaps even merge into one another if the critical nature of the emergency warrants it. But these eventualities are so rare and so little understood, the whole subject is so complicated by ambiguity and obscurity, that speculation is necessarily vague.

Actually, one is tempted to believe that the authorities are so perspicacious, so ingenious, that they have devised this method of tricking into conformity with the law people who might otherwise prove recalcitrant and badly adjusted. It is easy to see how a person of this type, thinking only of his own idiosyncrasies, would fall into the trap. He imagines that by going into retreat he will change his allegiance. And, indeed, once he is inside he becomes docile and content, believing that the old authorities control him no longer.

Meanwhile they, in a stronger position than ever, merely congratulate themselves on the success of their stratagem. The fact that their victory has been won in secret is immaterial; why should they, being all-powerful, wish to make an open display of their powers? All that they wanted has now been skilfully and pacifically achieved.

I hid my face in the lap of darkness like a lost child brought at last to his mother. Never again would I stray into the light: never again would I trust myself to a place where even those who sold their birthright for safety were not secure.

The dreamscape languidly opens up. Conspectus of university town; early morning mist slowly clearing. The mist dispersal not mere evaporation but a sort of gradual unswathing, very gentle protracted tearing, rolling up and discarding, as of webs or excessively fragile tissue paper, disclosing buildings in careful succession. This process, though necessarily long-drawn-out, progresses methodically with a certain businesslike efficiency. Enough should be seen of it to suggest the practised unpacking and setting out of, say, a stock of valuable china.

View narrows to disclosure, from ground upwards, of one particular tower. As mist wrappings are removed, there appears, on a carved ledge, a row of plump pigeons fast asleep with heads under their wings. Then, sighted up the shaft of the tower as if from its foot, the remote rococo summit, which in a second starts to revolve, discharges a musical-box carillon of tinkling notes which dance off, frisky white minims and semibreves, into the now blue sky. Back for a moment to the pigeons, untucking themselves, yawning, blinking, sleepily stretching their wings.

Now a switchover to an outlying residential street of the same town. Ahead, set back from the road in small flowerless lawn garden, a new white flat-roofed modern house, determinedly unembellished, simple rectangles superimposed like a construction of nursery building blocks. A path of concrete slabs leads to the front door which has a chromium ring, O-shaped, instead of a handle.

Inside, in one of the bedrooms upstairs, a child's cot. It is white, with bars at the sides; a brightly painted cock decorates the headboard, an owl the foot; the occupant lies motionless under puffed pale-blue eiderdown. Across the floor, which is covered in some hygienic greyish composition of cork or rubber, comes a tall brasslike woman of forty, her face somewhat like a photo of one of the hostesses seen in society papers; looking like and dressed like a hybrid nurse and socialite; her plucked eyebrows very arched, her lips painted bright red; costumed as if for a cocktail party; wearing a mackintosh apron tied round her waist.

In a series of brisk efficient motions she approaches the cot; lets down the side (with harsh buzz-saw rasp); bends stiff from the waist, her tightly sheathed hind parts glossy in taut satin; turns back the eiderdown. With her hard hands she reaches inside the woolly-white, lamb's-wool coverings (peeling them off as if they were part of a parcel or a cocoon) and grasps firmly, and after a moment lifts out a manikin, adeptly supported by her large hands under buttocks and shoulder-blades, dressed in grey-mottled and baggy tweeds: she sits on a chair; the manikin held on her knee and balancing there, limp dangling feet turned in like a ventriloquist's dummy. The woman zips open her diamanté-trimmed corsage; pulls out a long rubbery phallus-shaped nipple from the glans of which a few flakes of sawdust scale off; inserts this in the dummy's mouth in the style of a petrol feed.

Shot of the little pursed rosebud mouth under shaved upper lip busily sucking away (with lipsmacking and belching accompaniment). The pose held in gruesome travesty of madonna and child tableau. While this goes on the manikin visibly swelling, swelling, till at the end of the meal he is almost a full-sized man. The woman stands him on the floor while she tucks away the flaccid phallus-teat, zips up her dress, stands up.

Slight transitional pause. Next view is downwards from landing to hall (looking down steep-diving staircase), on the two foreshortened figures, the man's egghead with incipient bald tonsure spot. The woman hustles him into professorial gown, jerks, tugs, pats, brushes him off; takes his hand, leads him out of the front door. Through the open door is seen a sliver of venomous green-raffia stage grass.

Chug-chug sound of a child playing at cars; high-pitched tooting horn; the woman reappears in the doorway, watching departure; her watchfulness holds for a few seconds. The woman turning, comes back inside; closing the door, the lock snicks shut; ripping loose apron-strings. The apron falls on the floor. Denting it with her high heels she walks over it to the wall-mirror, extracts a lipstick from gold-mesh bag, starts to repaint her mouth. In the mirror, close-up of her enormously enlarged brilliant moist raw red mouth, suggestive of fancified genital organ.

Now a complete change of scene. The professor has reached the college and is lecturing to his class. He stands on a dais behind a desk on which is a carafe of water and a tin trumpet. He is not quite tall enough for the height of the desk and so he stands on an old-fashioned church hassock with flaps at the ends. To his left, on the wall behind him, a large blackboard scrawled over with indecipherable words and symbols in coloured chalks. (Conceivably some of these might be semi-intelligible words related to escapism; and one or two of the scribbles could be kindergarten obscenities, faces, figures.) On the right a phenomenally tall blank frosted-glass window reaches clear from floor to high domed ceiling. It holds its pair of stiff white fluted curtains rigidly to its sides in arms-downwards-stretch position. Semicircular tiers of benches rising in front. The back of each bench forms a continuous curved shelf for the books of the row above. Only two tiers towards the centre are occupied. (There could be a suggestion of upper and lower dentures in this.) The students are masks: upper row masculine, feminine lower. Except for the sex differentiation, which appears mainly in the arrangement and length of the painted hair, all are identical, characterless, with wide round eyes of respectful admiration, adulation, attention. The masks supported on spinal columns of spiral wire: similar wires representing arms terminated by limp chamois glove-hands half-stuffed with cotton. The hands are laid flat on the bookrests with books between; all are motionless.

The professor's voice continuous

wordless booming punctuated by an occasional NOW or YOU SEE. Sudden short tinny interjection of sound as he picks up toy trumpet and blows. Followed by immediate lifting and reaching out of curtain arms from the window, one arm to each row of students, arms gliding smoothly over the rows of limp glove-hands, touching off each hand in turn, retiring swiftly to the original attention posture at window. There is a faint twanging noise of quivering wires while the gloves are left gangling in palsied mimicry of jittery handwriting and the professor takes a long drink of water.

A resumption of the professorial booming (for a very short period this time), with attention gradually concentrating on the curtains, which appear holding themselves with watchdog vigilance at their window post. Climax comes with the curtains coiling, the curtain tentacles extending, delicately glissading along the mask rows, turning the masks to the blackboard (the professor chalks up O); masks spectrally twitching and trilling in twisted unison; the curtain arms coil high to the ceiling, weave there; then return to the window, to stiff and full arm's-length attention at each side of the window, resume the same tense rigidity as before. As the wire vibration dies down, one after another, the masks topple, tumble, tip out of sight behind the benches. As the last one disappears the professor comes down from the hassock, from the dais, walks to the door of the lecture room.

Four seconds after he has gone out of the door the left curtain slowly draws itself across half the window. The right curtain slowly crosses to meet it.

A series of transient views tracks the professor's progress from lecture room to outer door of college. His black-moth-gown seen fluttering down long perspective of shadowed, tunnel-like stone corridor; emerging into high-groined and vaulted entrance hall, the grey stones of the floor with faint localized stippling of amethyst, topaz, ruby light spillings from stained-glass windows.

Numerous indistinct indications of other figures, gowned professors, student masks topping garments on coat-hangers, wires, hockey-sticks; all flickering spasmodically in different directions; all very indefinite, ephemeral.

Finally, a static black-and-white punctuation mark, a heavy dark ancient door under gothic arch. An old man's gnarled, unsteady, veined hand with border of frayed shirt-cuff, wear-shined and threadbare porter's sleeve, draws back bolts, turns key, loosens chain, with rusty rasping, jarring complaint of unoiled metal.

The door slowly opens.

First the pepper-and-salt trousers, then the whole of the professor, stepping out of the door, crossing empty and sunlit pavement in the cracks of which wild flowers, daisies, harebells, cowslips, primroses, are in bloom. A toy motor car, painted red, stands at the kerb. The professor packs and stuffs and forces himself into it; settles his feet on the pedals; squeezes a captious toot out of the rubber horn-bulb; vigorously pedals off. There is a squeaky noise from the chain driving the wire-spoked wheels. Short distance up street he signals with left arm stiffly extended; turns left, disappears. The chain squeak briefly outlasts him.

Now the professor pedalling home through the quiet streets of the town; not a real-life town, of course. The sunshine is filtered through pink gauze. Colleges, churches, museums, etc., like birthday cakes in the gauzy light. Cuckoos fly out of belfries and cupolas as the clocks strike.

The professor keeps on pedalling, passes the entrance to a street which is in shadow. Glimpse down this street, emphasizing its shadowed contrast to the rest of the town. About two hundred yards along it, facing another way, a mass of full-sized people crowds silently outside a municipal building, a town hall or a police station, very dark-looking, very ominous, introducing an abrupt note of alarm. The professor does not look. He keeps on pedalling.

The sunlit street ribbons on unbroken down a gentle slope with the white play-block house at the end of it. The car, without free wheel, running faster and faster downhill; the professor's knees pistoning faster and faster, almost grazing his chin.

Inside the house the woman who appeared earlier on is playing mah-jong with three visitors. These people are seen only in profile and are feminine, bloodless; with long proboscis noses, like Javanese silhouettes stamped out of metal, very frigidly and ophidianly malignant. The mah-jong tiles forming the walls behind which they are sitting are covered with money symbols, deeds, bonds, coins of various currencies; power symbols, sceptres, whips, bribes; diapers, feeding bottles; phallic signs.

Rapid survey of this somewhat provincial pretentious drawing-room of a would-be-modern intellectual. Smooth, pale, faintly glazed planes of walls, built-in furniture, unstained woods: squarish, low, upholstered couch; easy chairs covered in zebra-stripe fabric: the emasculate fireplace, without mantelpiece, without fire, meekly impounded by chaste light wood bands: wall alcoves, interiorly tinted, and displaying such objects as negro carvings and/or very consciously quaint period pieces, china dogs, red and blue glinting lustres, wax flowers under fragile cloches. Bookshelves with volumes of philosophy, psychology by the more superficial writers, books issued by 'advanced' publishers, a few up-to-the-moment novels, poems, pamphlets, 'advanced' publications generally, a few literary quarterlies and art papers. There would be not more than two or three not-very-original paintings in pale frames on the walls: still life of the slick Slade student apple-and-wine-glass variety, or etiolated impressionist water-colour, or possibly pastel-smudged portrait or overloaded oil landscape in crude colour discords. There would probably be an absence of flowers in the room; or perhaps a white pottery jar of tall grasses or shell flowers.

This room the professor enters in his black gown; with light short tripping steps advances across the neutral carpet; pirouettes; simpers and postures. He stands holding the pose, feet in the fifth position, skirts of his gown extended to fullest width and held between thumbs and forefingers, both little fingers curled and archly pointing.

In their alcoves the dangling glass lobes of the lustres begin to swing and oscillate gently, set up a faint tinkling applause.

Now a quick circling view of the whole rather phoney prosperous enclosed room dithering faintly appreciative: into this circle, very complacent, the professor relaxes coyly from his pose: acknowledging the slight rustle of handclapping from the mah-jong players he sits down in the exact centre of the couch.

The players rise from the table, group themselves round him. The visitors (always in profile) take positions on each side of him on the couch, the third sits on the floor at his feet. From attitudes of admiration their flat snake eyes are upon him in bitter malice, contempt or envy. His own woman is standing behind him, her face tiger-possessive, triumphant; she sets her fingers proprietorially on his head, absently twists his thin hair into kewpie tuft.

This tableau abruptly shattered by sudden rude surge of clamouring, knocking, at outer door of the house. With utmost possible effect of shock, enormous figures, in dark uniforms, bursting into the room, crowding in one after the other, surrounding the couch, brandishing, with threatening gestures, some document (Demand? Indictment?) under the professor's nose.

He jumps up, astounded and outraged, thrusting the three visitors aside in rising (they collapse stiffly with metallic jingle and disappear); the woman behind the sofa gestures imperiously; calls out an unidentifiable order: she is at once submerged by the uniforms; seen struggling for a moment; disappears.

The professor is ringed, pressed on all sides by the massed uniforms, fear now coming out on his face like sweat. He glances round quickly, his face more and more afraid. He clutches his gown, pulls it higher and higher up round his shoulders, hunches his neck in it, muffles his head in its folds; and out of this hiding-place yells shrilly some protest or appeal, indignation in the start of the sounds, panic towards the end.

Two huge uniformed arms are extended from each side simultaneously.

They take hold of the gown, twitch at it derisively, contemptuously snatch it away.

The manikin cowers on the floor, grovels between them, his head with bald spot lolling limp on dummy stalk-neck to the floor.

As the arms grapple him every ornament in the room sets up a thin mad screeching.

A china dog leaps frantically from its shelf and dives under the couch with reversed curlicue tail between its legs.

A glass goblet falls; heavy boots tramp it to dust.

The boots and the forest of dark legs close in, amalgamate into black blob-blot. The blob bulges, spreads steadfastly up to and over everything; blots out the room with a bulging and bursting of black bubble, inky cuttlefish ejaculation; and the brittle death trills still bleating. Blotchout.

*Long ago I had embraced the night and given myself to darkness.
The gentle whispers of rain had consoled me; kind quiet shadows had been
my friends.*

*Why was I led astray by a tiger brightness? Why did a false sun lure me so
far from home?*

*True, I had not actually surrendered to daylight. But I had looked too long
into dazzling and sunbright faces and stayed too long within the gates of
day. My eyes had looked at something forbidden, and seen what they
should never have seen, and now sight itself had gone out of them.*

*Now from the dark and solitary place where I belonged I would not stir
again. When voices called to me I refused to answer. I stopped my ears with
the black robe of night and pulled the folds of darkness about my head.
Never again would I see the blinding glare of enemy eyes or hear the
thudding of disastrous feet.*

Is it or is it not the Liaison Officer who sits at a desk in the middle of this dream? The face looks the same and so does the little neat beard – can it be turning grey? – but why is he wearing an elegant dark suit instead of a uniform? Perhaps not his almost too elegant clothes, but his surroundings, including the big glossy desk where he sits writing, suggest the prosperous professional man, without precisely indicating which profession. On the whole, the room looks more like a doctor's consulting-room than anything else; and yet that doesn't seem quite the right label. The divan and the massive, costly, dead-looking furniture could belong to any successful practitioner. But there are some rather queer mystical pictures and ornaments which don't seem to fit in. Is it a crucifix or a primitive negro priapus hanging there on the wall? It's hard to make anything out in the dim light. A row of books under the desk-lamp can be distinguished as medical textbooks mixed up with books on magic, mythology, philosophy, metaphysics, religion.

The man sitting behind the books has finished his writing. He screws the cap on to his fountain-pen, looks up, and as he moves the gold lettering gleams on the epaulets which he is now seen to be wearing with the insignia of his rank. He leans back comfortably in his chair, gathering together the written sheets, which he holds in one hand (keeping the other free for an occasional restrained gesture) while he reads aloud from them in the smooth nicely modulated voice of a trained actor.

Who are the authorities and where are they to be found? Do they operate from one central focus or from various scattered bureaux with, possibly, a main headquarters in supreme control of the whole organization? These are questions which everyone asks but to which no satisfactory replies are forthcoming. Admittedly, there are so-called initiates who claim to possess information, and one has heard of people whose minds have been set at rest by these individuals. And yet if you or I decide to go into the matter for ourselves our investigations never seem to lead anywhere. Supposing that certain persons have, as they assert, obtained enlightenment from some unknown source, it would seem that they are unable, or perhaps not allowed, to illuminate others, except in rare and selected instances. What happens when you approach such a person with a genuine wish for communication? He will most likely start off by talking to you in a straightforward easy way that at once gives a favourable impression of frankness. Make yourself at home, my friend, he says, by implication if not in so many words. Relax, and listen while I explain everything to you in simple language.

This ingenious technique is, in fact, so convincing that anyone may well be taken in by it, lulled into an uncritical state of mind merely by the soothing quality of manner and words. Quite probably it is not until one has been ushered out of the warm room and is walking home through the frosty air that one really begins to reflect on the interview in an objective way, and to realize that one is absolutely no wiser than before.

At this stage I imagine the average inquirer is apt to abandon the whole affair, considering that he has made an effort adequate to preserve his integrity. Besides, he may think, matters so deep and so hard to approach are certainly dangerous and forbidden and I had better not dabble in them or I shall get into trouble.

On the other hand, someone of greater tenacity and tougher moral fibre may decide to return to the charge. I won't be fobbed off like this, he says to himself: and before his next visit he carefully thinks out and memorizes a series of leading questions. But no matter how cool headed he is or how well he has studied and framed his questions, the result is precisely the same as before. This time, to be sure, the technique will be somewhat different. Instead of the misleading simplicity of the previous occasion, the interrogator now encounters a complexity of specious rhetoric which is woven before him like those unbelievably fine Chinese embroideries which seem to be without beginning or end. The visitor doesn't forget a single question; he puts forward every point in due order. And to every question and point he receives not only an answer but an elaborate homily, a whole lengthy peroration full of learned allusions which a layman would hardly be likely to follow.

But the questioner is a man of superior intelligence, and determination as well. He sticks to his guns, he forces his brain to keep pace with all that is being said.

And now a curious and disheartening phenomenon makes its appearance; a phenomenon of which there appears to be no explanation. It seems to him that each separate sentence is comprehensible.

He is convinced that he understands everything. And, in fact, the various themes, taken one by one, do give an effect of being quite lucid and reasonable, and he hurries home to get the whole thing down on paper while it is fresh in his mind.

Yet no sooner does he begin to concentrate on the subject *as a whole* than he is overcome by a paralysing mental confusion. The explanations, the allusions, the arguments which individually seemed clear enough, inexplicably lose their significance when viewed as the component parts of a pattern, and dissolve into empty verbosity. Hour after hour the unfortunate inquirer sits motionless with his brain in a turmoil, his pen in his hand, unable to write down a single word. Disregarding the voices of his family or his friends, not noticing when it is time to eat or to go to bed, he ponders endlessly over what he has heard, forcing concentration to its nth power in a desperate endeavour to track and pin down the meaning which he once thought was within his grasp, but which has now tantalizingly and mysteriously concealed itself in an intricate maze of incomprehensible phraseology. So it goes on, his thoughts racing fruitlessly and interminably, until sheer mental exhaustion compels him to give in.

Ah, how well one knows the whole horrid cycle, from confidence to uncertainty, to bewilderment, and finally to utter chaos and despair. What is the key to it all? What attitude should one take up? The fact is, and I suppose we must accept it, that for the great majority it is impossible to find out anything about the authorities. But to resign oneself to ignorance is indeed hard. Everyone knows that the authorities exercise supreme control over each one of us, even down to the most trivial details of our lives: and this is even specifically stated in the writings of our ancient teachers. Human beings can hardly be expected to refrain from trying to throw a little light on such vital mysteries: particularly as some unconscious impulse deep in our natures seems to be continually turning our thoughts in that direction.

Who has not, when walking in an unfamiliar part of the town, felt one of those sudden queer psychological shocks which dart like arrows, like premonitions, out of the blue? One may be hurrying along thinking about some personal matter or about an important appointment ahead. All at once, quite without rhyme or reason, the thread of thought snaps, one looks up and sees a big dingy building on the other side of the street, a warehouse possibly, or an old-fashioned office block, which seems to be empty because the shutters are all closed and scraps of paper and leaves have blown on to the dusty doorstep. It's the sort of unattractive unremarkable place you might pass a hundred times without noticing; but today it catches your eye just as an importunate beggar might catch hold of your sleeve. After all it isn't deserted, because between the slats of the shutters dim lights are gleaming. And suddenly the idea comes into your head that perhaps now, at this very moment while you are passing by, in one of the rooms behind those drab shutters, at a worm-eaten desk, among bundles of papers tied up with red or green tape, with scratchy old-fashioned pen-strokes, your fate is being inscribed.

Or something like this may happen while you are out for a walk in the country: you feel yourself quite alone, for an hour you haven't seen one living creature, not even a dog or a horse in a field, you seem to be miles from anywhere. And then in this solitude, out of the bushes at the side of the road, a sly face looks out at you, the face of an old man with a beard and a big hat such as is seldom worn these days. Just for a second he looks out at you. It's really surprising to meet anyone in such a lonely place; but instead of saying Good-day, he draws back, disappears into the wood, and you don't see him again. What is it makes you feel that this old man has been watching you, perhaps following you for some time, hidden among the trees: that he has perhaps been sent to that out-of-the-way spot on purpose to see and report afterwards which track you are following, whether you turn to the right or the left at the crossroads at the foot of the hill?

Nobody knows the exact significance of these feelings which all of us have experienced: but that they bear some relation to our close surveillance by the authorities appears certain. If only it were possible to find out something definite. One feels under constant observation. One has the conviction that every trifling act is noted and set down against one or in one's favour. And at the same time one hasn't the faintest clue to the standards by which one is being judged. How is it possible to avoid anxiety and indecision when a move of any kind involves the whole of one's future status?

Well, it's no good trying to take matters into our own hands; nor is it much good consulting anyone else. All we can do is walk circumspectly and hope for the best; always remembering that whole trains of unimaginable events may follow some incident which seems quite trivial to us, such as, for example, the act of telephoning instead of writing a letter to someone we know.

When everything's said and done, unfortunately, we find ourselves in the position of children whose parents have gone to the theatre, leaving them alone in the dark house. Yes, we are forced, if we are honest, to make the saddest of all admissions when it comes to the last resort: Alas, we do not understand these things.

What ages it took us to get to the end of our journey. At times it seemed as if we never should arrive anywhere, but spend our whole lives travelling. The natives of the countries we passed through must have thought us a funny lot, all of us wearing the same face (though our sizes were different, and our clothes too, of course). Some of us would have liked to settle down in one of these countries, some in another. And I think we all occasionally wished in our secret hearts that we'd never embarked on the expedition. But we couldn't go back once we had started. There was nothing for it but to keep moving on, even if we didn't know where we were going. It wasn't a pleasure trip at any stage; but sometimes the going was terribly hard and slow and exhausting; those were the times when we tried to keep up our spirits by singing. We don't know where we're going, we sang then, but we're on our way. We got discouraged though, all the same, however loudly we sang.

Besides the hardships of the journey itself, there was the isolation and uncertainty about what we should find at the end of it, supposing we ever did get to our destination. It was impossible not to feel anxious from time to time, and homesick, as well. How could we help remembering the place where we'd lived long ago, where people were kind and smiling? How could we help reflecting that the smiles and the kindness would have been still there for us to enjoy if we hadn't been so independent? We used to think of that place always flooded with summer sunshine, while we were travelling far away in stony forgotten regions under a winter sky.

It was winter when we arrived at a place which we thought at first was the right one. The inhabitants came out to meet us and took us in: they took our arms and took us inside walls, and then we saw that the windows were barred and that the doors could not be opened. We became frightened, smelling the caged smell that was in the place, and seeing the locked garden where men with dead eyes swept the unfallen leaves. We saw sleepers laid out in a mass grave, and officials going among them with sleep in their hands. We were more frightened then, we looked at one another and whispered, What kind of sleep is this? knowing now that certainly we had not reached the right destination.

From there we escaped finally, and travelled farther, and in the end we arrived, in spite of all the obstacles. How glad we were to think we had got to our own place! How glad we were to be able to rest at last! Yes, it seems wonderful that the dangers are all behind us. But even now we sometimes wonder about things, and think of the lost sun and the smiles that we knew in the beginning. We suffered much in avoiding those treacherous smiles: we passed through many trials to escape that traitorous sun.

Now we are safe at last. We are secure. We are at peace. But even in the midst of the security and the peace ... still, at certain moments ... we wonder, secretly, if it was worth it ... if peace and security are really worth the splendour they cost to buy.

It is night; and there is nothing false here. Night is reliable. Night does not dazzle us with treacherous fires. Night keeps a dark enduring silence for us ... like sleep, deep sleep. By our own will we came here and tasted sleep before there was any need, because we loved to gaze at the face of night. But not quite at home ... even among loved shadows ... we can't forget altogether the splendid sun ... we sometimes have to dream of the place we came from.

The blissful eye, conscientiously keeping an eye on everything in its turn, takes a turn at eyeing microbic matters, applies itself to the eyepiece (microscope by Negretti and Zambra), and makes a leisurely tour of the slide-wide situation.

A peaceful pastoral scene is here displayed on the fluorescent field, quite in order and as it should be, unexciting, of course, but who is not prepared to sacrifice whatsit to whatsit these days? There is, we think, general agreement that we all have to face a period of whatsit and lessened whatsit for some time to come.

In addition to those of us who are actively engaged in one of the whatsits, very many other people are turning towards whatsit as an outlet for their thoughts and energies, and either as a means of increasing whatsit for whatsit motives, or as a whatsit to take the place of other whatsits not now within their reach.

There is no more gratifying sight for the enthusiast than a contented culture of healthy whatsits placidly browsing upon the pabulum scientifically prepared by those who have studied whatsits and understand the many problems which may cause anxiety.

What is it that emerges from this droplet of broth, or is it bouillon, deposited with professional precision upon the slide? What menacing creatures are these, battened on the nourishing fluid, which now encircle and stalk down their unconscious victims?

The successful preservation of whatsit often depends on the ability of the whatsit to combat and destroy the various whatsit and whatsit whatsits, which manœuvre so much more rapidly, and which, if not speedily checked, will often ruin the whole of a whatsit in a whatsit. The great secret is to be continually on the watch, and to attack the whatsit at the outset before it has had time to gain a whatsit.

On this occasion the experimenter (though doubtless familiar with every branch of the technique), perhaps in the pursuit of further knowledge, makes no attempt to interfere with the fate of these hapless humble martyrs to science, but dispassionately observes the onslaught of the voracious attackers who tear into their prey like tigers and devour them wholly until no single trace remains.

But Nemesis is not far away.

No whatsit need remain in any uncertainty about the kind of whatsit to use in a whatsit, for information is freely available to all and it is the duty of every whatsit one of us to make himself familiar with a few simple whatsits for whatsit. Remember that a whatsit's whatsit may depend on your whatsit. Whatsit now

Swift indeed is the retribution which overtakes the aggressors; and for a display of poetic justice it would be hard to rival the terrible scene which now ensues. A third infinitesimal drop is planted deftly on the slide, an agent so powerful that, extending rapidly in a thin film around and over the fierce corpuscular conquerors, it instantaneously absorbs them into itself, eliminating them in a second by a horrid process of ingurgitation.

Tiring, one imagines, of this close concentration upon bacillic dramatics, a simple adjustment on the part of the eye (Pinto et Issaverdens precision instruments) scales the operational field up to major proportions. A truly astounding scene is forthwith presented, one guaranteed to strike the stoutest heart with terror and amazement. The very seat of reason itself quakes under the visual impact of this awful spectacle, hardly to be expressed in ordinary words. How can one describe even the background, that dark and whirling storm of fiery particles, blinding and burning and asphyxiating at the same time? It's a fog and yet it's a fire, intolerable heat combined with suffocating obscurity. Through this murky inferno, huge armour-plated monsters, blind and mad, are charging in all directions, driven by their Gadarene frenzy to charge each other in indiscriminate fury, stampeded and possessed by maniacal fiends.

Even the perennially untroubled eye of the Heaven-Born prefers not to linger on this unspeakable shambles

and passes on through the world wilderness of death to a large remote semi-demolished, sham-antique building. Under powerful moonshine lamp-flood black forms are busily hauling and hoisting and heaving apart various beams, arches, windows, etc., of this fake medieval edifice. View of the partially dismantled whole narrows down to a doorway; moves over trampled ground to a mock mulberry tree which two sweaty workmen in singlets are preparing to remove. They unhook several large boughs hinged to the main trunk, drop them carelessly on the ground (the torn faded fabric leaves flutter dusty in dust); wrench remainder of tree from its socket; struggle off, lugging it between them.

The general view again, very briefly, indefinitely, outlines blurred and figures eliminated; retreating almost immediately to distant glimpse of roughly similarly shaped sand-castle on a deserted beach in moonlight. The tide comes in quickly. Views of successive small summer waves breaking (with soft soooooon sound), opening white-lipped mouths on the sand, each sucking a few inches nearer the castle.

The first wave reaches the castle wall. The white wavelips suck at

the sand with their sibilance, insidiously: soooon soooooon
soooon (each wave sucking a little harder, higher, undermining
the castle).

The sand walls spread, subside, sink, settle, submerge – their
soft almost soundless sigh sunk in the sea sound.

In a house where furnished seaside lodgings are rented a girl,
asleep in her bed, green slippers under the bed as she kicked them
off toe to heel, dreams, stirs and hears the subsidence (it is only a
dressing-gown slipping off the end of the bed); she does not wake;
although she changes position.

The empty beach with the sand now covered by water, smooth
and full. The moon gravely passes with quiet deliberation behind a
cloud, drawing after her all detail; leaving only the tranquilly
breathing breast of dark and murmurous water; which the eye
observes, as it seems, pensively, and one is anthropomorphically
inclined to believe, with relief in respite, until

goddess no longer of the moony crested tire, quick-change artist
and record-holder, out steps the twenty-one-year-old lieutenant-
colonel – the youngest in the whatsit army – wearing steel helmet,
rakishly askew, eccentric battledress copiously stippled with pig's
blood, bedroom slippers with soft woollen pompoms (I intend to
invade whatsit in comfort); his face is blacked like a nigger-
minstrel's with white eye-circles, one emitting searchlight illumination: through the second orifice a whizzing stream of machine-
gun bullets, exploding bombs, rockets, clods of earth, power-
diving planes, bombers, fighters, vampires, anopheles-size and
vicious, in inexhaustible swarms.

The searchlight beam points erratically hither and thither, in the
manner of a retriever questing for game, over the vast slow-
seething seabulk which is now apperceptible as a sort of time
symbol holding locked in its dark plasma the innumerable bubbles
of all past and future eventualities.

At irregular intervals the beam oscillates violently in the agitation of finding, then slowly fixes, freezing in its terminal circle
small distant sharp scenes of topical interest. As,

        an idealized country house in sunny summery landscape,
roses round the door, elm-muffled peaceable strokes of church
clock striking the tea hour, strawberries and cream and deck-

chairs on the lawn, unseen pigeons cooing, every exile's sentimental picture of home.

Twilight gathers quickly; a bleak wind rising overturns the deserted chairs: the roses droop, wither, fall, their petals are blown away; the pigeon-coos hoarsen to ominous hooting as a huge spectral white owl with lambent eyes sweeps stealthily past, concentrating to pounce as it disappears; immediately afterwards a thin mouse death-shriek is heard.

In deepening darkness dimly seen conspiratorial forms, wearing some kind of horrific disguise-uniform (Inquisition or Ku-Klux-Klan suggestion) by unclear and rapid manipulation convert the house to traditional haunted-house aspect.

The Hanged Man swings from a black tree; he is looking at something unseen in the air; spinning slowly in the wind with desolate bone creaking; muttering, I am too old to be in a tree. A mongrel pup, starved ribcage on four matchsticks, slinks in and out of sight. Mist wraiths coagulate, hover lugubriously, disintegrate, among dark shapes of bushes or tombstones or crouching things. After slight pause, a small white bone falls like a full stop on the black grass.

Now inside the house: a storm lantern flickers feebly on dusty and empty rooms that the wind whimpers through, and on the uneasy group of neophytes herded together. These are boys of about fourteen, with dumb-bucolic or vicious-urban-degenerate faces sniggering in discomfort, and with restless movements and whispers hiding their half-alarm. They are dressed in badly fitting uniforms of cheap coarse material, some with jackets sagging loose to the knees, some with tight sleeves which fail to cover their wrists. They are armed with weapons contrastingly expensive, efficient, ultra-modern and deadly looking. Carrying out their orders, they move through the rooms, a few displaying exaggerated toughness, the others alternately scared and vacuously amused by the various trick manifestations, hidden traps, skulls springing out of cupboards, chains clanking, lights suddenly flashing, doors suddenly opening or slamming, moans, screams, howls, etc.

Finally the roof lifts up like a lid and the lieutenant-colonel is seen hovering batlike and spraying from the poison ducts at the back of his vampire fangs a fine rain of blood with which the upturned faces are thinly spattered. Simultaneously his voice, very much amplified, yells through the loudspeaker, On your toes, boys. Remember whatsit. There's a whatsit. Kill the swine. Kick his guts out.

As his image slowly fades it develops a recognizable though incomplete resemblance to the Liaison Officer. At the instant of disappearance the rim of his steel helmet catches the light and hangs in mid-air, a halo-like, phosphorescent ellipse which evaporates as the loudspeaker switches to soundtrack of war horror film

linking up with

a cinema audience in tightly-packed hall. The rows of people seen from the back all exactly similar somewhat elongated heads with protuberant ears. A big flag with crossed emblems hangs over the screen where an air-raid is shown in progress. Deafening accompaniment of appropriate noises: bombs, rockets, ack-ack, sirens, shouts, clanging bells of fire engines, ambulances, etc. Walls seen crumbling, ARP and NFS personnel search through wreckage and rubble for victims under mobile arc-lamps. A woman is carried by on a stretcher; where her face was, foot-long splinters of glass project like porcupine quills. A growl of rage, baited-animal sound, travels along the watching rows of the audience.

Quick over the road to the movie theatre on the other side. The rows of people here seen from the back all exactly similar somewhat square heads with protuberant ears. A big flag with circular emblem hangs over the screen where an air-raid is shown in progress. Deafening accompaniment of appropriate noises: bombs, rockets, ack-ack, sirens, shouts, clanging bells of fire engines, ambulances, etc. Walls seen crumbling, ARP and NFS personnel hunt through wreckage and rubble for victims under mobile arc-lamps. A woman is carried by on a stretcher; where her face was, foot-long splinters of glass project like porcupine quills. A growl of rage, baited-animal sound, travels along the watching rows of the audience.

Quickly the audiences of the two theatres crowding blackly out, overflowing the street like opposing ant-swarms. A rumbling roar goes up as they converge upon one another, interpenetrate.

The searchlight beam (now for the sake of convenience to be identified with the untroubled eye up above) wanders restlessly:

after a not arbitrary number of glimpses of world happenings,

roams towards a huge solitary fang-shaped rock, almost a mountain, jutting sheer out of the ocean, sleek oil-black faintly polished, belted with white scalloped beading of foam. A sudden long inexplicable swell gathers on the smooth water, mounting quickly to tidal-wave size, travels increasingly rapidly and toweringly to the rock; at the moment of impact the eyebeam telescopes into close-up of the shattering wave with heavy spray mane wind combed and white from the black wave blown back.

In still closer analysis, the spray particles brightly illuminated, particularized, individualized, metamorphosed into papers of all descriptions.

Envelopes (with stamps of various countries, airmail stamps, Opened by Censor, DDA stickers, OHMS signs, etc.) addressed in various handwritings or typewritten to places all over the world. Letters from lovers, banks, businesses, ministries, consulates, etc.; on embossed paper, thin paper, papers with printed headings, pages torn from exercise books. Birth, marriage, death certificates; diplomas, passports, dossiers, warrants, licences, ballot cards, invitations, tickets, cheques, coupons, leaflets, cables, menus, currency notes, programmes, manuscripts, drawings, photographs, labels, press cuttings. These appear briefly (there is barely time to read them) with headlines in utter confusion. As

Gas leads suicide methods this winter. Shaw mumbles no in beard to love notes. Mayan temple hieroglyphics used as play-suit trimmings. No bass violinists in Folsom Prison. Atom Bomb opens new era in world destruction, entire city vaporized in black rain, victims vanish. Bishop thanks God for science.

There are perhaps one or two full paragraphs

Phosgene is the most practical and economical gas for the production of quick death. While mustard-gas casualties are a long time in hospital, sometimes several months, there is nothing about them, immediately after being gassed, to inspire terror in other troops. With phosgene, however, if heavily gassed, men will be dropping dead like flies in a few hours. . . .

The impact of his body loosened the jam and started the coal moving downward to the funnel in the centre of the floor. While his companions ran for aid, Seery flailed about and when police of

Emergency Squad 4 reached the scene only his head and shoulders were visible. The bottom of an ashcan was ripped out and lowered to him as an improvised caisson. A rope was then dropped and planks were laid on top of the moving coal on which Fire Captain Charles Kuchas of Hook and Ladder Co. 24 clambered to Seery and administered a hypodermic. Then the Rev. W. J. Faricker of the Church of the Epiphany made the same dangerous journey to administer the last rites of the Catholic Church. As Father Faricker finished the rope snapped and Seery was sucked beneath the surface. . . .

Take a pleasant breezy jaunt with Jimmy Fidler, on location every day at the Mirror. . . .

Finally the whole mass of papers flying, whirling through the air like Alice's pack of cards. The paper storm condenses, recedes, spirals into funnel-shaped white cloud-whirl, tornado, travelling away at great speed over perfectly featureless, blank, near-black field: vanishing. The neutral shadowblank holds for a moment of discharging tension as the blissful eyes up above defocus slowly.

I can't remember the journey or who arranged it. No one told me where I was going. No one told me the name of the shadow house or why I was brought there.

Some things about the place were confusing. There were wet nights when it seemed to be the house where my mother lived. Sometimes when the rain struck at the window I called my mother's face to the black glass in the way a fisherman draws a fish to the surface of the water. Then it was hard to tell which face was my own.

Sometimes the shadow house was extremely quiet: vigilant silence crouched against every door. Sometimes the walls rang with tremendous music, Israfel sang, whose heart-strings are a lute, and all the ghosts of China twittered like crazy birds.

Sometimes my mother's familiars, sadness and boredom, loitered among the shadows: then I looked out of the window quickly.

My window was a magic glass which gave everything it reflected a kind face. Even hostility and chaos smiled in that mirror. When I looked out of the window everything became friendly and clear and simple. All day I could watch the white sky children wreathing light-hearted dances in their playground, while the air cherished them like a mother. And in the night my own mother came to the window to meet me, strange, solitary; splendid with countless stars; my mother Night; mine, lovely, mine. My home.

It's rather dark in the house where B has gone, and this isn't because it's evening outside. Of course, sometimes it is night out of doors, and then you'd expect the house to be dark indeed: but curiously enough there's very little difference inside between the night and the day. It's always twilight in those rooms where a lamp or candle is just as likely to be burning at noon as in the small hours of the morning.

The house is really difficult to describe. You can say that it's in a town, in a long street of other houses. But that only conveys the vaguest impression, if it isn't actually misleading, for some of the upstairs windows look clean into the country with its lakes and streams and fields and forests and villages and the majestic mountains behind. It's no easier to give a picture of the interior either. Like most old places, this house has been altered and enlarged again and again so that the rooms are of all shapes and sizes and periods, opening one into another, or linked by galleries or flights of steps leading up and down in the most unexpected and unconventional way. One circular tower room, for instance, appears to have been built on quite haphazard, as if the architect had overlooked the necessity for connecting it with the rest of the building, and had only added as an afterthought a crooked little staircase hidden away in a corner which you might pass a dozen times without noticing. This irregularity of design makes it hard to find your way about the house. It's such a rambling old place, there are so many rooms, and all of them half-dark, that you can never be absolutely certain you've been into every one.

B herself is often surprised when she is wandering in the passages to find that she has come to a door which she has never seen before. And this is particularly apt to happen just when she feels that she has at last mastered the plan of the different floors.

It almost seems as if alterations were continually taking place in the outlying parts of the house, certain rooms changing their shape or position or even disappearing entirely, and other new rooms proliferating in distant corridors: while the main part of the construction, the hall, kitchens, dining-room, library, principal bedrooms and so on, remain more or less stabilized. Certainly, minor changes are liable to occur even in these rooms; but they are unimportant and chiefly confined to differences of furniture, decoration or general arrangement. Thus, in place of a window, there may one day appear some ancient, half-indistinguishable portrait of a state dignitary in solemn robes. And then very possibly within a few hours a window will again have taken the picture's place: but this time the window, instead of overlooking the street as before, will be facing on to a formal paved yard, bounded by high walls, and with a clipped shrub growing in each corner.

On the face of it, this looks like a lot of unnecessary expenditure of energy. It's hard to conceive any acceptable explanation of such changeability; unless the proprietors have adopted some complicated eclectic system with regard to the place. The best way, as in all these obscure matters, is simply to accept the situation without enquiring into causality, which would most likely be incomprehensible even if brought to light.

B, in any event, does not speculate about what goes on. These constant unpredictable variations, which some people might find disconcerting, to her constitute one of the great charms of the house. The pleasant anticipation of novelty turns the opening of every door into an adventure.

How does a girl like B feel, you may wonder, alone in this great dark place? The question can be answered in four simple words: B is at home. And she's not lonely either. Her companions are the many mirrors which hang all over the house in the various rooms. Probably there has never been a house which contained as many mirrors as this one. Mirrors framed in every imaginable style, from the huge glass in the salon with its magnificent eagle whose wide wings, glimmering with dim gilt in the dusk, seemed poised already in imperial flight, to the convex circle, no larger than a plate, which microcosmically reflects in steely recession the window at the turn of the stairs and a whole pinpoint Brueghel landscape beyond. Long cheval glasses lean inquiringly in the bedrooms like strangers wishing to ask the way. In alcoves, in the passages, on landings, you will unexpectedly catch, just as you sometimes catch someone else's eye in a crowd, the subdued and watchful gleam of a mirror. And in every one of these mirrors B recognizes the fair-haired girl who is her closest friend.

Even without this mirror friend there would be plenty of entertainment to be had just by looking out of the windows. Sometimes, on certain days or in certain rooms, the curtains are drawn, and then of course it's inadvisable to attempt to look outside. But usually there is nothing to prevent you from studying the view. What a variety of views there are too. That's what makes window-gazing from this house so delightful.

Perhaps it's Christmas time in the street. You can sit on the wide window-seat sheltered by a wine-coloured velvet curtain and watch the snow feathers falling. The children are throwing snowballs as they run home in the twilight, their cheeks are bright red, they wear ear-muffs and warm mittens and little round caps made of fur. Their movements are like a dance. What a joy it is to watch such spontaneous happiness.

The tongues of the bells in the church steeple at the end of the street dart sharp and clean as icicles in the freezing air. The sky is the deep blue of sapphires, the snow burns blue-white, lighted windows blossom one after the other.

In the house opposite they are having a party. A huge holly wreath tied with red satin ribbon hangs on the door knocker. Gold light streams from the windows, and inside you can see the gorgeous Christmas tree and the guests in their fine clothes. In one room people are dancing to the music of a piano and violin; in another, boys and girls are just sitting down to a table decorated with flowers and candles and toys. How gay all the faces are! What peace and friendliness inside the festive rooms; and the beautiful frozen night out of doors. It makes you feel warm and comfortable just to look at it all.

Or, maybe, delicate muslin ruffles are floating gently in and out of the open window in a warm breeze. The air enters scented with roses, with honeysuckle and clover, fresh with the smell of grass which men have been cutting all day long in the fields. Stripped to the waist, their torsos beautiful as light bronze, the strong young haymakers rhythmically swing their scythes through the final swaths. The heavy haywains lumber home in the dusk. From the village rises the sound of singing and laughter; a cheerful clatter of pans comes from the kitchens where women in bright aprons are preparing the evening meal. Lovers walk in the orchards under the ripening fruit. Grave and benign like archangels, the white winged mountains stand in the darkening sky.

Yes, there's always something fascinating to be seen from the windows. And then there's the house itself, a perpetual source of interest and surprise. Why, you could easily spend a lifetime investigating the library alone. Not to mention the pictures, the clocks, the tapestries, and the curious objects stored in the different rooms; the attics crowded with trunks, every one packed full of unimaginable and exciting treasures; the porcelain, silver, silk, crystal, ivory, jade, collected through many centuries and in many lands; the clothes folded away in the cupboards; the very pots and pans in the kitchen, the canisters full of strange spices, the herbs and cordials and preserves, the vast stone urnlike crocks on the store-room floor.

It's really impossible to mention even a fraction of the riches contained in a house so inexhaustibly endowed with wonders from all over the world, as well as with its own unique, complex, incomparable individuality. You get confused when you try to describe it; the mind is embarrassed by such a wealth of material; you hardly know where to begin or where to leave off.

Well, the line has to be drawn somewhere: and that's why it seems useless to say any more except that no discriminating person would ever willingly leave such a house once they had taken up residence in it; or find any other house even tolerable afterwards.

Ice

one

I was lost, it was already dusk, I had been driving for hours and was practically out of petrol. The idea of being stranded on these lonely hills in the dark appalled me, so I was glad to see a signpost, and coast down to a garage. When I opened a window to speak to the attendant, the air outside was so cold that I turned up my collar. While he was filling the tank he commented on the weather. 'Never known such cold in this month. Forecast says we're in for a real bad freeze-up.' Most of my life was spent abroad, soldiering, or exploring remote areas: but though I had just come from the tropics and freeze-ups meant little to me, I was struck by the ominous sound of his words. Anxious to get on, I asked the way to the village I was making for. 'You'll never find it in the dark, it's right off the beaten track. And those hill roads are dangerous when they're iced up.' He seemed to imply that only a fool would drive on under present conditions, which rather annoyed me. So, cutting short his involved directions, I paid him and drove away, ignoring his last warning shout: 'Look out for that ice!'

It had got quite dark by now, and I was soon more hopelessly lost than ever. I knew I should have listened to the fellow, but at the same time wished I had not spoken to him at all. For some unknown reason, his remarks had made me uneasy; they seemed a bad omen for the whole expedition, and I began to regret having embarked on it.

I had been doubtful about the trip all along. I had arrived only the previous day, and should have been attending to things in town instead of visiting friends in the country. I myself did not understand my compulsion to see this girl, who had been in my thoughts all the time I was away, although she was not the reason for my return. I had come back to investigate rumours of a mysterious impending emergency in this part of the world. But as soon as I got here she became an obsession, I could think only of her, felt I must see her immediately, nothing else mattered. Of course I knew it was utterly irrational. And so was my present uneasiness: no harm was likely to come to me in my own country; and yet I was becoming more and more anxious as I drove on.

Reality had always been something of an unknown quantity to me. At times this could be disturbing. Now, for instance. I had visited the girl and her husband before, and kept a vivid recollection of the peaceful, prosperous-looking countryside round their home. But this memory was rapidly fading, losing its reality, becoming increasingly unconvincing and indistinct, as I passed no one on the road, never came to a village, saw no lights anywhere. The sky was black, blacker untended hedges towering against it; and when the headlights occasionally showed roadside buildings, these too were always black, apparently uninhabited and more or less in ruins. It was just as if the entire district had been laid waste during my absence.

I began to wonder if I would ever find her in the general disorder. It did not look as if any organized life could have been going on here since whatever disaster had obliterated the villages and wrecked the farms. As far as I could see, no attempt had been made to restore normality. No rebuilding or work on the land had been done, no animals were in the fields. The road badly needed repairs, the ditches were choked with weeds under the neglected hedges, the whole region appeared to have been left derelict and deserted.

A handful of small white stones hit the windscreen, making me jump. It was so long since I had experienced winter in the north that I failed to recognize the phenomenon. The hail soon turned to snow, diminishing visibility and making driving more difficult. It was bitterly cold, and I become aware of a connexion between this fact and my increasing uneasiness. The garage man had said he had never known it so cold at this time, and my own impression was that it was far too early in the season for ice and snow. Suddenly my anxiety was so acute that I wanted to turn and drive back to town; but the road was too narrow, I was forced to follow its interminable windings up and down hill in the lifeless dark. The surface got worse, it got steeper and more slippery all the time. The unaccustomed cold made my head ache as I stared out, straining my eyes in the effort of trying to avoid icy patches, where the car skidded out of control. When the headlights fled over roadside ruins from time to time, the brief glimpse always surprised me, and vanished before I was sure I had really seen it.

An unearthly whiteness began to bloom on the hedges. I passed a gap and glanced through. For a moment, my lights picked out like searchlights the girl's naked body, slight as a child's, ivory white against the dead white of the snow, her hair bright as spun glass. She did not look in my direction. Motionless, she kept her eyes fixed on the walls moving slowly towards her, a glassy, glittering circle of solid ice, of which she was the centre. Dazzling flashes came from the ice-cliffs far over her head; below, the outermost fringes of ice had already reached her, immobilized her, set hard as concrete over her feet and ankles. I watched the ice climb higher, covering knees and thighs, saw her mouth open, a black hole in the white face, heard her thin, agonized scream. I felt no pity for her. On the contrary, I derived an indescribable pleasure from seeing her suffer. I disapproved of my own callousness, but there it was. Various factors had combined to produce it, though they were not extenuating circumstances.

I had been infatuated with her at one time, had intended to marry her. Ironically, my aim then had been to shield her from the callousness of the world, which her timidity and fragility seemed to invite. She was over-sensitive, highly strung, afraid of people and life; her personality had been damaged by a sadistic mother who kept her in a permanent state of frightened subjection. The first thing I had to do was to win her trust, so I was always gentle with her, careful to restrain my feelings. She was so thin that, when we danced, I was afraid of hurting her if I held her tightly. Her prominent bones seemed brittle, the protruding wrist-bones had a particular fascination for me. Her hair was astonishing, silver-white, an albino's, sparkling like moonlight, like moonlit Venetian glass. I treated her like a glass girl; at times she hardly seemed real. By degrees she lost her fear of me, showed a childish affection, but remained shy and elusive. I thought I had proved to her that I could be trusted, and was content to wait. She seemed on the point of accepting me, though immaturity made it hard to assess the sincerity of her feelings. Her affection perhaps was not altogether pretence, although she deserted me suddenly for the man to whom she was now married.

This was past history. But the consequences of the traumatic experience were still evident in the insomnia and headaches from which I suffered. The drugs prescribed for me produced horrible dreams, in which she always appeared as a helpless victim, her fragile body broken and bruised. These dreams were not confined to sleep only, and a deplorable side effect was the way I had come to enjoy them.

Visibility had improved, the night was no less dark, but the snow had stopped. I could see the remains of a fort on the top of a steep hill. Nothing much was left of it but the tower, it had been gutted, empty window-holes showed like black open mouths. The place seemed vaguely familiar, a distortion of something I half-remembered. I seemed to recognize it, thought I had seen it before, but could not be certain, as I had only been here in the summer, when everything looked quite different.

At that time, when I accepted the man's invitation, I suspected him of an ulterior motive in asking me. He was a painter, not serious, a dilettante; one of those people who always have plenty of money without appearing to do any work. Possibly he had a private income; but I suspected him of being something other than what he seemed. The warmth of my reception surprised me, he could not have been more friendly. All the same, I was on my guard.

The girl hardly spoke, stood beside him, glancing sideways at me with big eyes through her long lashes. Her presence affected me strongly, though I scarcely knew in what way. I found it difficult to talk to the two of them. The house was in the middle of a beech wood, so closely surrounded by many tall trees that we seemed to be actually in the tree tops, waves of dense green foliage breaking outside every window. I thought of an almost extinct race of large singing lemurs known as the Indris, living in the forest trees of a remote tropical island. The gentle affectionate ways and strange melodious voices of these near-legendary creatures had made a great impression on me, and I began speaking about them, forgetting myself in the fascination of the subject. He appeared interested. She said nothing, and presently left us to see about lunch. The conversation at once became easier when she had gone.

It was midsummer, the weather was very hot, the rustling leaves just outside made a pleasant cool sound. The man's friendliness continued. I seemed to have misjudged him, and began to be embarrassed by my suspicions. He told me he was glad I had come, and went on to speak of the girl. 'She's terribly shy and nervous, it does her good to see someone from the outside world. She's too much alone here.' I couldn't help wondering how much he knew about me, what she had told him. To remain on the defensive seemed rather absurd; still, there was some reservation in my response to his amiable talk.

I stayed with them for a few days. She kept out of my way. I never saw her unless he was there too. The fine hot weather went on. She wore short, thin, very simple dresses that left her shoulders and arms bare, no stockings, a child's sandals. In the sunshine her hair dazzled. I knew I would not be able to forget how she looked. I noted a marked change in her, a much increased confidence. She smiled more often, and once in the garden I heard her singing. When the man called her name she came running. It was the first time I had seen her happy. Only when she spoke to me she still showed some constraint. Towards the end of my visit he asked whether I had talked to her alone. I told him I had not. He said: 'Do have a word with her before you go. She worries about the past; she's afraid she made you unhappy.' So he knew. She must have told him all there was to tell. It was not much, certainly. But I would not discuss what had happened with him and said something evasive. Tactfully, he changed the subject: but returned to it later on. 'I wish you would set her mind at rest. I shall make an opportunity for you to speak to her privately.' I did not see how he was going to do this, as the next day was the last I would spend with them. I was leaving in the late afternoon.

That morning was the hottest there had been. Thunder was in the air. Even at breakfast time the heat was oppressive. To my surprise, they proposed an outing. I was not to leave without having seen one of the local beauty spots. A hill was mentioned, from which there was a celebrated view: I had heard the name. When I referred to my departure I was told it was only a short drive, and that we should be back in plenty of time for me to pack my bag. I saw that they were determined on the arrangement, and agreed.

We took a picnic lunch to eat near the ruins of an old fort, dating from a remote period when there had been fear of invasion. The road ended deep in the woods. We left the car and continued on foot. In the steadily increasing heat, I refused to hurry, dropped behind, and when I saw the end of the trees, sat down in the shade. He came back, pulled me to my feet. 'Come along! You'll see that it's worth the climb.' His enthusiasm urged me up a steep sunny slope to the summit, where I duly admired the view. Still unsatisfied, he insisted that I must see it from the top of the ruin. He seemed in a queer state, excitable, almost feverish. In the dusty dark, I followed him up steps cut inside the tower wall, his massive figure blocking out the light so that I could see nothing and might have broken my neck where a step was missing. There was no parapet at the top, we stood among heaps of rubble, nothing between us and the drop to the ground, while he swung his arm, pointing out different items in the extensive view. 'This tower has been a landmark for centuries. You can see the whole range of hills from here. The sea's over there. That's the cathedral spire. The blue line beyond is the estuary.'

I was more interested in closer details: piles of stones, coils of wire, concrete blocks, and other materials for dealing with the coming emergency. Hoping to see something that would provide a clue to the nature of the expected crisis, I went nearer the edge, looked down at the unprotected drop at my feet.

'Take care!' he warned, laughing. 'You could easily slip here, or lose your balance. The perfect spot for a murder, I always think.' His laugh sounded so peculiar that I turned to look at him. He came up to me saying: 'Suppose I give you a little push ... like this—' I stepped back just in time, but missed my footing and stumbled, staggering on to a crumbling, precarious ledge lower down. His laughing face hung over me, black against the hot sky. 'The fall would have been an accident, wouldn't it? No witnesses. Only my word for what happened. Look how unsteady you are on your feet. Heights seem to affect you.' When we got down to the bottom again I was sweating, my clothes were covered in dust.

The girl had set out the food on the grass in the shade of an old walnut tree growing there. As usual she spoke little. I was not sorry my visit was ending; there was too much tension in the atmosphere, her proximity was too disturbing. While we were eating I kept glancing at her, at the silvery blaze of hair, the pale, almost transparent skin, the prominent, brittle wrist-bones. Her husband had lost his earlier exhilaration and become somewhat morose. He took a sketchbook and wandered off. I did not understand his moods. Heavy clouds appeared in the distance; I felt the humidity in the air and knew there would be a storm before long. My jacket lay on the grass beside me; now I folded it into a cushion, propped it against the tree trunk and rested my head on it. The girl was stretched out full length on the grassy bank just below me, her hands clasped over her forehead, shielding her face from the glare. She kept quite still, without speaking, her raised arms displaying the slight roughness and darkness of the shaven armpits, where tiny drops of sweat sparkled like frost. The thin dress she was wearing showed the slight curves of her childish body: I could see that she wore nothing underneath it.

She was crouching in front of me, a little lower down the slope, her flesh less white than the snow. Great ice-cliffs were closing in on all sides. The light was fluorescent, a cold flat shadowless ice-light. No sun, no shadows, no life, a dead cold. We were in the centre of the advancing circle. I had to try to save her. I called: 'Come up here – quick!' She turned her head, but without moving, her hair glinting like tarnished silver in the flat light. I went down to her, said: 'Don't be so frightened. I promise I'll save you. We must get to the top of the tower.' She seemed not to understand, perhaps did not hear because of the rumbling roar of the approaching ice. I got hold of her, pulled her up the slope: it was easy, she was almost weightless. Outside the ruin I stopped, holding her with one arm, looked round and saw at once that it was useless to go any higher. The tower was bound to fall; it would collapse, and be pulverized instantly under millions of tons of ice. The cold scorched my lungs, the ice was so near. She was shivering violently, her shoulders were ice already; I held her closer to me, wrapped both arms round her tight.

Little time was left, but at least we would share the same end. Ice had already engulfed the forest, the last ranks of trees were splintering. Her silver hair touched my mouth, she was leaning against me. Then I lost her: my hands could not find her again. A snapped-off tree trunk was dancing high in the sky, hurled up hundreds of feet by the impact of the ice. There was a flash, everything was shaken. My suitcase was lying open, half-packed, on the bed. The windows of my room were still wide open, the curtains streamed into the room. Outside the treetops were streaming, the sky had gone dark. I saw no rain, but thunder still rolled and echoed, and as I looked out lightning flashed again. The temperature had fallen several degrees since morning. I hurried to put on my jacket and shut the window.

I had been following the right road, after all. After running like a tunnel between unpruned hedges that met overhead, it wound through the dark beech wood to end in front of the house. No light was visible. The place looked derelict, uninhabited, like the others I had passed. I sounded the horn several times and waited. It was late, they might be in bed. If she was there I had to see her, and that was all there was to it. After some delay, the man came and let me in. He did not seem pleased to see me this time, which was understandable if I had woken him up. He appeared to be in his dressing gown.

The house was without electricity. He went first, flashing a torch. I kept my coat on, although the living-room fire gave out some warmth. In the lamplight I was surprised to see how much he had altered while I had been abroad. He looked heavier, harder, tougher; the amiable expression had gone. It was not a dressing gown he was wearing, but the long overcoat of some uniform, which made him seem unfamiliar. My old suspicions revived; here was someone who was cashing in on the emergency before it had even arrived. His face did not appear friendly. I apologized for coming so late, explaining that I had lost my way. He was in the process of getting drunk. Bottles and glasses stood on a small table. 'Well, here's to your arrival.' There was no cordiality in his manner or in his voice, which had a sardonic tone that was new. He poured me a drink and sat down, the long overcoat draping his knees. I looked for the bulging pocket, the protruding butt, but nothing of the sort was visible under the coat. We sat drinking together. I made conversation about my travels, waiting for the girl to appear. There was no sign of her; not a sound from the rest of the house. He did not mention her, and I could tell that he refrained deliberately by his look of malicious amusement. The room I remembered as charming was now neglected, dirty. Plaster had fallen from the ceiling, there were deep cracks in the walls as from the effect of blast, black patches where rain had seeped in, and with it, the devastation outside. When my impatience became uncontrollable I asked how she was. 'She's dying.' He grinned spitefully at my exclamation. 'As we all are.' It was his idea of a joke at my expense. I saw that he meant to prevent our meeting.

I needed to see her; it was vital. I said: 'I'll go now and leave you in peace. But could you give me something to eat first? I've had nothing since mid-day.' He went out and in a rough overbearing voice shouted to her to bring food. The destruction outside was contagious and had infected everything, including their relationship, and the appearance of the room. She brought a tray with bread and butter, a plate of ham, and I looked closely to see if her appearance had changed too. She only looked thinner than ever, and more nearly transparent. She was completely silent, and seemed frightened, withdrawn, as she had been when I knew her first. I longed to ask questions, to talk to her alone, but was not given the chance. The man watched us all the time as he went on drinking. Alcohol made him quarrelsome; he got angry when I refused to drink any more, determined to pick a quarrel with me. I knew I ought to go, but my head ached abominably and made me reluctant to move. I kept pressing my hand over my eyes and forehead. Evidently the girl noticed this, for she left the room for a minute, came back with something in the palm of her hand, murmured: 'An aspirin for your head.' Like a bully, he shouted: 'What are you whispering to him?' Touched by her thought for me, I would have liked to do more than thank her; but his scowl was so vicious that I got up to leave.

He did not come to see me off. I felt my way through the darkness by walls and furniture, faced a pale shimmer of snow when I opened the outer door. It was so cold that I hurriedly shut myself in the car and put on the heater. Looking up from the dashboard, I heard her call softly something of which I caught only the words 'promise' and 'don't forget'. I switched on the headlights, saw her in the doorway, thin arms clasped round her chest. Her face wore its victim's look, which was of course psychological, the result of injuries she had received in childhood; I saw it as the faintest possible hint of bruising on the extremely delicate, fine, white skin in the region of eyes and mouth. It was madly attractive to me in a certain way. I had barely caught sight of it now before the car began moving; I was automatically pressing the starter, not expecting it to work in the freezing cold. At the same moment, in what I took for an optical delusion, the black interior of the house prolonged itself into a black arm and hand, which shot out and grasped her so violently that her shocked white face cracked to pieces and she tumbled into the dark.

I could not get over the deterioration in their relationship. While she was happy I had dissociated myself, been outside the situation. Now I felt implicated, involved with her again.

two

I heard that the girl had left home suddenly. No one knew where she was. The husband thought she might have gone abroad. It was only a guess. He had no information. I was agitated and asked endless questions, but no concrete facts emerged. 'I know no more than you. She simply vanished, I suppose she's entitled to go if she wants to – she's free, white and twenty-one.' He adopted a facetious tone, I could not tell if he was speaking the truth. The police did not suspect foul play. There was no reason to think harm had come to her, or that she had not gone away voluntarily. She was old enough to know her own mind. People were constantly disappearing; hundreds left home and were not seen again, many of them women unhappily married. Her marriage was known to have been breaking up. Almost certainly she was better off now, and only wanted to be left in peace. Further investigation would be resented and lead to more trouble.

This was a convenient view for them, it excused them from taking action. But I did not accept it. She had been conditioned into obedience since early childhood, her independence destroyed by systematic suppression. I did not believe her capable of taking such a drastic step on her own initiative: I suspected pressure from outside. I wished I could talk to someone who knew her well, but she seemed to have had no close friends.

The husband came to town on some mysterious business, and I asked him to lunch at my club. We talked for two hours, but in the end I was none the wiser. He persistently treated the whole affair lightly, said he was glad she had gone. 'Her neurotic behaviour nearly drove *me* demented. I'd had all I could take. She refused to see a psychiatrist. Finally she walked out on me without a word. No explanation. No warning.' He spoke as if he was the injured party. 'She went her own way without considering me, so I'm not worrying about her. She won't come back, that's one thing certain.' While he was away from home I took the opportunity of driving down to the house and going through the things in her room, but found nothing in the way of a clue. There was just the usual collection of pathetic rubbish: a china bird; a broken string of fake pearls; snapshots in an old chocolate box. One of these, in which a lake reflected perfectly her face and her shining hair, I put into my wallet.

Somehow or other I had to find her; the fact remained. I felt the same compulsive urge that had driven me straight to the country when I first arrived. There was no rational explanation. I could not account for it. It was a sort of craving that had to be satisfied.

I abandoned all my own affairs. From now on my business was to search for her. Nothing else mattered. Certain sources of possible information were still available. Hairdressers. Clerks who kept records of transport bookings. Those fringe characters. I went to the places such people frequented, stood about playing the fruit machines until I saw a chance of speaking. Money helped. So did intuition. No clue was too slender to follow up. The approaching emergency made it all the more urgent to find her quickly. I could not get her out of my head. I had not seen all the things I remembered about her. During my first visit I was in their living-room, talking about the Indris, my favourite subject. The man listened. She went to and fro arranging flowers. On an impulse I said the pair of them resembled the lemurs, both so friendly and charming, and living together so happily here in the trees. He laughed. She looked horrified and ran out through the french window, silvery hair floating behind her, her bare legs flashing pale. The secret, shady garden, hidden away in seclusion and silence, was a pleasant cool retreat from the heat of summer. Then suddenly it was unnaturally, fearfully cold. The masses of dense foliage all round became prison walls, impassable circular green ice-walls, surging towards her; just before they closed in, I caught the terrified glint of her eyes.

On a winter day she was in the studio, posing for him in the nude, her arms raised in a graceful position. To hold it for any length of time must have been a strain, I wondered how she managed to keep so still; until I saw the cords attached to her wrists and ankles. The room was cold. There was thick frost on the window panes and snow piled up on the sill outside. He wore the long uniform coat. She was shivering. When she asked, 'May I have a rest?' her voice had a pathetic tremor. He frowned, looked at his watch before he put down his palette. 'All right. That'll do for now. You can dress.' He untied her. The cords had left deep red angry rings on the white flesh. Her movements were slow and clumsy from cold, she fumbled awkwardly with buttons, suspenders. This seemed to annoy him. He turned away from her sharply, his face irritable. She kept glancing nervously at him, her mouth was unsteady, her hands would not stop shaking.

Another time the two were together in a cold room. As usual, he wore the long coat. It was night, freezing hard. He had a book in his hand, she was doing nothing. She looked cold and miserable, huddled up in a thick grey loden coat with a red and blue check lining. The room was silent and full of tension. It could be felt that neither of them had spoken for a long time. Outside the window, a twig snapped in the iron frost with a sound like a handclap. He dropped the book and got up to put on a record. Instantly she began to protest. 'Oh, no! Not that awful singing, for heaven's sake!' He ignored her, went on with what he was doing. The turntable started revolving. It was a record I had given them from my tape recording of the lemurs' song. To me, the extraordinary jungle music was lovely, mysterious, magical. To her it was a sort of torture, apparently. She covered her ears with her hands, winced at the high notes, looked more and more distraught. When the record ended and he re-started it without a moment's pause, she cried out as if he had struck her, 'No! I won't listen to it all over again!', threw herself at the mechanism, stopped it so abruptly that the voices expired in uncanny wailing. He faced her angrily. 'What the hell do you think you're doing? Have you gone off your head?' 'You know I can't stand that horrible record.' She seemed almost beside herself. 'You only play it because I hate it so much ...' Tears sprang unchecked from her eyes, she brushed them away carelessly with her hand.

He glared at her, said: 'Why should I sit in silence for hours just because you don't choose to open your mouth?' His angry voice was full of indignant resentment. 'What's wrong with you, anyhow, these days? Why can't you behave like a normal being?' She did not answer, dropped her face in her hands. Tears dripped between her fingers. He gazed at her with a disgusted expression. 'I might as well be in solitary confinement as alone with you here. But I warn you I'm not going to put up with it much longer. I've had enough. I'm sick and tired of the way you're carrying on. Pull yourself together, or else—' With a threatening scowl, he went out, banging the door behind him. A silence followed, while she stood like a lost child, tears wet on her cheeks. Next she started wandering aimlessly round the room, stopped by the window, pulled the curtain aside, then cried out in amazement.

Instead of the darkness, she faced a stupendous sky-conflagration, an incredible glacial dream-scene. Cold coruscations of rainbow fire pulsed overhead, shot through by shafts of pure incandescence thrown out by mountains of solid ice towering all round. Closer, the trees round the house, sheathed in ice, dripped and sparkled with weird prismatic jewels, reflecting the vivid changing cascades above. Instead of the familiar night sky the aurora borealis formed a blazing, vibrating roof of intense cold and colour, beneath which the earth was trapped with all its inhabitants, walled in by those impassable glittering ice-cliffs. The world had become an arctic prison from which no escape was possible, all its creatures trapped as securely as were the trees, already lifeless inside their deadly resplendent armour.

Despairingly she looked all round. She was completely encircled by the tremendous ice-walls, which were made fluid by explosions of blinding light, so that they moved and changed with a continuous liquid motion, advancing in torrents of ice, avalanches as big as oceans, flooding everywhere over the doomed world. Wherever she looked, she saw the same fearful encirclement, soaring battlements of ice, an overhanging ring of frigid, fiery, colossal waves about to collapse upon her. Frozen by the deathly cold emanating from the ice, dazzled by the blaze of crystalline ice-light, she felt herself becoming part of the polar vision, her structure becoming one with the structure of ice and snow. As her fate, she accepted the world of ice, shining, shimmering, dead; she resigned herself to the triumph of glaciers and the death of her world.

It was essential for me to find her without delay. The situation was alarming, the atmosphere tense, the emergency imminent. There was talk of a secret act of aggression by some foreign power, but no one knew what had actually happened. The government would not disclose the facts. I was informed privately of a steep rise in radioactive pollution, pointing to the explosion of a nuclear device, but of an unknown type, the consequences of which could not be accurately predicted. It was possible that polar modifications had resulted, and would lead to a substantial climatic change due to the refraction of solar heat. If the melting antarctic ice cap flowed over the South Pacific and Atlantic oceans, a vast ice-mass would be created, reflecting the sun's rays and throwing them back into outer space, thus depriving the earth of warmth. In town, everything was chaotic and contradictory. News from abroad was censored, but travel was left unrestricted. Confusion was increased by a spate of new and conflicting regulations, and by the arbitrary way controls were imposed or lifted. The one thing that would have clarified the position was an overall picture of world events; but this was prohibited by the determination of the politicians to ban all foreign news. My impression was that they had lost their heads, did not know how to deal with the approaching danger, and hoped to keep the public in ignorance of its exact nature until a plan had been evolved.

No doubt people would have been more concerned, and would have made greater efforts to find out what was taking place in other countries, if, at home, they had not been obliged to contend with the fuel shortage, the power cuts, the breakdown of transport, and the rapid diversion of supplies to the black market.

There was no sign of a break in the abnormal cold. My room was reasonably warm, but even in hotels heating was being reduced to a minimum, and, outside, the erratic, restricted services hampered my investigations. The river had been frozen over for weeks, the total paralysis of the docks was a serious problem. All essential commodities were in short supply; rationing, at least of fuel and food, could not be delayed much longer, despite the reluctance of those in power to resort to unpopular measures.

Everyone who could do so was leaving in search of better conditions. No more passages were available, either by sea or air; there were long waiting lists for all ships and planes. I had no proof that the girl was already abroad. On the whole it seemed unlikely she would have managed to leave the country, and an obscure train of thought suggested that she might embark on a certain vessel.

The port was a long way off, to reach it involved a long complicated journey. I was delayed, got there, after travelling all night, only an hour before sailing time. The passengers were already aboard, crowding the decks with friends who were seeing them off. The first thing I had to do was to speak to the captain. He turned out to be maddeningly talkative. While I became more and more impatient, he complained at great length about the way the authorities allowed overcrowding: it was a danger to his ship, unfair to himself, to the company, the passengers, the insurance people. That was his business. As soon as I got permission to get on with my own, I made a methodical search of the ship, but without finding a trace of the person I wanted.

Finally I gave up in despair and went out on deck. Too tired and disheartened to push through the crowds of people milling about there, I stood by the rail, overcome by a sudden urge to abandon the whole affair. I had never really had a valid reason for supposing the girl would be on this ship. Suddenly it seemed neither sensible, nor even sane, to continue a search based solely on vague surmise; particularly as my attitude to its object was so undefined. When I considered that imperative need I felt for her, as for a missing part of myself, it appeared less like love than an inexplicable aberration, the sign of some character flaw I ought to eradicate, instead of letting it dominate me.

At this moment a big black-backed gull sailed past, almost brushing my cheek with its wing tip, as if on purpose to draw my attention and eyes after it up to the boat deck. At once I saw her there, looking away from me, where no one had been before; and everything I had just been thinking was swept out of my head by a wave of excitement, my old craving for her returned. I was convinced it was she without even seeing her face; no other girl in the world had such dazzling hair, or was so thin that her fragility could be seen through a thick grey coat. I simply had to reach her, it was all I could think of. Envying the gull's effortless flight, I plunged straight into the solid mass of humanity separating me from her, and forced my way through. I had hardly any time, in a moment the boat would be sailing. Visitors were leaving already, forming a strong cross current I had to fight. My one idea was to get to the boatdeck before it was too late. In my anxiety, I must have pushed people aside. Hostile remarks were made, a fist shaken. I tried to explain my urgency to those who obstructed me, but they would not listen. Three tough-looking young men linked arms and aggressively barred my way, their expressions threatening. I had not meant to offend, hardly knew what I was doing. I was thinking only of her. Suddenly an official voice shouted through a loudspeaker: 'All visitors ashore! The gangway will be raised in exactly two minutes.' The ship's siren sounded an earsplitting blast. An immediate rush followed. It was quite impossible to resist the human flood surging towards the gangway. I was caught up in the stampede, dragged along with it, off the boat, and on to the quay.

Standing at the water's edge, I soon saw her high above me, considerably farther off now. The ship had already moved away from the shore and was gathering speed every second, already divided from me by a strip of water too wide to jump. In desperation, I shouted and waved my arms, trying to attract her attention. It was hopeless. A whole sea of arms waved all round me, innumerable voices were shouting unintelligibly. I saw her turn to speak to somebody who had just joined her, at the same time pulling a hood over her head, so that her hair was hidden. Immediate doubts invaded me, and increased as I watched her. After all, perhaps she was not the right girl; she seemed too self-possessed. But I was not certain.

The boat was now beginning the turn that would bring it round facing the mouth of the harbour, leaving behind it a curving track of smoother water, like the swath left by a scythe. I stood staring after it, although cold had driven the passengers off the decks and there was no more hope of recognition. I dimly remembered what I had been thinking just before I caught sight of her, but only as one might recall an incident from a dream. Once again the urgency of the search had reclaimed me; I was totally absorbed in that obsessional need, as for a lost, essential portion of my own being. Everything else in the world seemed immaterial.

All round me people were walking away, stamping their feet in the cold. I hardly noticed the mass departure. It did not occur to me to leave the edge of the water, over which I continued to gaze at the vessel's diminishing shape. I had been an utter fool. I was furious with myself for letting it go without discovering the identity of the girl on board. Now I would never be sure whether she had, or had not, been the right one. And if she had been, how would I ever find her again? A mournful hoot travelled across the water: the ship was leaving the protection of the harbour, heading out into the open sea. Already meeting the off-shore rollers, it kept disappearing behind grey masses of water surging along the horizon. It looked absurdly small, a toy boat. I lost sight of it, my eyes could not find it again. It was lost irretrievably.

I only became aware that everyone else had gone and that I was alone there, when two policemen approached, marching along side by side, and pointed to a sign, 'Loitering on the waterfront strictly forbidden: War Department.' 'Why are you hanging about here? Can't you read?' Needless to say, they refused to believe that I had not seen it. Hugely tall in their helmets, they stood on each side, so close that their guns stuck into me, and demanded my papers. These were in order. There was nothing against me. Nevertheless, my conduct had been suspicious, they insisted on writing down my name and address. Again I had acted stupidly, this time by drawing attention to myself. Now that my name had been noted, it would appear in the records; I would be known to the police everywhere, my movements would be kept under observation. It would be a serious handicap in my search.

As the two men hustled me through the gates, something made me look up at a row of big black-backed gulls perched on a wall, all facing into the wind and pointing out to sea, as motionless as if they had been stuffed and put up there to act as a message. On the spot I decided to leave the country before any of my visas lapsed or were cancelled. No particular place seemed more or less promising than another as a base from which to start searching. But to attempt to operate from here while under suspicion would surely invite failure.

I had to leave at once, before the police report circulated. It could not have been done through the normal channels. By employing other methods, I managed to board a northbound cargo boat carrying a few passengers, and booked to the end of the voyage. The purser was willing to vacate his cabin for a consideration. Next day, at the first port of the trip, I went on deck to watch our arrival. I remembered the complaints I had been forced to listen to about overcrowding when I saw a lot of people packed together on the deck below waiting to disembark. Twelve was the authorized number of passengers. I wondered how many more were on board.

It was extremely cold. Loose fragments of pack ice drifted past in the green water. Everything was misty and indistinct. The landing-stage was quite close, but the buildings at the end of the jetty looked insubstantial, amorphous. A girl in a heavy grey coat with a hood was standing a little apart from the other passengers, leaning on the rail. Occasionally a fold of the coat would blow back, showing a quilted check lining. It was the coat I noticed: although I knew perfectly well that such coats had become almost a uniform among women since the start of the cold, and were to be seen everywhere.

The mist began to lift and break up, the sun would shine later. A rugged coastline appeared with many inlets and jagged rocks, snow-covered mountains behind. There were many small islands, some of which floated up and became clouds, while formations of cloud or mist descended and anchored themselves in the sea. The white snowy landscape below, and above the canopy of misty white light, the effect of an oriental painting, nothing solid about it. The town appeared to consist of ruins collapsing on one another in shapeless disorder, a town of sandcastles, wrecked by the tide. A great wall which had protected it was broken in many places, both ends subsiding uselessly into the water. The place had once been important. Its fortifications had lain in ruins for centuries. It was still of some historical interest.

Sudden silence fell. The engines had stopped. The boat was still moving forward under its own momentum. I heard the faint swish of water against the sides, the plangent crying of sea birds, that sad northern sound. Otherwise all was silent. No sounds of traffic, of bells or voices, came from the land. The town of ruins waited in utter silence under the brooding mountains. I thought of long narrow ancient ships, vast collections of loot preserved in barrows, winged helmets, drinking horns, great heavy ornaments of gold and silver, piles of fossilized bones. It looked a place of the past, of the dead.

There was a shout from the bridge. On the jetty a group of sullen-faced men rose out of the ground. They were armed and wore uniform: black padded tunics, belted tight at the waist, high boots, fur caps. The knives in their belts caught the light as they moved. They looked outlandish, even menacing. I heard somebody say they were the warden's men, which meant nothing: I had not heard of this warden. Their presence surprised me since private armies were forbidden by law. Ropes were thrown; they caught them and made them fast. The gangway crashed down. A slight stir started among the passengers, who picked up luggage, got out passports and papers, began a slow shuffling progress towards a barrier that had been set up.

Only the girl in the grey coat did not concern herself with landing, did not change her position. As the others moved forward and she was left isolated, my interest increased, I could not detach my attention from her, kept on watching. What most struck me was her complete stillness. Such a passive attitude, suggesting both resistance and resignation, did not seem entirely normal in a young girl. She could not have been more motionless if she had been tied to the rail, and I thought how easily bonds could be hidden by the voluminous coat.

A bright strand of glittering blonde hair, almost white, escaped from the hood and blew loose in the wind; I felt a sudden excitement; but reminded myself that many northerners were extremely fair. All the same, my interest now became compelling, I was longing to see her face. She would have to look up towards me before that could happen.

The passengers' forward movement was interrupted. Men in uniform came aboard and cleared a way through them, demanding room for the warden, shouting peremptory orders. Space was made

for a tall man, yellow haired, handsome in a tough, hawk-hard
northern fashion, his height jutting above those near him. His
arrogant manner, his total disregard for the feelings of others, made
an unpleasant impression. As if he sensed my criticism, he glanced
up for a second. His eyes were startling pieces of bright blue ice. I
saw that he was making for the girl in the grey coat, the one person
who had not seen him. Everyone else was staring. When he called
out, 'Why are you standing there? Have you gone to sleep?' she
swung round as if terribly startled. 'Hurry up! The car's waiting.'
He went close and touched her. He was smiling, but I detected a
hint of a threat in his voice and behaviour. She hung back, seemed
unwilling to go with him. He linked arms with her, apparently
friendly, but really forcing her forward against her will, pulling her
along with him through the bunched, staring people. She still did
not look up, I could not see her expression, but I could imagine his
iron grip on her thin wrist. They left the ship before anyone else,
and were immediately driven off in a big black car.

I had been standing there as if petrified. Suddenly now I made a
decision. It seemed worth taking a chance. Though without having
seen her face . . . I had no other clue to follow, in any case.

I ran down to the cabin, sent for the purser, told him I had
changed my plans. 'I'm going ashore here.' He looked at me as
though I was out of my mind. 'Please yourself.' He shrugged his
shoulders indifferently, but could not quite conceal an incipient
grin. He had already received his money. Now he would be able to
collect a second payment from somebody else for the remainder of
the voyage.

I hurriedly threw into my suitcase the few things I had unpacked.

three

Carrying my suitcase, I walked into the town. Silence obtruded
itself. Nothing moved. The devastation was even greater than it had
seemed from the boat. Not a building intact. Wreckage heaped in

blank spaces where houses had been. Walls had crumbled; steps ascended and stopped in mid-air; arches opened on to deep craters. Little had been done to repair this wholesale destruction. Only the main streets were clear of rubble, the rest obliterated. Faint tracks, like the tracks of animals, but made by human beings, twisted among the debris. I looked in vain for somebody to direct me. The whole place seemed deserted. A train whistle at last guided me to the station, a small makeshift building constructed with materials salvaged from ruins, which reminded me of a discarded film set. Even here there was no sign of life, though presumably a train had just left. It was hard to believe the place was really in use; that anything really functioned. I was aware of an uncertainty of the real, in my surroundings and in myself. What I saw had no solidity, it was all made of mist and nylon, with nothing behind.

I went on to the platform. They must have dynamited some of the ruins to lay the track. I could see the single line running out of the town, crossing a strip of open ground before it entered the fir forest. This fragile link with the world did not inspire confidence. I had the feeling it stopped just beyond the first trees. The mountains rose close behind. I shouted, 'Is anyone here?' A man appeared from somewhere, made a threatening gesture. 'You're trespassing – get out!' I explained that I had just come off the boat and wanted to find a room. He stared, hostile, suspicious, uncouth, saying nothing. I asked the way to the main street. In a sulky voice I could hardly understand he muttered a few words, staring at me the whole time, as if I had dropped from Mars.

I walked on with my bag, came to an open square where people were going about. The men's black tunics were variations of those I had already seen, and most of the wearers carried knives or guns. The women also wore black, producing a gloomy effect. All the faces were blank and unsmiling. For the first time I saw signs that some buildings were occupied, a few even had glass in the windows. There were market stalls and small shops; wooden huts and lean-tos had been tacked on to some of the patched-up ruins. A café was open at the end of the square, and there was a cinema, shut, displaying a tattered advertisement of a year-old programme. This evidently was the living heart of the town; the rest was just the remains of the dead past.

I invited the proprietor of the café to drink with me, hoping to establish good relations before I asked for a room. All these people seemed insular and suspicious, antagonistic to strangers. We drank the local brandy made out of plums, potent and fiery, a good drink for a cold climate. He was a big, robust man, better than a peasant. At first I could hardly get a word out of him, but over the second glass he relaxed enough to ask why I had come. 'Nobody ever comes here; we have nothing to attract foreigners – only ruins.' I said: 'The ruins of your town are famous. They're the reason for my coming. I'm making a study of them for a learned society.' I had decided beforehand to say this. 'You mean people in other countries are interested?' 'Certainly. This town is a place of historic importance.' He was flattered, as I expected. 'That's true. We have a glorious war record.' 'And also a record of discovery. Did you know that a map has been found recently which indicates that your long-boats crossed the Atlantic and were the first to reach the new world?' 'You expect to find proof of this in the ruins?' It had not occurred to me, but I assented. 'I know of course that I must get permits; everything must be done correctly. Unfortunately I don't know who's the right man to approach.' Without hesitation he said: 'You must ask the warden. He controls everything.' Here was an unexpected stroke of luck. 'How do I get in touch with him?' I had a vision of an iron hand gripping a girl's thin wrist, crushing the brittle prominent bones. 'That's simple. You make an appointment through one of the secretaries at the High House.' I was delighted by such good fortune. I had been prepared to wait and scheme for a chance of seeing this man; now the opportunity had presented itself at the very beginning.

The business of the room was also settled without difficulty. I was having a run of good luck. Although the proprietor could not accommodate me himself, his sister who lived nearby had a spare room I could rent. 'She's a widow and can do with the extra money, you understand.' He went off to telephone to her; returned after rather a long absence, saying that it was all arranged. He would provide my two main meals at the café; breakfast would be brought to my room. 'You won't be disturbed there while you're working, it's very quiet. The house looks away from the street, faces the water; and nobody ever goes *there*.' His cooperation was valuable, so to keep the conversation going I asked why people avoided the vicinity of the fjord. 'Because they're afraid of the dragon that lives at the bottom.' I looked at him, thought he was joking; but his face was perfectly serious, his voice had been matter-of-fact. I had never before met anyone who owned a telephone and believed in dragons. It amused me, and also contributed to my sense of the unreal.

The room proved to be dark and devoid of comfort or convenience. It was not warm enough. However, it had a bed, a table and chair – the basic necessities. I was lucky to get it as no other accommodation was available. The sister looked older and much less sophisticated than her brother, who must have persuaded her to take me in against her will during their long talk on the telephone. She was evidently reluctant to admit a foreigner to the house where she lived alone; I could feel her suspicious dislike. To avoid trouble I paid the exorbitant price she asked without question, a week in advance.

I asked for the keys, saying I would have a duplicate cut for the outer door; I had to be independent. She brought the two keys, but gave me only the key of my own door, hiding the other one in the palm of her hand. I told her to hand it over. She refused, I insisted. She became stubborn and retreated into the kitchen. I followed and took the key from her forcibly. I did not much care for this sort of behaviour, but a principle was involved. She would not oppose me again.

I went out and walked about, exploring the town: the empty lanes silent between shapeless shapes of decay, the ruined forts jutting into the greengage sea, the huge slab-steps of a giant's staircase where the great wall had fallen, subsiding in solid sections. Everywhere the ubiquitous ruins, decayed fortifications, evidences of a warlike, bloodthirsty past. I searched for buildings of a more recent date. There were none. The dwindling population lived like rats in the ruins of a lost martial supremacy. If one place became uninhabitable its occupants moved to another. The community was gradually dying out, each year its numbers declined. There were enough disintegrating structures to last them out. At first it was hard to distinguish the inhabited buildings; I learnt to look for the signs of occupation, the reinforced door, the boarded-up windows.

I made an appointment to see the warden at the High House,

which dominated the town, a fortress-like mass built at its highest point. At the time agreed, I climbed a steep road, the only one that led to it. From the outside the place looked like an armed fort, enormously massive, thick walls, no windows, some narrow slits high up that might have been meant for machine guns. Batteries flanked the entrance, apparently trained on the road. I assumed they were relics of some old campaign, though they did not look especially obsolete. I had spoken to a secretary on the telephone; but now I was met by four armed guards in black tunics, who escorted me down a long corridor, two walking in front, two behind. It was dark. High above, thin pencils of daylight, entering through the slits in the outer wall, dimly revealed glimpses of other corridors, galleries, stairs, bridge-like landings at different levels, radiating in different directions. The invisible ceiling must have been enormously high, the full height of the building, for all these indistinct ramifications were far overhead. Something moved at the end of one vista: a girl's figure. I rushed after her as she started to climb some stairs, her silvery hair lifting, glimmering in the darkness, at every step.

The short steep stair led to one room only, large, sparsely furnished, its polished floor bare like a dance floor. I was immediately struck by the unnatural silence, a curious hushed quality in the air, which reduced her movements to mouselike scratchings. Not a sound penetrated from outside or from other parts of the building. I was puzzled, until it dawned on me that the room had been soundproofed, as that whatever took place there would be inaudible beyond its four walls. Then it at once became obvious why this particular room had been allotted to her.

She was in bed, not asleep, waiting. A faint pinkish glow came from a lamp beside her. The wide bed stood on a platform, bed and platform alike covered in sheepskin, facing a great mirror nearly as long as the wall. Alone here, where nobody could hear her, where nobody was *meant* to hear, she was cut off from all contact, totally vulnerable, at the mercy of the man who came in without knocking, without a word, his cold, very bright blue eyes pouncing on hers in the glass. She crouched motionless, staring silently into the mirror, as if mesmerized. The hypnotic power of his eyes could destroy her will, already weakened by the mother who for years had persistently crushed it into submission. Forced since childhood into a victim's pattern of thought and behaviour, she was defenceless against his aggressive will, which was able to take complete possession of her. I saw it happen.

He approached the bed with unhurried steps. She did not move until he bent over her, when she twisted away abruptly, as if trying to escape, buried her face in the pillow. His hand reached out, slid over her shoulder, strong fingers feeling along her jaw bone, gripping, tilting, forcing her head up. She resisted violently, in sudden terror, twisting and turning wildly, struggling against his strength. He did nothing at all, let her go on fighting. Her feeble struggles amused him, he knew they would not last long. He looked on in silence, in half-smiling amusement, always tilting her face with a slight but inescapable pressure, while she exhausted herself.

Suddenly she gave in, worn out, beaten; she was panting, her face was wet. He tightened his grip slightly, compelled her to look straight at him. To bring the thing to a finish, he stared into her dilated eyes, implacably forced into them his own arrogant, ice-blue gaze. This was the moment of her surrender; opposition collapsed at this point, when she seemed to fall and drown in those cold blue mesmeric depths. Now she had no more will. He could do what he liked with her.

He leaned further, knelt on the bed, pushed her down with his hands on her shoulders. Will-less, she submitted to him, even to the extent of making small compliant movements fitting her body to his. She was dazed, she hardly knew what was happening, her normal state of consciousness interrupted, lost, the nature of her surrender not understood. He was intent only on his enjoyment.

Later she did not move, gave no indication of life, lying exposed on the ruined bed as on a slab in a mortuary. Sheets and blankets spilled on to the floor, trailed over the edge of the dais. Her head hung over the edge of the bed in a slightly unnatural position, the neck slightly twisted in a way that suggested violence, the bright hair twisted into a sort of rope by his hands. He sat with his hand upon her, asserting his right to his prey. When his fingers passed over her naked body, lingering on thighs and breasts, she was shaken by a long painful shudder; then she went still again.

He lifted her head with one hand, looked into her face for a moment, let the head fall back on the pillow: it lay as it fell. He stood up, moved away from the bed; his foot caught in the fold of a blanket, he kicked it back and went on to the door. He had not spoken a single word since he entered the room, and he left it without a sound, apart from the faint click of the closing door. To her, this silence was one of the most terrifying things about him, in some way associated with his power over her.

I wondered where I was being taken. The place was colossal, the passages wound on and on. We passed the trapdoors of oubliettes, cells hacked out of the rock. The walls of these hutches were running with water, with some noisome exudation. Perilous steps led down to still deeper dungeons. We went through several pairs of huge doors, which the guards in front unlocked and the others slammed shut behind us.

The warden received me in a civilized room. It was spacious and well-proportioned, the wood floor reflecting dim old chandeliers. The windows faced away from the town, over park-like grounds, sloping down to the distant fjord. His perfectly fitting black tunic was of superb material, his high boots shone like mirrors. He was wearing the coloured ribbon of some order I did not know. This time my impression was more favourable; the arrogant look I disliked was less in evidence, although it was clear that he was a born ruler, a law unto himself, not to be judged by the usual standards. 'What can I do for you?' He greeted me with formal politeness, his blue eyes looked me straight in the face. I told him the story I had prepared. He agreed at once to have the necessary permits made out and signed. I would get them tomorrow. On his own initiative he suggested adding a note to the effect that I was to be given help in my investigations. To me it seemed superfluous. He said: 'You don't know these people. They are naturally lawless and have an innate dislike of strangers, their ways are violent and archaic. I've tried hard to introduce more modern attitudes. But it's useless, they're embedded in the past like Lot's wife in her pillar of salt; you can't detach them from it.' I thanked him; at the same time I was thinking about the guards, who hardly seemed to fit in with his enlightened outlook.

He remarked that I had chosen a strange time for my visit. I asked why. 'The ice will be here very soon. The harbour will freeze, we shall be cut off.' He flashed a blue glance at me. Something had not been said. He had a trick of blinking his very bright eyes, which then seemed to emit blue flames. He went on: 'You may be stranded here longer than you bargained for.' Again the sharp look, as if something more were implied. I told him: 'I'm only staying for a week or so. I don't expect to find anything new. It's more a matter of getting the atmosphere.' In spite of my original aversion, I suddenly had a curious sense of contact with him, almost as though some personal link existed between us. The feeling was so unexpected, unaccountable and confusing that I added, 'Please don't misunderstand me,' without knowing quite what I meant. He seemed gratified, smiled, and at once became more friendly. 'So we speak the same language. Good. I'm glad you've come. We need closer contact in this country with the sophisticated nations. This is a beginning.' Still somewhat hazy as to what we were talking about, I stood up to go, thanking him again. He shook my hand. 'You must come and dine one evening. Let me know in the meantime if I can be of any further service to you.'

I was jubilant. My luck was holding. I seemed almost to have attained my object already, I was sure of a chance of seeing the girl. If the dinner invitation failed to materialize, I could always fall back on his final offer.

four

The signed permits arrived the next day. The warden had initialled an additional sentence saying that I was to receive every assistance. This impressed the café proprietor, and I left it to him to circulate the message.

I began making notes on the town; my performance had to be convincing and thorough. I had sometimes thought vaguely of writing about the fascinating singing lemurs; now I had a perfect opportunity to describe them before the memory faded. Each day I wrote a little about my surroundings and a lot more on the other subject. There was nothing else to do, I would have been bored without this occupation, which became an absorbing interest and kept me busy for hours. The time passed surprisingly fast. In some ways I was better off than I had been at home. It was exceedingly cold, but I was warm in my room, having organized a daily supply of logs for the stove. No fuel problem existed here, close to these great forests. To think of the ice coming nearer all the time was very disturbing. But for the present the harbour remained open, occasional ships came and went. From these I sometimes managed to obtain a few delicacies to supplement my meals at the café, which were ample, but lacking in variety. I had arranged for my food to be served in a sort of alcove off the main room, where I was out of the noise and smoke and had a certain amount of privacy.

The work I was supposed to be doing among the ruins enabled me to keep the High House unobtrusively under observation. I never once caught sight of the girl, though on several occasions I saw the warden emerge, always accompanied by his bodyguard. He usually jumped straight into his big car and was driven off at tremendous speed. I gathered that threats from political opponents accounted for these precautions.

After two or three days I became impatient. I was getting nowhere and time was short. As she never seemed to leave the High House, I should have to get in. But no invitation arrived. I was trying to decide on the best excuse for approaching the warden again when he sent one of his guards to fetch me to lunch. The man intercepted me on my way to the café at mid-day. I disliked the absence of notice, and the whole imperious style of the summons and its delivery. It was more a command than an invitation, and, feeling obliged to protest, I said it was hardly possible to cancel the meal already prepared and waiting for me at that very moment. Instead of answering me, the guard shouted. Two more black tunics appeared from nowhere: the wearer of one was sent to explain things to the café proprietor, while the other stationed himself beside me. I now had no alternative but to go with this double escort. Of course I was glad to do so, it was what I wanted. But I would have preferred less high-handed treatment.

The warden led me straight into a large dining hall with a long table intended for twenty people. He took his chair at the head, an imposing figure. I was seated beside him. A third place was laid opposite. Seeing me glance at it, he said: 'A young friend from your country is staying with me; I thought you might like to meet her.' He gave me one of his piercing looks as I replied calmly that I would be delighted. Inwardly I was exulting; it seemed almost too good to be true, the climax of my good fortune, to be spared the tricky business of asking to see her.

Dry Martinis were brought in a frosted jug. Immediately afterwards someone came in, whispered something, gave him a note. His face changed as he read the few words, he ripped the paper across and across, reducing it to minute fragments. 'It appears the young person is indisposed.' I hid my disappointment by murmuring something polite. He was frowning furiously, obviously could not bear to be thwarted over the least thing; his anger pervaded the atmosphere. Saying no more to me, he signed for the extra setting to be removed, glasses and cutlery were whipped out of sight. The food was served, but he hardly touched what was on his plate, sat pounding the shreds of paper into a pulp with his clenched fist. I became more and more annoyed the longer he ignored me, particularly resenting this additional rudeness after the peremptory way he had sent for me. I wanted to get up and walk out, but knew it would be fatal to break off relations at this stage. To distract myself, I thought of the girl, decided I was probably responsible for her absence; she must have guessed who I was, if she had not known all along. I tried to imagine her alone in a silent room overhead. But she seemed miles away, a dream figure, inaccessible and unreal.

The warden gradually became calmer, although his expression remained forbidding. I would not speak first, but waited for him to acknowledge my presence. A joint of excellent young lamb was carved, and while we were eating he referred abruptly to my investigations. 'I notice you confine them to the ruins in my vicinity.' I was disconcerted, I had not known I was being watched. Luckily there was a ready-made answer. 'As you know, these have always been the administrative buildings, so anything of interest is more likely to turn up here than anywhere else.' He said nothing, but made the sound of a player whose opponent claims a dubious point in the game. I could not tell whether my reply had satisfied him or not.

Coffee was put on the table, and to my surprise, everybody

withdrew from the room. I felt apprehensive, I could not imagine what he could have to say to me in private. His mood appeared to have hardened; he looked formidable, cold, distant. It was difficult to believe he had ever showed friendliness when he remarked ominously: 'People who try to trick me usually regret it; I'm not easily taken in.' His voice was controlled and quiet, but the threat I had detected in it on a former occasion had become open. I said I did not understand what he meant; the obvious implication did not apply to me. He subjected me to a prolonged stare, which I returned with more coolness than I was feeling. An aura of danger and duplicity surrounded him, I was on my guard.

Pushing aside his cup, he leaned his elbows on the table, brought his face close to mine and went on gazing fixedly at me without a word. His eyes were startlingly bright, I could feel them trying to dominate me, and found it hard not to lower my own. He must have practised hypnosis at some time: I had to keep up a sustained effort of resistance. It was a relief when he drew back a little, and said bluntly: 'I want you to do something for me.' 'What on earth can I possibly do for you?' I was astonished. 'Listen. This is a small, poor, backward country, without resources. In an emergency we would be lost without the help of the big powers. Unfortunately the big powers consider us too insignificant to be of any interest. I want you to convince your government that we can be useful, if only because of our geographical position. I'm assuming you have the necessary influence?' I supposed I had; but I was taken aback, I had not expected anything like this. My instinct was against it, and I began: 'That sort of thing's not my line at all—' He interrupted impatiently: 'I'm simply asking you to point out to your politicians the advantage of cooperation with us. It should be easy. They've only got to look at the map.' Before I could think what to say, he pressed me again with increased impatience: 'Well, will you do it?' His habit of dominance and his personal magnetism made it virtually impossible to refuse; almost involuntarily I made a sound of assent. 'Good. It's a bargain. Of course you'll receive an adequate return.' As if to clinch the matter, he stood up and held out his hand, adding: 'You'd better write immediately to prepare the ground.' He picked up a small silver bell, rang it vigorously, people came trooping into the room. As he went to meet them, he dismissed me with a casual nod. I felt confused and uneasy, and was glad to get out of the place. I did not like this new turn of events. I had the impression my luck was changing.

A day or two later his big car stopped beside me and he looked out, wearing a magnificent fur-lined overcoat. He wanted a word with me; would I come to the High House? I got in, we raced up to the entrance.

We went into a room full of people waiting to speak to him: the guards moved them back so that we could pass through to a room beyond. I heard him mutter, 'Get rid of this fellow after five minutes,' before he dismissed his men. To me he said: 'I presume you've written to someone about that bargain of ours?' I muttered something evasive. In quite a different tone he rapped out: 'The post office informs me you have not communicated with any useful person. I took you for a man of your word: it seems I was mistaken.' To avoid a quarrel I took no notice of the insult, replied peaceably: 'I haven't heard yet what I'm to get out of the bargain.' Curtly he told me to state my terms. I decided to speak in a frank, simple manner, hoping to make him less hostile. 'My request seems almost too trivial to mention after these preliminaries.' I gave him what I hoped was a disarming smile. 'It's simply this: I believe your guest may be an old acquaintance of mine, and should like to meet her in order to settle the point.' I was careful not to show too much interest.

He said nothing, but I could feel opposition behind his silence. Evidently there had been a change in his attitude since the day when he had proposed to introduce us at lunch. Now I felt pretty sure he would not agree to the meeting.

Suddenly remembering the time, I looked at my watch. The five minutes had almost gone. I had no intention of waiting until the guards came in, according to orders, to throw me out, and began to make the opening moves of departure. He came to the door with me, kept his hand on the knob, preventing me from leaving. 'She's been unwell, and is nervous about meeting people. I shall have to ask if she'll see you.' I was convinced he would not allow the meeting to take place, and looked at my watch again. There was only one minute left. 'I really must go now. I've taken up too much of your time already.' His unexpected laughter took me by surprise;

he must have known what was going on in my head. His mood seemed to alter suddenly, all at once his manner was easy. Once more I was momentarily aware of an obscure sense of inner contact with him. He opened the door and gave an order to the men standing outside, who saluted and marched away down the corridor, their boots thumping on the polished floor. He turned to me then, and as if demonstrating his goodwill, said: 'We can go to her now, if you like. But I'll have to prepare her first.'

He took me back into the crowded waiting-room, where everybody surged round, eager to speak to him. He had a smile and a friendly word for those nearest, raised his voice to apologize generally for keeping them waiting, begged them all to be patient a few minutes longer, promised that everyone would be heard in due course. In a tone audible all over the room, he demanded, 'Why is there no music?' then spoke sharply to a subordinate. 'You know these people are my guests. The least we can do is try to entertain them if they have to wait.' The notes of a string quartet started to fill the room, and followed us out of it.

He led the way past more guards, strode quickly along winding corridors ahead of me, ran up and down several flights of stairs. It was all I could do to keep pace with him. He was in far better condition than I was, and seemed to enjoy demonstrating the fact, looking back at me, laughing, showing off his fine physique. I did not quite trust this sudden good humour. But I admired his tough athlete's body, the wide shoulders and elegant, narrow waist. The passages seemed never-ending. I was breathless, he had to wait for me finally, standing at the top of yet another short staircase. The landing was in deep shadow. I could just distinguish the rectangle of a single door, and realized that the stairs led only to this one room.

He told me to stay where I was for a minute while he explained the situation to the girl, adding, with a malicious grin: 'It'll give you time to cool off a bit.' With his hand on the doorknob, he went on: 'You understand, don't you, that it's entirely up to her to decide. There's nothing I can do if she prefers not to see you.' He opened the door without knocking and vanished into the room.

Left out there in the semi-darkness, I felt gloomy and irritated. He seemed to have got the better of me by a trick. Nothing satisfactory to myself could come of an interview arranged and introduced by him. Most probably it would not materialize at all; either she would refuse to see me, or he would forbid her to do so. In any case, I did not want to talk to her in his presence, when she would be under his influence.

I listened, but could hear nothing through the sound-proofed wall. After some moments I went down the stairs and wandered round dark passages until I met a servant who showed me the way out. My lucky period certainly seemed to be over.

five

My window overlooked an empty landscape where nothing ever moved. No houses were visible, only the debris of the collapsed wall, a bleak stretch of snow, the fjord, the fir forest, the mountains. No colour, only monotonous shades of grey from black to the ultimate dead white of the snow. The water lifeless in its dead calm, the ranks of black trees marching everywhere in uniform gloom. Suddenly there was a movement, a shout of red and blue in that silent grey monotone. I seized my overcoat, struggled into it as I rushed to the door; changed my mind and went back to the window, which was stuck fast. I managed to heave it up, stepped out on to the piles of rubble, then pulled it shut behind me with the tips of my fingers. Slithering on the frozen grass, I ran down the slope; it was the quickest way; and I had eluded the woman of the house, whom I suspected of keeping watch on my movements. There was no one on the narrow path skirting the fjord, but the person I was chasing could not be far off. The path plunged into the forest. At once it got colder and darker under the trees, which grew close together, their black branches meeting in dense entanglements overhead, intertwining with the undergrowth lower down. Twenty invisible people could have been near me, but I saw the ghostly grey coat flicker among the firs, and occasionally caught a glimpse of its checked lining. The wearer's head was uncovered: her bright hair shimmered like silver fire, an *ignis fatuus* glimmering in the forest.

She hurried on as fast as she could, anxious to get out of the trees. She was nervous in the forest, which always seemed full of menace. The crowding trees unnerved her, transformed themselves into black walls, shutting her in. It was late, after sunset; she had come too far and must hurry back. She looked about for the fjord, failed to see it, lost her bearings, and at once became really frightened, terrified of being overtaken by night in the dark forest. Fear was the climate she lived in; if she had ever known kindness it would have been different. The trees seemed to obstruct her with deliberate malice. All her life she had thought of herself as a foredoomed victim, and now the forest had become the malign force that would destroy her. In desperation she tried to run, but a hidden root tripped her, she almost fell. Branches caught in her hair, tugged her back, lashed out viciously when they were disentangled. The silver hairs torn from her head glittered among black needles; they were the clues her pursuers would follow, leading them to their victim. She escaped from the forest at length only to see the fjord waiting for her. An evil effluence rose from the water, something primitive, savage, demanding victims, hungry for a human victim.

For a second she stood still, appalled by the absolute silence and loneliness all around. A new ferocity pervaded the landscape now that night was approaching. She saw the massed armies of forest trees encamped on all sides, the mountain wall above bristling with trees like guns. Below, the fjord was an impossible icy volcano erupting the baleful fire of the swallowed sun.

In the deepening dusk every horror could be expected. She was afraid to look, tried not to see the spectral shapes rising from the water, but felt them come gliding towards her and fled in panic. One overtook her, wound her in soft, clammy, adhesive bands like ectoplasm. Wildly choking a scream, she fought herself free, raced on blindly, frantic and gasping. Her brain was locked in nightmare, she did not think. The last light fading, she stumbled against unseen rocks, bruising knees and elbows. Thorns lacerated her hands, scratched her face. Her flying leaps shattered the thin ice at the fjord's edge and she was deluged in freezing water. Each breath was painful, a sharp knife repeatedly stabbing her chest. She dared not stop or slacken speed for an instant, terrified by the loud thud of pursuing steps close behind her, not recognizing her own agonized heartbeats. Suddenly she slipped on the edge of a snowdrift, could not stop herself, fell face down in a deep snow-grave. There was snow in her mouth, she was done for, finished, she would never get up again, could not run any farther. Cruelly straining muscles relentlessly forced her up, she had to struggle on, pulled by the irresistible magnet of doom. Systematic bullying when she was most vulnerable had distorted the structure of her personality, made a victim of her, to be destroyed, either by things or by human beings, people or fjords and forests; it made no difference, in any case she could not escape. The irreparable damage inflicted had long ago rendered her fate inevitable.

A pitch black mass of rock loomed ahead, a hill, a mountain, an unlighted fortress, buttressed by regiments of black firs. Her weak hands were shaking too much to manipulate a door, but the waiting forces of doom dragged her inside.

Stretched out on her bed, she could feel the hostile, alien, freezing dark pressed to the wall like the ear of a listening enemy. In the utter silence and solitude, she lay watching the mirror, waiting for her fate to arrive. It would not be long now. She knew that something fearful was going to happen in the sound-proof room, where nobody could or would come to her rescue. The room was antagonistic as it had always been. She was aware of the walls refusing protection, of the frigid hostility in the air. There was nothing she could do, no one to whom she could appeal. Abandoned, helpless, she could only wait for the end.

A woman came in without knocking and stood in the doorway, handsome, forbidding, dressed all in black, tall and menacing as a tree, followed by other indistinct shapes, which kept to the shadows behind her. The girl at once recognized her executioner, whose enmity she had always felt without understanding it, too innocent or too preoccupied with her own dream world to guess the obvious cause. Now, cold bright pitiless eyes swam in the glassy depths of the mirror, darted towards their victim. *Her* eyes were widely dilated and black with dread, two deep pits of terror, of intuitive nightmare foreknowledge. Then a sense of fatality overcame her: she experienced a regression, became a submissive, terrorized child, cowed by persistent ill-treatment. Intimidated, obedient to the woman's commanding voice, she got up and with faltering steps left the platform, her white face blank as paper. When her arms were seized she cried out, struggled feebly. A hand was clamped over her mouth. Several figures towered above her. She was gripped from all sides, roughly handled, hustled out of the room, her hands tied behind her back.

Under the trees it got darker and darker, I kept losing sight of the path. In the end I lost it entirely and came out at a different place. I was close to the wall. It was impressive, intact, no break in it anywhere. I saw the black shapes of sentries posted along the top. Two of them were approaching each other and would cross quite near me. I stood still in the shadow of the black trees where I should not be seen. Their steps were loud, the hard frost magnified every sound. They met, stamped their feet, exchanged passwords, separated again. I walked on when the footsteps grew fainter. I had a curious feeling that I was living on several planes simultaneously; the overlapping of these planes was confusing. Huge rounded boulders as big as houses, resembling the heads of decapitated giants, were lying near, where they had fallen long ago from the mountainside. Suddenly I heard voices, looked everywhere, but could see no one. The sound seemed to come from among the boulders, so I went to investigate. A light flowered yellow in the blue dusk: I was looking at a cottage, not a mass of rock. People were talking inside it.

I heard yells, crashes, the frightened neighing of horses, all the noises of battle. Arrows flew in clouds. War clubs thumped. There was loud clashing of steel. Strangely dressed men came at the wall in waves, swarming up it, using their feet as well as their hands, holding cutlasses in their teeth. Agile as gorillas, they came in their thousands; however many were thrown back, a new wave always came on. Finally all the defenders of the wall were exterminated, the second-line defences forced back. Invaders already inside opened the gates, and the rest burst in like a tidal wave. People barricaded themselves in their houses. In the town there was utter chaos. Hand to hand fighting in the narrow streets; savage meaningless cries like the cries of wild animals resounding between the walls. The strangers raced through the town like madmen, pouring wine down their throats, slaughtering all they met, every man, woman, child, animal. The wine streamed down their faces mingled with sweat and blood so that they looked like demons. A little snow fell: this seemed to excite them to frenzy, they laughed insanely, trying to catch the falling flakes in their mouths. The horsemen carried long lances with pennants or feathers attached. Hacked-off heads were impaled on these lances, sometimes infants or dogs. Huge fires blazed everywhere, it was as bright as day. The air was full of the reek of burning, of charred wood and old dust. As people were smoked out of their homes they were massacred by the enemy. Many preferred to die in the flames.

I had no weapon, and searched for something with which to defend myself. I was in a street where dead horses had been piled up to form a barricade, among them a man who had been killed with his mount. He had not had time even to draw his sword, which was still in the scabbard, engraved with intricate patterns, a beautiful piece of work. I tugged at the projecting hilt, but in falling the blade had jammed and I could not move it. The dead beasts had been heaped up in such frantic haste that my persistent efforts were shaking the whole construction; carcasses worked loose, rolled down, forming a breach. Before I could repair the damage, a troop of horsemen galloped along the street with a fearful clattering din, waving their lances, yelling their senseless cries. I threw myself flat on the ground, hoping they had not seen me, expecting the worst. As they came up, one of them jabbed his long lance ahead of him into the dead rider, dislodging the body so violently that it fell on top of me, probably saving my life. I kept perfectly still while the whole troop went careering past, rolling their bloodshot, demented, animalic eyes.

When they had gone, I pushed the corpse aside and got up to go and search for the girl. I had not much hope of finding her; I knew the fate of girls in sacked towns. The sword was loose now, I pulled it out easily. I had never used such a weapon and tried slashing at some of the bodies I passed. The thing was heavy and hard to handle, but I discovered the balance and began to get the feel of it as I walked, thus gaining some much-needed confidence. As it happened, I was not attacked. Most of the fighting was going on in the lower streets, round the harbour forts, which appeared to be holding out. When I saw anyone I took cover, and in the general confusion escaped observation. The High House was almost burnt out already, only the shell still standing. Smoke and flames spouted towards the sky, the whole interior was incandescent. I approached as close as I could, but was driven back by the smoke and intense heat. It was quite impossible to get inside. In any case, nobody could have survived in such an inferno. My face was scorched, sparks were smouldering in my hair, I crushed them out with my hands.

I came upon her by chance, not far away, lying face down on the stones. A little blood had trickled out of her mouth. Her neck had an unnatural twist; a living girl could not have turned her head at that angle: the neck was broken. She had been dragged by the hair, hands which had twisted it into a sort of rope had dulled its silvery brightness. On her back blood was still fresh in places, wet and bright red; in other places it had caked black on the white flesh. I looked particularly at one arm, on which the circular marks of teeth stood out clearly. The bones of the forearm were broken, the sharp pointed ends of bone projected at the wrist through the torn tissue. I felt I had been defrauded: I alone should have done the breaking with tender love; I was the only person entitled to inflict wounds. I leaned forward and touched her cold skin.

I went to look in at the cottage window, taking care not to go near enough to be seen from inside. A lot of people were crowded into a small smoky room, firelight flickering red on their faces, reminding me of a medieval picture of hell. At first I could not make out any words; they were all talking at once. I recognized one woman, unusually tall, handsome in a forbidding way; I had seen her at the High House. Now she was with a man she called father who sat just inside the window. Because he was so close to me, his was the first voice I understood. He was relating the legend of the fjord, how every year at the winter solstice a beautiful girl had to be sacrificed to the dragon that lived in its depths. The other voices gradually became silent when he began describing the rite itself. 'We untie her as soon as we get her up there on the rock. She must struggle a bit, otherwise the dragon might think we'd palmed off a dead girl on him. The water foams down below. The monster's great scaly coils appear. Then we hurl her down. The whole fjord becomes a maelstrom, blood and foam flying in all directions.'

A lively discussion of the sacrifice followed, different people speaking in turn. They might have been talking about a football match between their team and a rival town. Somebody said: 'We haven't so many good-looking girls to spare. Why should we give one of them to the dragon? Why not sacrifice a stranger, some foreign girl who means nothing to any of us?' The tone of voice suggested that the speaker referred to a special person, whose identity was known to all present. The father started raising objections, but was silenced by his daughter, who called out her agreement, launching into a vicious tirade of which I only caught isolated phrases. 'Pale girls who look as pure as if they were made of glass ... smash them to smithereens. ... And I *will* smash this one ...' The end was shouted. 'I'll hurl her down off the rock myself, if none of you have the guts to do it!'

I walked away in disgust. These people were worse than savages. My hands and face were numb, I felt half frozen, and could not think why I had stood there so long listening to their preposterous rigmarole. I had a vague feeling that something was wrong with me, though I could not decide what it was. For a moment this was disturbing; then I forgot it. A small, cold, bright moon shone high in the sky, showed the landscape distinctly. I recognized the fjord but not the scene. Tall perpendicular rocks rose straight out of the water, supporting a flat horizontal rock like a high-diving platform. Some people appeared, dragging the girl between them, her hands tied. As she passed me, I caught a glimpse of her pitiful white face of a child-victim, terrified and betrayed. I sprang forward, tried to reach her, to cut her bonds. Somebody went for me. I threw him off, tried again to get near her, she was dragged away. I rushed after the group, shouting: 'Murderers!' Before I could overtake them, they were hauling her up the rock.

I was close to her on the platform high above the fjord. We were alone there, although a mixture of vague sounds behind me indicated the presence of numerous onlookers. They did not concern me. I was completely concentrated on the trembling figure, half kneeling, half crouching, at the extremity of the rock, overhanging the dark water. Her hair glittered as if with diamond dust under the moon. She was not looking at me, but I could see her face, which was always pale, but now drained of colour right to the bone. I observed her extreme slenderness, felt I could enclose the whole of her with my two hands, even the rib-cage containing her heart. Her skin was like white satin, shadowless in the brilliant moonlight. The circular marks the cords had left on her wrists would have been red in daylight, but now looked black. I could imagine how it would feel to take hold of her wrists and to snap the fragile bones with my hands.

Leaning forward, I touched her cold skin, the shallow hollow in her thigh. Snow had fallen between her breasts.

Armed men came up, pushed me back, seized her by her frail shoulders. Big tears fell from her eyes like icicles, like diamonds, but I was unmoved. They did not seem to me like real tears. She herself did not seem quite real. She was pale and almost transparent, the victim I used for my own enjoyment in dreams. People behind me muttered, impatient at the delay. The men did not wait any longer but hurled her down, her last pathetic scream trailing after her. The night exploded then like a paper bag. Huge jets of water sprang up; waves dashing wildly against the rocks burst in cascades of spray. I hardly noticed the freezing showerbath, but peered over the edge of the platform, and saw a circle of scaly coils emerge from the seething water, in which something white struggled frantically for an instant before the crunch of armour-plated jaws.

I was in a hurry to get back to my lodging. My feet and fingers were numb, my face stiff, my head starting to ache with the cold. As soon as I had thawed out a little in my warm room, I began to write. My main topic, of course, was the Indris, but I still kept up the pretence I had started by writing down anything that seemed of interest about the town. I did not think the security people would bother to read my notes, although they could easily do so while I was out of the room. The childishly simple form of scrambling I used, mixing up sentences about the lemurs with others on local affairs, would at least defeat the woman of the house, who pried into everything.

I derived great satisfaction from describing the gentle mysterious singing creatures, and seemed to grow more deeply involved with them as I wrote. With their enchanting other-world voices, their gay, affectionate, innocent ways, they had become for me symbols of life as it could be on earth, if man's destructiveness, violence and cruelty were eliminated. I enjoyed writing as a rule, the sentences came to me without effort as if they formed in my head of their own accord. But now it was quite different, I could not find the right words: I knew I was not expressing myself lucidly, or remembering accurately, and after some minutes put down my pen. Immediately I saw a mental picture of many people crowded into a smoky room, and felt I ought to inform the warden of what I had overheard. At the same time, there was a curious unreality about the memory of that scene, as if I could have dreamt it. And when it occurred to me that the girl might be in real danger I did not quite believe this. I got up, all the same, to go to the telephone. Then, restrained by the peculiar uncertainty as to what was real more than the thought of the woman who would be listening to every word, I decided not to ring up until I got to the café.

My sense of unreality became overwhelming as I left the house. A strong colourless light was making everything outside as clear as day, though I was quite unable to see where it came from. My amazement increased when I observed that this extraordinary light revealed details not normally visible to the naked eye. It was snowing slightly, and the complex structure of each individual snowflake appeared in crystalline clearness, the delicate starlike, flowerlike forms perfectly distinct and as bright as jewels. I looked round for the familiar ruins, but they were no longer there. I was used to the sight of destruction, but this was different. Nothing whatever was left of the ruined town; its structures had disintegrated, the remains were flattened, spread as though a giant steam-roller had passed over them. The one or two vertical fragments seemed to have been left intentionally, with the deliberate object of emphasizing the general levelling. With a dreamlike feeling, I walked on, seeing no one, either alive or dead. The air was full of a sweetish smell, not unpleasant, which I could smell on my own hands and clothes, and presumed had been left by some gas. The absence of fires surprised me; nothing seemed to be burning, I saw no smoke. I only now noticed thin trickles of a white milky fluid moving among the debris, collecting in pools here and there. These white pools continually widened as the liquid eroded their edges, eating away whatever came in contact with it; it was only a question of time before the entire mass of wreckage would be disposed of in this way. I stood still for a moment to watch the process, fascinated by such a practical, thorough method of clearance.

I remembered that I had to find the girl, searched for her desperately through the endless rubble. I thought I saw her a long way off in the distance, shouted, ran; she changed, disappeared. Like a mirage I saw her still farther away; then she vanished again. A girl's arm protruded from a heap of detritus; I took hold of the wrist, pulled gently; it came away in my hand. All at once I heard sounds and movements behind me, quickly swung round, caught sight of living objects which moved with a gliding motion, made warbling noises. Their shapes were queer, only partially human, reminding me of mutants in science fiction stories. They took no notice of me, ignored my existence completely, and I hurried on without going any closer.

When I came to a place where bodies were lying about, I stopped to examine them in case one was hers. I went up to the nearest corpse and looked at it carefully. It was not recognizable, the skeleton and what was left of the flesh had become phosphorescent. To look at the others would only be wasting time, so I left them alone.

six

The owner of the house heard me pass her door, opened it, peered out frowning. I pretended not to have seen her and hurried on, but the outer door would not move, there was some obstruction. I pushed hard, scattering the snow piled against it, and letting in icy wind that rattled something behind me. There was an angry shout, 'Mind what you're doing!' which I ignored.

Outside I was astonished by the quantity of snow that had fallen. A different town, white and spectral, had replaced the old one. The few feeble lights showed how the shapes of the ruins were altered by their thick white covering, the details of destruction obscured, all outlines muffled and blurred. The effect of the heavy snowfall was to deprive structures of solidity and precise location: my old impression revived of a scene made of nylon with nothing behind. Only a few snowflakes were in the air at first; then a white flurry passed me, driven along parallel to the ground by the strong wind. I lowered my head against this freezing wind, and saw the small grains of snow, dry and frozen, swirling round my legs. The flurries thickened, became incessant, filling the air; I could not see where I was. I got only intermittent glimpses of my surroundings, which seemed vaguely familiar, and yet distorted, unreal. My ideas were confused. In a peculiar way the unreality of the outer world appeared to be an extension of my own disturbed state of mind.

Collecting my thoughts with an effort, I remembered that the girl was in danger and must be warned. I gave up trying to find the café, and decided to go straight to the warden. I could just make out the fort-like mass of his home looming over the town.

Except for the main square, the streets were always deserted after dark, so I was amazed to see quite a number of figures climbing the steep hill in front of me. Next moment I remembered hearing talk, without paying attention, of some public dinner or celebration at the High House, which evidently was being held tonight. I reached the entrance only a few steps behind the nearest group of people, and was glad they were there; without them, I should not have been sure this was the right place, the snow made everything look so different. Two hillocks, one on each side, might have been the batteries; but there were other white mounds I could not account for. A cluster of long pointed icicles, sharp as swords, clung to a lantern over the huge main door, glistening ferociously in the dim light. As those ahead of me were admitted, I stepped forward and went inside with them. The guards would most likely have let me in if I had been alone, but this seemed the easiest way.

Nobody took the least notice of me. I must have been recognized, but received no sign of recognition from anyone, felt increasingly derealized, as familiar faces came up and passed me without a glance. The gloomy great place was already crowded, the group I had come in with must have been one of the last. If this was a celebration, it was singularly subdued. All the faces were dour as usual; there was no laughing and little talking. Such conversation as went on took place in tones too low to be overheard.

Ceasing to notice the people, I considered how I was to reach the girl. The warden had taken me to the door of her room, but I knew I would never be able to find it again without a guide. Somebody would have to help me. Wondering who would be the best person to approach, I wandered from room to room, presently found myself in a huge vaulted hall, where trestle tables had been set up, with jugs and bottles of wine and spirits placed at intervals between vast platters of meat and bread. Standing in a dark corner where I would not be seen, I watched the servants bringing in more plates of food and arranging them on the tables. In spite of an almost feverish anxiety over the girl, instead of attempting to find her, I stood there doing nothing at all; became aware of an odd sort of fragmentation of my ideas.

Hundreds of torches flared, lighting the great hall, a banquet had been arranged to celebrate victory. I went first with one of my aides to look over the prisoners. It was the commander's traditional privilege, a routine. The women were herded together behind a barrier. They had already retreated as far from everyone as they could, but when they saw us coming contrived to move back farther still, pressing against the wall. They did not attract me. I could not tell one from another; suffering had given them all the same features. In other parts of the hall there was much noise, but here only silence; no pleadings, no curses, no lamentations; just staring eyes, the red flicker of torchlight on naked limbs, breasts.

Torches were fixed like bundles of rockets to the enormous pillars supporting the high arched roof. Leaning against one of these pillars a young girl stood a little apart, unclothed except by her shining hair. The death of hope had tranquillized her white face. She was scarcely more than a child, did not see us; her eyes were looking far inward at dreams. Arms like peeled wands, silvery streaming hair . . . a young moon among clouds . . . I wanted to stay and watch her. But they came to escort me to the presence.

His splendid gold seat was carved with the faces and exploits of heroes, his ancestors. His magnificent cloak, lined with sable and gold embroidered, draped his knees in stiff statuesque folds. Sparks dripped from the torches and warmed the cold white of his long, thin, restless hands. A blue flash from his eyes; a matching blue flash from a tremendous jewel worn on his hand. I did not know the name of this stone. Neither his hands nor his eyes were ever at rest, there was a constant bombardment of blue. He would not let me move to a different place, kept me standing beside him. Because I had led the victorious army, he gave me a glittering order I did not want: I had too many already. I told him I only wanted the girl. A gasp went up. The people round him waited to see me struck down. I was indifferent. I had lived half my life, seen as much as I wanted. I was sick of war, sick of serving this difficult, dangerous master who loved war and killing and nothing else. There was a kind of insanity in his war-making. Conquest was not enough. He wanted a war of extermination, all enemies slaughtered without exception, nobody left alive. He wanted to kill me. But, though he could not live without war, he was unable to plan a campaign, take a city; I had to do that. So he could not kill me. He wanted my war skills and he wanted me dead. Now he gave me a deadly glance, kept me at his side; but, at the same time, beckoned closer those standing around him. They formed a close sycophantic circle, the only gap was the point where I stood. A small man slipped in, crept under my arm, lifted a long-nosed face like a vicious dog ready to bite, cringing before his master, snarling at me. Now the circle was closed. But I could still watch the ring flashing blue, the gesticulations of the unquiet hands, their long thin white fingers and long pointed nails. The fingers curved inwards in a strange way, like a strangler's, the blue stone was anchored by the curved bone. Commands were given, too low for me to hear. Earlier, he had praised my skill and courage extravagantly, promised me great rewards, I was his guest of honour. I knew him well, could well imagine what sort of reward he planned for me now. I had already prepared my face.

Six guards brought her to him, bundled up in a soldier's cloak. These men had been taught a trick of grasping that left no bruises. I had never learnt it, did not see now how it was done. There was a moment's pause. I wondered if, after all, generosity might be shown . . . in the circumstances, it seemed just possible.

Then I saw his hand move towards her, the curved predatory fingers, the blazing blue. She gave a small choked cry as the huge ring tore through her hair; it was the one time I heard her voice. I heard too the faint clank of the metal rings round her wrists and ankles when she fell with violence across his knees. I stood motionless, looking on with an expressionless face. That cold, hard, mad, murderous man; her soft young girl's body and dreaming eyes . . . a pity, sad . . .

I had decided to approach one of the servants who were still busy round the long tables. I was watching a scared-looking peasant girl, one of the youngest of them, slow, clumsy and obviously new to the work. She seemed frightened, downtrodden, the others teased her, slapped her, jeered, called her half-witted. She was tearful, kept making mistakes, I saw her drop things several times. Her sight could have been defective. I went and stood in a doorway she had to pass, grabbed her and dragged her through, my hand over her mouth. Luckily, the passage beyond was empty. While I was saying I would not harm her, only wanted her help, she looked at me in horror, her red eyes filling with tears; blinked, trembled, seemed too stupid to understand. There was no time, in a moment people would come looking for her, but she would not speak. I spoke to her kindly; argued with her; shook her; showed her a wad of notes. Absolutely no response, no reaction. Increasing the amount of money, I held it under her nose, told her: 'Here's your chance to get away from people who treat you badly. With this you won't have to work again for a long time.' Finally she saw the point, agreed to take me to the room.

We started off, but she was slow and kept hesitating, so that I began to wonder whether she really knew the way. My nerves were on edge, I wanted to hit her, it was hard to control myself. I was afraid of being too late. I said I had to speak to the warden, which would be impossible once the party had started. It was a relief to hear that he never appeared during the early part of the evening, but only when the eating and drinking were over, in about two hours' time. At last I recognized the final steep staircase. She pointed to the top, clutched the money I was holding ready for her, bolted back the way we had come.

I went up and opened the solitary door. The sound-proof room was in darkness, but a little of the faint light from the landing came in behind me. I saw the girl lying on the bed, fully dressed, with a book beside her; she had fallen asleep while reading. I spoke her name softly. She started up, her hair glinting. 'Who's that?' There was fear in her voice. I moved, let the dim light touch my face; she knew me at once, said: 'What are you doing here?' I said: 'You're in danger; I've come to take you away.' 'Why should I go with *you*?' 'She sounded astonished. 'There's no difference—' We both heard a sound at the same moment; footsteps were starting to mount the stairs. I stepped back, froze, held my breath. The feeble light outside the door was extinguished. I stood in black shadow, I was pretty safe; unless she gave me away.

The man's ungentle hands gripped her. 'Put on your outdoor things quickly. We're leaving at once.' His voice was low and peremptory. 'Leaving?' She stared, saw him as a blacker shadow against the black, her cold lips murmuring: 'Why?' 'Don't talk. Do as I tell you.' Obediently she stood up, the draught from the door made her shiver. 'How am I supposed to find anything in the dark? Can't we have a light?' 'No. Somebody might see.' He flashed a torch briefly, saw her pick up a comb and start pulling it through her hair, snatched it away from her. 'Leave that! Get your coat on – hurry!' The irritable impatience radiating from him made her movements slower, more awkward. Feeling about the dark room she found her coat but could not find the way into it; she held it the wrong way round. He seized it angrily, turned it, forced her arms through the sleeves. 'And now come on! Don't make a sound. Nobody must know we've gone.' 'Where are we going? Why do we have to go at this time of night?' She expected no answer, doubted whether she heard correctly when he muttered, 'It's the one chance,' adding something about the approaching ice. He grasped her arm then, pulled her across the landing and on to the stairs. The beam of the torch, intermittently stabbing pitch blackness, showed his looming repressive shadow, which she followed as if sleepwalking through all the ramifications of the huge building, out into the icy snow-filled night.

Although snow was falling heavily, there was none on the black car; it had just been cleared away: yet no one had passed them, nobody was in sight. She shivered as she got in, sat in silence while he quickly inspected the chains. Yellow oblongs stained the pure white in front of the windows. In the air, the snow was transformed into showering gold as it passed the lights. A confused noise from the dining hall, voices, clattering plates, drowned the noise of the car starting up, and impelled her to ask: 'What about all those people who are expecting you? Aren't you going to see them?'

Already in a state of irritable nervous tension, he was exasperated by the question, lifted one hand from the wheel in a threatening gesture. 'I told you not to talk!' His voice was frightening, his eyes flashed in the dark interior of the car. She moved fast to avoid the blow, but could not get out of reach, crouched down, shielding herself with her raised arm, made no sound when the glancing blow struck her shoulder and crushed her against the door; afterwards huddled there in silence, shrinking away from his silent rage.

Snow-muffled silence outside; silence filling the car. He drove without lights, his eyes like cats' eyes, able to see through the snowy darkness. A ghost-car, invisible, silent, fled from the ruined town. The ancient snow-covered fortifications fell back and vanished in snow, the broken wall vanished behind. In front loomed the black living wall of the forest, ghostly whiteness fuming along its crest like spray blown back from the crest of a breaking wave. She waited for the black mass to come crashing down on them, but there was no crash, only the silence of snow and forest outside, and in the car, his silence, her apprehension. He never spoke, never looked at her, handled the powerful car recklessly on the rough frozen track, hurling it at speed over all obstacles, as if by the force of his will. The violent lurching of the car threw her about; she was not heavy enough to keep in her seat. Thrown against him, forced to touch his coat, she winced away as though the material burned. He seemed unaware. She felt forgotten, forsaken.

It was incomprehensible to her, this extraordinary flight that went on and on. The forest went on for ever. The silence went on and on. The snow stopped, but the cold went on and even increased, as if some icy exudation from the black trees congealed beneath them. Hour after hour passed before a little reluctant daylight filtered down through the roof of branches, revealing nothing but gloomy masses of firs, dead and living trees tangled together, a dead bird often caught in the branches, as if the tree had caught it deliberately. She shuddered, identifying herself, as a victim, with the dead bird. It was she who had been snared by nets of black branches. Armies of trees surrounded her on all sides, marching to infinity in all directions. Snow flew past the window again, waving white flags. She was the one who long ago had surrendered. She understood nothing of what was happening. The car leapt in the air, she was flung painfully on to her bruised shoulder, tried ineffectually to shield it with the other hand.

The man drove the car brutally throughout the short day. It seemed to her that she had never known anything but the terrifying drive in the feeble half-light; the silence, the cold, the snow, the arrogant figure beside her. His cold statue's eyes were the eyes of a Mercury, ice-eyes, mesmeric and menacing. She wished for hatred. It would have been easier. The trees receded a little, a little more sky appeared, bringing the last gleams of the fading light. Suddenly, she was astonished to see two log huts, a gate between, blocking the road. Unless the gate was opened they could not pass. She watched it racing towards them, reinforced with barbed wire and metal. The car burst through with a tremendous shattering smash, a great rending and tearing, a frantic metallic screeching. Broken glass showered her, she ducked instinctively as a long, sharp, pointed sliver sliced the air just over her head, and the car rocked sickeningly on two wheels before turning over. At the last moment then, by some miracle of skill, or strength, or sheer will power, the driver brought it back on to its axis again, and drove on as if nothing had happened.

Shouts exploded behind them. A few shots popped ineffectively and fell short. She glanced back and saw uniforms running; then the small commotion was over, cut off by black trees. The road improved on this side of the frontier, the car travelled faster, more smoothly. She shifted her position, leaning away from the stream of ice-vapour entering through the smashed window, shook bits of broken glass off her lap. There was blood on her wrists, both hands were cut and bleeding; she looked at them in remote surprise.

I raced down stairs and passages. In sight of the main door I hid in the shadows, watched the men guarding it. Sounds of the party, now growing more animated, came from the dining hall, where drinking was evidently in full swing. Someone shouted to the guards out in the cold corridor. The men I was watching put their heads together, then left their post, passed close to me as they went to join the rest. Unnoticed by anyone, I slipped out through the door they were supposed to be guarding.

It was snowing hard. I could barely distinguish the nearest ruins, white stationary shadows beyond the moving fabric of falling white.

Snowflakes turned yellow like swarms of bees round the lighted windows. A wide expanse of snow lay in front of me, a hollow marking the place where the warden's black car had stood. I realized that various white mounds must be other cars, belonging, presumably, to his household, and waded towards them through the deep snow. I tried the door of the first one, found it unlocked. The whole vehicle was buried in snow, which had drifted deep against wheels and windscreen. Snow fell all over me when I opened the door, filled my sleeve as I tried to clean the glass. I thought the starter would never work, but at last the car began to move slowly forward. I revved the engine just enough to keep the tyres gripping, and followed the warden's hardly visible tracks, which were rapidly being obliterated by fresh snow. Outside the encircling wall they practically vanished. I lost them altogether at the edge of the forest, blindly drove into a tree, scraping off the bark. The car stopped and refused to move. The wheels just spun round, uselessly churning the snow. As I got out, a mass of snow fell on me from the branches above. In two seconds my clothes were caked solid with driving snow. I tore down fir branches, threw them under the wheels, got back into the car and restarted. It was no good; the tyres would not grip, still went on spinning and hissing. I was sliding sideways, I pulled on the brake, jumped straight into a snowdrift, sank up to my armpits. The snow kept collapsing on me as I moved, slipped inside my collar, my shirt, I felt snow in my navel; to struggle out was an exhausting business. After breaking off more branches and piling them under the car without the least effect, I knew I was beaten and would have to give up. Weather conditions were quite impossible. Somehow or other I got the car going, and crawled back to the town. It was the only thing to do in the circumstances.

I started skidding again just as I reached the wall, lost control this time. Suddenly I saw the front wheels crumbling the edge of a deep bomb crater; one more second, and I would be over; the drop was of many feet. I stood on the foot brake, the car spun right round, executed a complete circle before I jumped out and it nosedived, vanishing under the snow.

I was freezing, very tired, shivering so much I could hardly walk. Luckily my lodging was not far off. I slithered and staggered back there, crouched over the stove just as I was, plastered in frozen snow, my teeth chattering. The shivering was so violent I could not unfasten my coat, only succeeded in dragging it off by slow stages. In the same laborious fashion, by prolonged painful effort, I finally got rid of the rest of my freezing clothes, struggled into a dressing gown. It was then that I saw the cable and ripped open the envelope.

My informant reported the crisis due in the next few days. All air and sea services had ceased operating, but arrangements had been made to pick me up by helicopter in the morning. Still holding the flimsy paper, I crawled into bed, went on shivering under piles of blankets. The warden must have received the news earlier in the day. He had fled to save himself, abandoning his people to their fate. Of course such conduct was highly reprehensible, scandalous: but I did not condemn him. I did not think I would have acted differently in his place. Nothing he could have done would have saved the country. If he had revealed the critical situation a panic would have resulted, the roads would have been jammed, nobody would have escaped. In any case, judging by what I had just experienced, his chance of reaching the frontier was extremely slim.

seven

The aircraft deposited me at a distant port just before the ship sailed. I was suffering from some kind of fever, shivering, aching, apathetic. I sat at the back of the car rushing me to the docks, did not even look out, went on board in a daze. The ship was already moving when I crossed the deck, meaning to go straight to my cabin. But now the scene caught my eyes, and it gave me a shock; I stopped and stood staring. A sunlit harbour was sliding past me, a busy town; I saw wide streets, well-dressed people, modern buildings, cars, yachts on the blue water. No snow; no ruins; no armed guards. It was a miracle, a flashback to something dreamed. Then another shock, the sensation of a violent awakening, as it dawned on me that this was the reality, and those other things the dream. All of a sudden the life I had lately been living appeared unreal: it simply was not credible any longer. I felt a huge relief, it was like emerging into sunshine from a long cold black tunnel. I wanted to forget what had just been happening, to forget the girl and the senseless, frustrating pursuit I had been engaged in, and think only about the future.

Later, when the fever left me, my feelings remained unchanged. Thankful to have escaped from the past, I decided to go to the Indris; to make that tropical island my home, and the lemurs themselves my life work. I would devote the rest of my time to studying them, writing their history, recording their strange songs. No one else had done it, as far as I knew. It seemed a satisfactory project, a worthwhile aim.

From the shop on board I bought a big notebook and a stock of ball-point pens. I was ready to plan my work. But I could not concentrate. After all, I had not escaped the past. My thoughts kept wandering back to the girl; incredible that I should have wished to forget her. Such a forgetting would have been monstrous, impossible. She was like a part of me, I could not live without her. But now I wanted to go to the Indris, so there was a conflict. She prevented me, holding me back with thin arms.

I tried to stop thinking about her, to fix my mind on those innocent gentle creatures, their sweet, eerie singing. But she persistently distracted me with thoughts that were less than innocent. Her face haunted me: the sweep of her long lashes, her timid enchanting smile; and then a change of expression I could produce at will, a sudden shift, a bruised look, a quick change to terror, to tears. The strength of the temptation alarmed me. The black descending arm of the executioner; my hands seizing her wrists ... I was afraid the dream might turn out to be real ... Something in her demanded victimization and terror, so she corrupted my dreams, led me into dark places I had no wish to explore. It was no longer clear to me which of us was the victim. Perhaps we were victims of one another.

I was desperately worried when I thought of the situation I had left behind. I walked round and round the decks, wondering what had happened, whether the warden had got away, whether she had been with him. No news was received on board ship. I could only wait, in great anxiety and impatience, to reach a port where I could go ashore and get some information. At last the day came. The steward had pressed my suit. He brought it back with a buttonhole, a red carnation he had got hold of somehow. Its strong colour looked well against the light grey material.

Just as I was ready to leave my cabin, there was a peremptory bang on the door, and a plain-clothes policeman came in without waiting for me to answer. He did not take off his hat, but opened his jacket to show the official badge, the pistol in its armpit holster. I gave him my passport. He flipped over the pages contemptuously, looked me up and down in an insolent way, stared hard and with particular disapproval at the red carnation. Everything about my appearance obviously confirmed the low opinion he had already formed. I asked what he wanted with me, received no answer but an insulting silence: I would not ask again. He produced a pair of handcuffs, dangled them in front of me. I said nothing. When he tired of the jingling, he put them away, observing that, out of respect for my country, handcuffs would not be used. I was to be allowed to walk off the ship with him. But I had better not play any games.

The sun shone, everybody was going ashore. In the crowd I kept close beside him, as agreed. I was not worried. Such things happened. I gathered that I was wanted for interrogation, and wondered what questions I would be asked, and how they had got hold of my name. Uniformed police were waiting for us in a side street just off the quay. They ordered me into an armoured car with black glass in the windows. After a short drive, we stopped at a large municipal building in a quiet square. Birds were singing. I noted the sound specially after the days at sea.

The few passers-by paid no attention to us. But a girl standing at the corner a few yards away took some interest, judging by her frequent glances in my direction. I saw that she was selling spring flowers, jonquils, dwarf irises, wild tulips, and among them a bunch of red carnations, like the one I was wearing. Then armed figures fell in round me, marched me into the building and down a long corridor. 'Get a move on.' A powerful hand gripped my elbow, pushed me up some steps. Double doors at the top opened into a hall where people sat in tiers as at a theatre, a magistrate enthroned facing them. 'In you go!' Various hard hands pulled and shoved me into a sort of pew. 'Halt!' Feet stamped smartly to right and left, and I looked round, feeling detached from the situation. A high ceiling, closed windows, no sun, no singing birds, on each side of me men with guns, everywhere staring faces. People whispered or cleared their throats. The jury looked tired, or bored. Somebody read out my name and particulars, all quite correct. I confirmed them and took the oath.

The case was that a girl had vanished, supposed kidnapped, possibly murdered. A well-known person had been suspected and questioned, and had accused someone else who could not be found. The girl's name was mentioned; I was asked if I knew her. I replied that I had known her for several years. 'You were intimate with her?' 'We were old friends.' There was laughter; somebody asked: 'What was your relationship with her?' 'I've told you; we were old friends.' More laughter, silenced by an official. 'You expect us to believe that you changed your plans all at once, dropped everything you were doing, in order to follow a friend to a foreign country?' They seemed to know all about me. I said: 'That is the truth.'

I sat on the bed, smoking, watching her face in the mirror as she combed her hair, the smooth sheen of the glittering mass of palely shining hair, its silvery fall on her shoulders. She leaned forward to look at herself, the glass reflected the beginning of her small breasts. I watched them move with her breathing, went and stood behind her, put my arms round her, covered them with my hands. She pulled away from me. Not wanting to see her frightened expression, I blew smoke in her face. She went on resisting, and I had an impulse to do certain things with the lighted cigarette, dropped it on the floor, put my foot on it. Then I pulled her closer to me. She struggled, cried: 'Don't! Leave me alone! I hate you! You're cruel and treacherous ... you betray people, break promises ...' I was impatient, I let her go and went over to lock the door. Before I got there, a sound made me turn round. She was holding a big bottle of eau-de-Cologne over her head, meaning to hit me with it. I told her to put it down; she took no notice, so I went back and twisted it out of her hand. She was not strong enough to put up a fight. There was no more strength in her muscles than in a child's.

While she was getting dressed I continued to sit on the bed. We did not speak to each other. She was ready, fastening her coat, when the door opened suddenly: in my impatience just now, I had forgotten to go back and lock it. A man came in. I jumped up to throw him out, but he walked past as though I was invisible or not present.

A tall, athletic, arrogant-looking man, with an almost paranoid air of assurance. His very bright and blue eyes flashed a danger signal, seemed not to see me. The girl was petrified, she did nothing at all. I did nothing either, simply stood watching. It was unlike me. But he was a man who had entered with a revolver for a specific purpose, and could not be prevented from carrying it out. I wondered if he would shoot us both, and if so which first, or if only one of us, which one. Such points were of interest to me.

It was clear that he regarded her as his property. I considered that she belonged to me. Between the two of us she was reduced to nothing; her only function might have been to link us together. His face wore the look of extreme arrogance which always repelled me. Yet I suddenly felt an indescribable affinity with him, a sort of blood-contact, generating confusion, so that I began to wonder if there *were two* of us ...

I was asked: 'What happened when you met your friend?' 'We did not meet.' Subdued excitement broke out, an official voice had to order silence. The next voice sounded like an actor's trained in elocution. 'I wish to state that the witness is a psychopath, probably schizoid, and therefore not to be believed.' Someone interjected: 'Produce a psychiatrist's confirmation.' The theatrical voice continued: 'I repeat, with all possible emphasis, that this man is known to be a psychopath and totally unreliable. We are investigating an atrocious crime against an innocent pure young girl: I asked you to note his unnatural callousness, his indifferent expression. What cynicism to come here with that flower in his buttonhole! How arrogantly he displays his utter contempt for the sanctity of family life, and for all decent feeling! His attitude is not only abnormal, but depraved, infamous, a desecration of all we hold sacred ...'

Somewhere high up in the room, where I could not see it, a bell rang. A superior, unimplicated voice stated: 'A psychopath is not an acceptable witness.'

I was taken away, locked in a cell for seventeen hours. In the early morning they released me without an explanation. In the meantime, the ship had gone, and with it my luggage. I was stranded with only the clothes I was wearing. Luckily, I had not been deprived of either my passport or my wallet, and was well provided with money.

I had a shave, a wash and brush up, and looked carefully at my reflection. I needed a clean shirt, but the shops were not yet open; I would buy one later and change. For the moment my appearance was passable, or would be when I had got rid of the dead carnation. I meant to throw it into the gutter as I left the barber's shop, but a boy just outside offered to clean my shoes, and while he did so I asked him which was the best café. He pointed out one farther along the same street; I walked on, liked the look of it, and sat down at one of the tables outside in the sun. At that hour the place was deserted. The solitary waiter on duty brought coffee and rolls on a tray, then returned to the dark interior, leaving me there alone. I drank the coffee, wondered what to do next, watched the passers-by; there were not many of them so early.

A girl went past carrying a basket of flowers, reminding me that, in the end, I had not disposed of the carnation. I tried to pull it out of my buttonhole, but the stem had been securely pinned by the steward. I turned back my lapel, peered down, felt about for the pin. Someone said: 'Let me do that for you.' I looked up; the flower girl was smiling at me. I seemed to have seen her face somewhere, I felt I already knew her and liked her. Having removed the carnation neatly, she prepared to replace it with one exactly the same from her basket. I was on the point of saying I did not want it, when something occurred to me and I kept silent. She fixed the fresh flower in my buttonhole and continued to stand beside me, though not as if she was merely waiting for payment. It looked as if my idea was correct but I said nothing in case I was mistaken. I knew I had been right when she asked: 'Is there anything else you'd like me to do?' I glanced round. The other tables were still deserted, the people on the pavement were out of earshot. She had put down her basket on a chair; I pretended to examine the flowers, picking up one bunch after another. To anyone watching, even through field-glasses, we would have appeared to be conducting a normal trans-action. I said, 'Certainly'; though I wondered if she ... But I had to find out without delay what had been going on in the world. 'I've been at sea; out of touch. There are lots of things you can tell me.'

I asked cautious questions, trying not to show the extent of my ignorance of the latest developments. It appeared that the situation at home was obscure and alarming, no precise information was coming through, the full extent of the disaster was not yet known. The warden of a northern country had escaped to the interior and joined forces with one of the various warlords, between whom hostilities had broken out.

I went on questioning her. She was always polite and friendly, and tried to be helpful. But her answers grew vague, she seemed afraid to commit herself. When one or two people drifted into the café and sat down near us, she said in a whisper: 'You'll have to discuss these matters with somebody higher up. Do you want me to arrange it?' I agreed at once, but was rather sceptical about her power to do this. She told me to wait, picked up her basket, and rushed off down the street, half running. I thought I had probably seen the last of her, but ordered more coffee, waited; I had nothing else to do. The news she had given me of the warden's escape had relieved my mind, up to a point; it seemed likely, though by no means certain, that he had taken the girl with him. Time passed. There were plenty of people about now. I watched the street for my informant's return. Just as I had decided she was not coming back, I saw her hurrying towards me between the passers-by. As she came to my table she called out: 'Here are the violets you wanted. I had to go all the way to the flower market for them. I'm afraid they're rather expensive.' She was out of breath, but made her voice sound clear and gay for the benefit of the people around us. I saw that it would be no good trying to persuade her to stay, and asked: 'How much?' She named a sum, I handed over the money. She thanked me with a charming smile, darted away, and disappeared in the crowd.

The stalks of the violets were wrapped in paper with words written on it. I was told where to find the man who might help me. The message was to be destroyed immediately. I bought a canvas bag with leather handles and straps to hold a few necessities, then booked at a hotel. When I had bathed and changed, I went to the office of the man named on the paper, who saw me at once. He too was wearing a red carnation. I should have to be careful.

I went straight to the point, there was no object in prevaricating. Naming the town from which the warden was operating, I asked if it was possible for me to get there. 'No. Fighting is going on in the area, night raids on the town. No foreigners allowed in.' 'No exceptions?' He shook his head. 'Anyway, there's no transport except for official personnel.' After all these negative statements, I could only say: 'Then you advise me to give up the idea?' 'Officially speaking, yes.' He looked at me slyly. 'But not necessarily.' His expression was more encouraging. 'There's just a chance I may be able to help you. Anyway, I'll see what can be done. But don't count on it. It will probably be a few days before I have anything to report.' I thanked him. We stood up and shook hands. He promised to notify me immediately he had any news.

I felt bored and restless. I had nothing to do. On the surface, the life of the town appeared normal, but underneath it was coming gradually to a standstill. The news from the north was scanty, confused, frightening. I realized that the destruction must have been on a gigantic scale. Little could have survived. The local broadcasters were cheerfully reassuring. It was the official policy, the population had to be kept calm. But these men actually seemed to believe their country would escape the cataclysm. I knew no country was safe, no matter how far removed from the present devastation, which would spread and spread, and ultimately cover the entire planet. Meanwhile, universal unrest was inevitable. It was the worst possible sign that war had already started, even though on a minor scale. That the more responsible governments were doing their utmost to pacify the belligerents only stressed the explosive nature of the situation, and the ominous threat of all-out warfare augmenting the present catastrophe. My anxiety about the girl, which had subsided slightly, revived again. She had gained nothing by escaping the destruction of one country, if she had gone to another about to engage in a full-scale war. I tried to believe the warden had sent her to safety, but knew too much about him to feel sure of that. It was absolutely essential for me to see him; otherwise I would never find out what had happened to her. I spent the evening in different bars, listening to the talk. His name was often mentioned, occasionally as a traitor to his own people, more frequently as a new, powerful, unknown influence on the war issue, a significant figure, a man to watch.

First thing in the morning the telephone rang in my room: someone wanted to see me. I said the person was to come up, hoping for a message from the official. 'Hullo.' The flower girl entered, smiling and unselfconscious. She saw my surprise. 'Forgotten me already?' I said I had not expected her here. *She* looked surprised now. 'But you know it's part of my job to bring your flower every morning.' I kept quiet while she fixed the carnation. It was fatally easy to show my ignorance of the organization to which she belonged. I was curious about it, but afraid of giving myself away. It occurred to me that, by spending more time with her, I might pick up information without asking questions. Besides, she was young and attractive. I liked her natural, matter-of-fact behaviour. It would relieve the boredom.

I invited her to dinner that evening. Her manners were charming, she acted in her usual engaging, unaffected way. Later we went to two night clubs, danced. She was a delightful partner, seemed relaxed and talked freely, but told me nothing I did not already know. I took her back to the hotel with me; the porter looked the other way when we came in together. I was rather drunk. Her full skirt fell in a shining ring on the floor of my room. Very early in the morning, while I was still asleep, she left to go to the flower market; was back at breakfast time with a fresh carnation, bright eyed, cheerful and full of life, more attractive than she had been in the dark. I wanted to keep her with me, to anchor myself in the present through her. But she said: 'No, I must go now, I have my work to do', then smiled in the friendliest way and promised to dance with me in the evening. I never saw her again.

The official sent for me while I was reading the papers. I hurried round to his office. He greeted me with a mysterious, conspiratorial air. 'I've been able to arrange that matter for you. It'll be a bit of a rush.' He grinned, pleased with himself, pleased to show me how he could manipulate events. I was surprised and excited. He went on: 'A lorry happens to be leaving today with important replacements for the new transmitter that's going up on our side of the frontier. It's quite near the town you want. I've got you signed on as a foreign consultant. You can do your homework on the way. It's all in here.' He handed me a thick folder full of papers, a travel permit on top, told me to be at the main post office in half an hour.

I thanked him profusely. He patted my arm. 'Think nothing of it. Glad I could be useful.' Withdrawing his hand, he touched the flower in my buttonhole and gave me a fright. Did he suspect something? If I had discovered nothing else about his organization, I at least knew now that it had considerable power. I was relieved when he said with a smile: 'Hurry back and collect your things. You mustn't be late on any account. The driver has orders to leave on the dot, and he won't wait for anyone.'

The room had been getting darker, a sudden storm had blown up. As his hand moved to the light, a livid flash and a crash came together, a splatter of rain hit the windows, and somebody wearing the long overcoat of a uniform entered and signed to him not to touch the switch. I could only just distinguish a big, heavily built man, whose massive shape seemed vaguely familiar. He stood talking to the official in undertones at the far end of the room, while I tried unsuccessfully to hear the low but heated discussion, of which I knew I was the subject, for they both kept glancing at me. It was obvious that I was being denigrated. Although the newcomer's face remained indistinct, between thunderclaps I could hear the accusing tone of his voice, but without being able to catch the words. He seemed already to have succeeded in discrediting me with the other man, who stood nearer the light, and showed signs of uneasiness and suspicion.

I was getting very uneasy myself. My position would be most unpleasant if he turned against me. Not only would I lose all hope of reaching the warden, but be shown up as having made use of the red carnation under false pretences. There was a serious danger that I would be re-arrested and put in prison again.

I looked at my watch. Several minutes of the half hour had elapsed, and, feeling that I had to get out of the room quickly, I made an unobtrusive move to the door, opening it with my hand behind me.

A terrific flash split the air, luridly lit up a sudden flurry of movement, the folds of the overcoat swinging, its wearer pointing a gun. As I raised my hands, he half turned to shout above the exploding thunder to the man to whom he had been talking: 'What did I tell you?' The momentary dividing of his attention gave me time to dive at his legs in a tackle I learnt at school, while the shot went over my head. I did not manage to bring him down, but caught him off balance, hampered by the length of the coat. Before he could aim again, I had knocked the revolver out of his hand, sent it flying across the room. He came at me directly, threw his whole weight against me in a vicious onslaught, hitting hard with both fists. He was much heavier than I was, I almost fell. The door saved me; clinging to it, I heard steps coming along the passage. My opponent attacked me fiercely again, shouting to the official to retrieve his gun. Once he got hold of it I was done for. In desperation, I bashed the door into him, kicked him with all my strength, had the satisfaction of seeing him fold up before I swung round. Two new figures materialized in my way. I did not look at them, simply hurled them aside, one after the other, heard one fall with a cry, and the crash of the door as he fell against it. Nobody else tried to stop me; without looking back, I rushed down the corridor and out of the building. Thanks to the thunder, the shot could not have been heard beyond the adjoining office.

The storm continued to help me. I was not noticed outside, everyone had taken shelter from the torrential rain. The streets were swimming with water, I was wet through in a second, kept running as fast as I could, splashing along as if in a shallow stream. Luckily I knew where the main post office was and made straight for it. Instructions to detain me would have been telephoned to my hotel, and anyhow I had no time to go there. As it was, the lorry driver was starting his engine when I came up, waving my travel documents for him to see. He scowled at me, and jerked his thumb at the back of the vehicle. I made a final effort and scrambled up, subsided on to something extremely hard. Someone immediately shut out the rain and the daylight; there was a tremendous lurch; we were off. I was breathless, bruised all over and soaked wet, but I felt triumphant.

Four of us were crowded inside the lorry. It was dark, noisy and uncomfortable, like being in some sort of tent with planks to sit on, but not enough head room to sit up straight. Two on each plank, we crouched face to face in the congested darkness, among stacked packing cases of different shapes and sizes. I hardly noticed the painful jolting, I was so relieved to be there, actually on my way, shut inside that cramped, comfortless, moving tent, where nobody could see me. The storm gradually died out, but the rain still streamed down, and eventually found its way through our canvas walls without damping my spirits. It could not possibly make me any wetter than I already was.

eight

I tried to make friends with my companions, young fellows straight from a technical college; but they would not talk. They distrusted me because I was a foreigner. When I asked questions, they suspected me of trying to find out things that were to be kept secret, although I could see that they themselves knew no secrets. They were incredibly naïve. I felt I belonged to another dimension, and became silent. By degrees they forgot about me and started talking among themselves. They spoke of their work; of difficulties in assembling the transmitter. Lack of materials; lack of trained personnel; lack of funds; bad workmanship; unaccountable errors. I heard the word sabotage muttered back and forth. The work was far behind schedule. The transmitter should have been functioning at the end of the month. Now no one knew when it would be finished. Exhausted, I closed my eyes, stopped listening.

Now and again an odd sentence reached me. Once I realized I was the subject of their conversation; they thought I was asleep. 'He's been sent to spy on us,' one of them said. 'To find out if we can be trusted. We must never tell him anything, never answer his questions.' Their voices dropped, they were almost whispering. 'I heard the professor say ... They don't explain ... Why send us to the danger zone when other people ...' They were dissatisfied and uneasy, and could not give me any information. I need not waste my time on them.

Late at night we stopped at a small town. I knocked up a shopkeeper, and, for the second time, provided myself with a few essentials: soap, a razor, a change of clothing. The place had only one garage: before we left in the morning, the driver insisted on buying up the entire stock of petrol. The owner protested indignantly; with supplies so restricted, he might not get any more. Our man ignored this, told him to empty the pumps, and, in response to further outraged protests, said: 'Shut up, and get on with it! That's an order.' Standing beside him, I remarked mildly that the next person expecting to fill up here would be in trouble. He gave me a scornful glance. 'He's got more hidden away somewhere. They always have.' The petrol cans were crammed into the back with the rest of the load, hardly leaving room for the four of us. I had the most uncomfortable place, over the back axle.

Flaps were rolled up, we could see out. We were driving towards a distant forest with a chain of mountains behind. A few miles from the town, the metalled road ended. Now there were only two narrow tarred strips for the wheels, as far apart as the width of the chassis. It got colder as we drove on; the climate was changing, like the character of the land. The edge of the forest was always in sight, gradually coming nearer: we passed less and less cultivation, fewer and fewer people and villages. I began to see the sense of storing the petrol. The road got steadily worse, full of ruts and holes. Progress was difficult, slow, the driver kept swearing. When even the tarred strips came to an end, I leant over and tapped his shoulder, offered to take turns with him at the wheel. Rather to my surprise, he agreed.

I had a more comfortable seat beside him, but found it an effort to handle the heavy lorry. I had never driven one before, and until I got used to it, had to concentrate on what I was doing. It was necessary to stop at intervals to remove fallen rocks or tree trunks that blocked the way. The first time this happened, I prepared to climb out to help the others, who had already jumped down from the back and were struggling to shift the obstruction. I felt a light touch and looked round. The driver's head made a just perceptible negative movement. My ability to drive the truck had apparently raised me above such duties in his estimation.

I offered him a cigarette. He accepted. I ventured a comment on the state of the road. As the transmitter was so important and involved so much traffic, I could not understand why a decent road had not been made. He said: 'We can't afford new roads. We asked the other nations associated with us in the undertaking to contribute, but they refused.' Frowning, he gave me a sidelong glance to see where my sympathies lay. I said in a non-committal tone that this seemed unfair. 'Just because we're a small, impoverished country, they've treated us badly all along the line.' He could not suppress his resentment. 'The transmitter could never have been built here at all if we hadn't donated the site. They should remember that we made the whole thing possible. We sacrifice a piece of our land for the general good, but get nothing in return. They won't even send ground troops to help to protect the position. It's their unsympathetic attitude that creates bad feeling.' He spoke bitterly. I could feel his grudge against the big powers. 'You're a stranger . . . I shouldn't be saying such things to you.' He looked at me with anxiety: I assured him I was not an informer.

Now that he had begun, he wanted to go on talking. I encouraged him to tell me about himself; it was the way to get him to speak of the things I was interested in. When the project first started, he had driven parties of workers along the road; they used to sing on the way. 'You remember the old formula – "all men of goodwill to unite in the task of world recovery and against the forces of destruction". They made the words into a sort of part song, men and women singing them together. It was inspiring to listen. We were all full of enthusiasm in those days. Now everything's different.' I asked what had gone wrong. 'Too many setbacks, delays, disappointments. The work would have been finished long ago if we'd had the materials. But everything had to come from abroad; from countries with different standards of measurement. Sometimes parts did not fit together; whole consignments had to go back. You can imagine the effect of such incidents on young enthusiasts, eager to get the job done.' It was the usual story of mistakes and muddles due to different ideologies, lack of direct contact. I thanked him for speaking frankly about these matters. A ball neatly volleyed, back bounced the cliché: 'Contact between individuals is the first step towards a better understanding between peoples.'

I seemed to have won his confidence. He became quite friendly, told me about his girl, showed snapshots of her playing with a dog. I considered it unwise to let people know that I carried a sum of money, so drew his attention to something at the roadside while I quickly took out of my wallet the photograph I still kept there of the girl standing beside a lake. I showed it to him, saying that she had disappeared and that I was looking for her. Without any special feeling, he commented: 'Wonderful hair. You're in luck.' I asked rather sharply whether he would think himself lucky if his girl had vanished off the face of the earth, and he had the grace to look slightly embarrassed. I put the photo away, asked if he'd ever seen hair like that. 'No, never.' He shook his head emphatically. 'Most of our women are dark.' It was no use talking to him about her.

We changed places. I was tired after my stint of driving and shut my eyes. When I opened them again he had a gun lying across his knees. I asked what he expected to shoot. 'We're getting near the frontier. It's dangerous here. Enemies everywhere.' 'But this country is neutral.' 'What's neutral? It's just a word.' He added mysteriously: 'Besides, there are various kinds of enemies.' 'Such as?' 'Saboteurs. Spies. Gangsters. All sorts of scoundrels who flourish in times of disorder.' I asked if he thought the lorry would be attacked. 'It has happened. The stuff we've got on board is urgently needed. If they've got to hear about it they may try to stop us.'

I brought out my automatic, saw him glancing at it with interest, evidently impressed by the foreign weapon. We had just entered the forest. He seemed nervous. 'This is where the danger begins.' The tall trees had long grey beards of moss hanging down from their branches, forming opaque screens. It looked a good place to hide. The light was starting to fade, and what was left of it fell on the road, so that it was easy to imagine invisible eyes watching us. I kept a lookout for gunmen, but had other things on my mind.

I spoke to the driver about the warden. He knew only what he had read in the newspapers. The distance to his headquarters from the transmitter was about twenty miles. 'Can one go there?' 'Go there?' He stared at me blankly. 'Of course not. It's enemy country. And they've destroyed the road, blocked the pass. There can't be much of the town left, anyhow. We hear the guns pounding it at night.' He was more interested in reaching our destination in daylight. 'We must get out of the forest before dark. We'll just make it, with any luck.' He drove furiously, the lorry bounced and skidded over loose stones.

I was too depressed to go on talking. The situation was hopeless. I needed the girl, could not live without her. But I should never be able to find her. There was no road to the town, I should never get there, it was impossible. In any case the place was under constant bombardment and must have been destroyed. There was no object in going there. She had either left or been killed long ago. I felt in despair. I seemed to have come all this way for nothing.

The site for the transmitter had been carefully chosen, high up, surrounded by forest, backed by mountains, an easy place to defend against ground attack. They had cleared the area immediately around the installation, but the trees were not far away. We lived in prefabricated buildings that let in the rain. Everything felt damp to the touch. The floors were concrete, always covered in mud. Everywhere we walked became a morass. Everyone grumbled about the discomfort and the poor quality of the food.

Something had gone wrong with the weather. It should have been hot, dry, sunny; instead it rained all the time, there was a dank chill in the air. Thick white mist lay entangled in the top of the forest trees; the sky was a perpetually steaming cauldron of cloud. The forest creatures were disturbed, and departed from their usual habits. The big cats lost their fear of man, came up to the buildings, prowled round the transmitter; strange unwieldy birds flopped overhead. I got the impression that birds and animals were seeking us out for protection against the unknown danger we had unloosed. The abnormalities in their behaviour seemed ominous.

To pass the time and for want of something better to do, I organized the work on the transmitter. It was not far from completion, but the workers had grown discouraged and apathetic. I assembled them and spoke of the future. The belligerents would listen and be impressed by the impartial accuracy of our reports. The soundness of our arguments would convince them. Peace would be restored. Danger of universal conflict averted. This was to be the final reward of their labours. In the meantime, I divided them into teams, arranged competitions, awarded prizes to those who worked best. Soon we were ready to start broadcasting. I recorded events on both sides with equal respect for truth, put out programmes on world peace, urged an immediate cease-fire. The minister wrote, congratulating me on my work.

I could not make up my mind whether to cross the frontier or to stay where I was. I did not think the girl could be alive in the demolished town. If she had been killed there it was pointless to go.

If she was safe somewhere else there was no point in going either. Considerable personal risk was involved. Although a non-combatant, I was liable to be shot as a spy, or imprisoned indefinitely.

But I was becoming tired of the work here now that everything was running smoothly. I was tired of trying to keep dry in the perpetual rain, tired of waiting to be overtaken by ice. Day by day the ice was creeping over the curve of the earth, unimpeded by seas or mountains. Without haste or pause, it was steadily moving nearer, entering and flattening cities, filling craters from which boiling lava had poured. There was no way of stopping the icy giant battalions, marching in relentless order across the world, crushing, obliterating, destroying everything in their path.

I made up my mind to go. Without telling anyone, in the drenching rain, I drove to the blocked pass, and from there found my way over the tree-covered mountains on foot. I had only a pocket compass to guide me. It took me several hours of climbing and struggling through wet vegetation to reach the frontier station, where I was detained by the guard.

nine

I asked to be taken to the warden. He had lately moved his headquarters to a different town. An armoured car drove me there; two soldiers with sub-machine-guns came too, 'for my protection'. It was still raining. We crashed through the downpour under heavy black clouds which shut out the last of the day. Darkness was falling as we entered the town. The headlights showed the familiar scene of havoc, rubble, ruins, blank spaces, all glistening in rain. The streets were full of troops. The least damaged buildings were used as barracks.

I was taken into a heavily guarded place and left in a small room where two men were waiting. The three of us were alone: they stared at me, but said nothing. We waited in silence. There was only the sound of the rain beating down outside. They sat together on one bench; I, wrapped in my coat, on another. That was all the furniture in the room, which had not been cleaned. Thick dust lay over everything.

After a while they began to converse in whispers. I gathered that they had come about some post that was vacant. I stood up, started pacing backwards and forwards. I was restless, but knew I should have to wait. I was not listening to what the others were saying, but one raised his voice so that I had to hear. He was certain that he would get the job. He boasted: 'I've been trained to kill with my hands. I can kill the strongest man with three fingers. I've learnt the points in the body where you can kill easily. I can break a block of wood with the side of my hand.' His words depressed me. This was the kind of man who was wanted now. The two were presently called to an interview and I was left waiting alone. I was prepared to have to wait a long time.

It was not so long before a guard came to conduct me to the officers' mess. The warden was sitting at the head of the high table. Other long tables were more crowded. I was to sit at his table, but not near him, at the far end. We should be too far apart to talk comfortably. Before taking my seat, I went up to salute him. He looked surprised and did not return my greeting. I noticed all the men sitting around immediately leaned together and began speaking in undertones, glancing furtively at me. I seemed to have made an unfavourable impression. I had assumed he would remember me, but he appeared not to know who I was. To remind him of our former connexion might make things worse, so I sat down in my distant place.

I could hear him talking amiably to the officers near him. Their conversation was of arrests and escapes. I was not interested until he told the story of his own flight, involving a big car, a snowstorm, crashing frontier gates, bullets, a girl. He never once looked in my direction or took any notice of me.

From time to time troops could be heard marching past outside. Suddenly there was an explosion. Part of the ceiling collapsed and the lights went out. Hurricane lamps were brought and put on the table. They showed fragments of plaster lying among the dishes. The food was ruined, uneatable, covered in dust and debris. It was

taken away. A long and tedious wait followed; then finally bowls of
hard-boiled eggs were put down in front of us. Intermittent
explosions continued to shake the building, a haze of whitish dust
hung in the air, everything was gritty to the touch.

The warden was playing a game of surprising me. He beckoned
at the end of the meal. 'I enjoyed your broadcasts. You have a gift
for that sort of thing.' I was astonished that he knew of the work I
had been doing. His voice was friendly, he spoke to me as an equal,
and just for a moment, I felt identified with him in an obscure sort
of intimacy. He went on to say I had timed my arrival well. 'Our
transmitter will soon be in operation, and yours will be put out of
action.' I had always told the authorities we needed a more powerful
installation; that it was only a question of time before the existing
apparatus was jammed by a stronger one. He assumed that I had
heard this was about to happen, and had defected accordingly. He
wanted me to broadcast propaganda for him, which I agreed to do,
if he would do something for me. 'Still the same thing?' 'Yes.' He
looked at me in amusement, but suspicion flashed in his eyes.
Nevertheless he remarked casually, 'Her room's on the floor above;
we may as well pay her a visit,' and led the way out. But when I said,
'I have to deliver a personal message; could I see her alone?' he did
not reply.

We went down one passage, up some stairs and along another.
The beam of his powerful torch played on floors littered with
rubbish. Footprints showed in the dust; I looked among them for
her smaller prints. He opened a door into a dimly lit room. She
jumped up. Her white startled face; big eyes staring at me under
glittering hair. 'You again!' She stood rigid, held the chair in front
of her as for protection, hands clenched on the back, knuckles
standing out white. 'What do you want?' 'Only to talk to you.'
Looking from one of us to the other, she accused: 'You're in league
together.' I denied it: though in a strange way there seemed to be
some truth in the charge . . . 'Of course you are. He wouldn't bring
you here otherwise.'

The warden approached her, smiling. I had never seen him look
so benevolent. 'Come now, that's not a very kind way to greet an old
friend. Can't we all have a friendly talk? You've never told me how
you first got to know each other.' It was clear that he had no

intention of leaving us alone. I gazed at her silently, could not talk to her in front of him. His personality was too dominant, his influence too strong. In his presence she was frightened, antagonistic. Barriers were created. I was distracted myself. No wonder he smiled. I might as well not have found her. A distant explosion shook the walls; she watched the white dust float down from the ceiling. For the sake of saying something, I asked if the bombing disturbed her. Her face blank, her bright hair shimmering, she silently moved her head in a way that meant anything, nothing.

The warden said: 'I've tried to persuade her to go to a safer place, but she refuses to leave.' He smiled complacently, showing me his power over her. I found it hard to accept. I looked round the room: the chair, a small mirror, a bed, paperbacks on the table, dust everywhere, fallen plaster thick on the floor. Her grey loden coat hung from a hook. I saw no other personal belongings except a comb and a square of chocolate in torn silver paper. I turned away from the man and addressed her directly, trying to speak as if he was not there. 'You don't seem very comfortable here. Why not go to a hotel, somewhere farther away from the fighting?' She did not answer, shrugged her shoulders slightly. A silence followed.

Troops marched past under the window. He went across, opened the shutters a crack and looked down. I muttered hurriedly, 'I only want to help you,' moved my hand towards hers, which was snatched back. 'I don't trust you. I don't believe a word you say.' Her eyes were wide and defiant. I knew I would never succeed in making contact with her while he was in the room. Nothing was to be gained by staying longer. I left.

Outside the door, I heard his laugh, his step on the floorboards, his voice: 'What have you got against that one?' Then her voice, changed, blurred with tears, high-pitched, hysterical. 'He's a liar. I know he's working with you. You're both the same, selfish, treacherous, cruel. I wish I'd never met either of you, I hate you both! One day I'll go . . . you won't see me again . . . ever!' I walked on down the passage, stumbling over the rubble, kicking it aside. I had not thought of providing myself with a torch.

For the next few days I considered taking her away from him to a neutral country. Theoretically it was quite possible. Occasionally ships still called at the local port. It was a matter of speed, secrecy and exact timing. Success depended on getting to sea before we were followed. I began making cautious enquiries. The answers could be bought. The difficulty was that no one could be trusted. The person I was paying for information might sell my questions to somebody in the warden's pay. This made the whole thing highly dangerous. I was nervous; I could not afford to take such risks; nevertheless, the risk had to be run.

Voices whispered secrets: names, addresses, destinations, departures. 'Go to ... ask for ... hold yourself in instant readiness ... documents ... proof ... ample funds ...' I needed to speak to her before taking my plans a stage further. I went to her room, heard a shot, paid no attention; shooting was going on in the streets all the time. The man emerged, shut the door behind him. I said I wanted to see her. 'You can't.' He turned the key, dropped it into his pocket, threw a pistol down on the table. 'She's dead.' A knife went through me. All other deaths in the world were outside; this one was in my body, like a bayonet, like my own. 'Who killed her?' Only I could do that. When he said, 'I did,' my hand moved, touched the gun, the barrel was hot. I could have seized it and shot him. It would have been easy. He made no move to prevent me, stood motionless, gazing at me. I looked back at him, at his face with its arrogant bone structure; our eyes met.

In an indescribable way our looks tangled together. I seemed to be looking at my own reflection. Suddenly I was entangled in utmost confusion, not sure which of us was which. We were like halves of one being, joined in some mysterious symbiosis. I fought to retain my identity, but all my efforts failed to keep us apart. I continually found I was not myself, but him. At one moment I actually seemed to be wearing his clothes. I fled from the room in utter confusion; afterwards did not know what had happened, or if anything had.

On another occasion he met me at the door of the room, said at once: 'You're too late. The bird's flown.' He was grinning, his face wore an expression of naked malice. 'She's gone. Run away. Disappeared.' My fists clenched. 'You sent her away so that I shouldn't see her. You've deliberately kept us apart.' I started towards him in fury. Then again our looks tangled, confusion came back; a wider confusion, not of identity only, but also of time and place. Cold blue eyes flashing, the blue flash of a ring, curved cold strangler's fingers. He had fought bears and strangled them with his hands. Physically I was no match ... As I left, I heard his voice jeering: 'That's more sensible.'

I went into an empty room. I needed time in which to collect myself. I was disturbed, I longed for the girl, could not bear to have lost her. I thought of the journey I had been planning with her beside me, which would now never take place. My face was wet as with rain, drops ran down into my mouth, tasted salt. I covered my eyes with my handkerchief, brought myself under control by a violent effort.

I should have to start searching for her all over again. The repetition was like a curse. I thought of placid blue seas, tranquil islands, far away from war. I thought of the Indris, those happy creatures, symbols of life in peace, on a higher plane. I could clear out, go to them. No, that was impossible. I was tied to her. I thought of the ice moving across the world, casting its shadow of creeping death. Ice-cliffs boomed in my dreams, indescribable explosions thundered and boomed, icebergs crashed, hurled huge boulders into the sky like rockets. Dazzling ice stars bombarded the world with rays, which splintered and penetrated the earth, filling earth's core with their deadly coldness, reinforcing the cold of the advancing ice. And always, on the surface, the indestructible ice-mass was moving forward, implacably destroying all life. I felt a fearful sense of pressure and urgency, there was no time to lose, I was wasting time; it was a race between me and the ice. Her albino hair illuminated my dreams, shining brighter than moonlight. I saw the dead moon dance over the icebergs, as it would at the end of our world, while she watched from the tent of her glittering hair.

I dreamed of her whether I was asleep or awake. I heard her cry: 'One day I'll go ... you won't see me again ...' She had gone from me already. She had escaped. She hurried along a street in an unknown town. She looked different, less anxious, more confident. She knew exactly where she was going, she did not hesitate once. In a huge official building she made straight for a room so crowded she could hardly open the door. Only her extreme slimness enabled her to slip between the many tall silent figures, unnaturally silent, fantastically tall, whose faces were all averted from her. Her anxiety started to come back when she saw them towering over her, surrounding her like dark trees. She felt small and lost among them, quickly became afraid. Her confidence had vanished; it had never been real. Now she only wanted to escape from that place: her eyes darted from side to side, saw no door, no way out. She was trapped. The faceless black tree-forms pressed closer, extended arm-branches, imprisoning her. She looked down, but was still imprisoned. Filled trouser-legs, solid treetrunks, stood all around. The floor had become dark earth, full of roots and boles. Quickly looking up at the window, she saw only white weaving meshes of snow, shutting out the world. The known world excluded, reality blotted out, she was alone with threatening nightmare shapes of trees or phantoms, tall as firs growing in snow.

Global conditions were worsening. There was no sign of destruction coming to a halt, and its inexorable progress induced general demoralization. It was more impossible than ever to find out what was really happening, impossible to know what to believe. No reliable source of information existed. Very little news of any description came from abroad; none whatsoever from once-prominent states which had simply dropped out of existence. More than any other single factor, it was the implacable spread of these unnerving areas of total silence that undermined public morale.

In certain countries civil unrest had resulted in the army taking command. A world-wide swing towards militarism had taken place during recent months, with deplorable and brutalizing effects. Frequent clashes occurred between civilians and the armed forces. The killing of police and soldiers, with retributory executions, had become commonplace.

As was to be expected, in the absence of any genuine news, fantastic rumours kept circulating. Monstrous epidemics, appalling famines, were said to have broken out in remote districts, fearsome deviations to have occurred from the genetic norm. Stocks of thermonuclear weapons, previously supposed to have been destroyed, were periodically reported to be in possession of this or that power. Persistent rumours concerned the existence of a self-detonating cobalt bomb, timed, at a pre-set, unknown moment, to destroy all life, while leaving inanimate objects intact. Spying and counter-spying went on everywhere. There were growing acute shortages in all countries, food riots followed as a matter of course. The lawless element in the population was much in evidence, decent people were terrorized. The death penalty imposed for looting had little or no effect as a deterrent.

I got news of the girl indirectly. She was alive, in a certain town, in another country. I was almost sure the place was in the area of immediate danger, though there was no means of checking the point, since all reference to the advancing ice was forbidden. By intense persistence and extensive bribery, I managed to board a ship travelling in that direction. The captain wanted to make money fast, and for a large sum agreed to put in at the port I named.

We arrived. It was early morning, unbelievably cold, dark when it should have been light. No sky, no clouds, they were hidden by falling snow. It was not a morning like other mornings, but what it was: an unnatural freezing of day into darkness, spring into arctic winter. I went to say goodbye to the captain, who asked if I had changed my mind about going ashore. I said I had not. 'Then for God's sake get going. Don't keep us hanging about.' He was angry, antagonistic. We parted without more words.

I went on deck with the first officer. The air stung like acid. It was the breath of ice, of the polar regions, almost unbreathable. It scarified the skin, seared the lungs; but the body quickly adjusted itself to this stringency. The density of the snow created a curious foglike gloom in the upper air. Everything was obscured by the small flakes falling ceaselessly out of the shrouded sky. The cold scalded my hands when I collided with iced-up parts of the ship's superstructure, which only became visible when it was too late to avoid them. In the silence I noted a rhythmic vibration below, and spoke to my escort: 'The engines; they haven't stopped.' For some reason it seemed surprising. 'You bet they haven't. The skipper can't wait to turn the ship round. He's been cursing you for days for making us put in here.' The man showed the same antagonism as the captain, plus a disagreeable curiosity which came out now. 'Why the devil *have* you come, anyhow?' 'That's my business.' In unfriendly silence we reached the rail. It was cased in thick ice, a rope ladder dangling from it towards the sound of a motor running below. Before I had time to look down, he swung his leg over. 'Harbour's frozen. We've got to put you ashore by launch.' While

he quickly descended with practised ease, I followed more awkwardly, clinging on with both hands, blinded by the snow. I did
not see who pulled me into the rocking launch, or who pushed me
towards a seat, as it immediately shot forward. Travelling at full
speed, it plunged and reared continually like a bucking horse,
sheets of spray flew over the roof of the little cabin. There was too
much noise for voices to be audible; but I could feel the almost
murderous hostility of those on board, all hating me for keeping
them here in danger when they might have been on the way to
safety. To them my behaviour must have seemed perverse and
utterly senseless. I began to wonder myself whether it made any
sense, sitting huddled up in my coat, in the brutal paralysing cold.

A sudden long-drawn-out yell startled me; it was really more of
a howl. The officer jumped up, shouted back through a mega-
phone, then resumed his seat with the words: 'One-way traffic.'
Seeing that I did not understand, he added, 'Plenty going the
other way,' and pointed ahead.

A confused indistinct commotion revealed itself as a ship,
motionless in the midst of the feverish activity of small boats
seething round it. In frantic competition, they fought to get near
enough for their occupants to climb aboard. There was not room
for all. Spectators crowded the rails of the ship as if at a race
course, watching the collisions and capsizings below. Those in the
boats had probably lived easily and been unaccustomed to danger,
for they battled clumsily for their lives, with a sort of headlong
terror, wasting their strength in useless jostling and surging. One
boat floated upside down, surrounded by frenzied hands and arms
struggling out of the water. The people in the next boat swarmed
over it, hit out, kicked, stamped on the clinging hands, beat off the
drowning. Even the most powerful swimmer could not survive
long in that freezing sea. Several of the overcrowded, unskilfully
handled boats turned over and sank. Some broke up after col-
liding. In those that remained afloat, the passengers crushed and
trampled each other in senseless panic, drove off clutching swim-
mers with oars. People already dying were battered and beaten.
The muffled uproar of screams, thuds, splashes continued long
after the scene was hidden behind the snow. I recalled polite
voices announcing over the air that people were desperate, fighting

to get away from the threatened countries to safer regions.

The frozen harbour was a grey-white expanse, dotted with black abandoned hulks, embedded immovably in the ice. Banks of solid ice edged the narrow channel of blackish water, fringed with grinning icicle-teeth. I jumped ashore, snow blew out in great fans, the launch disappeared from sight. There were no goodbyes.

ten

It could have been any town, in any country. I recognized nothing. Snow covered all landmarks with the same white padding. Buildings were changed into anonymous white cliffs.

A confused disturbance, shouts, the noise of wood splintering and glass breaking came from one of the streets where looting was going on. A crowd had broken into the shops. They had no leader, no fixed objective. They were just a disorderly mob surging about in search of excitement and booty, frightened, hungry, hysterical, violent. They kept fighting among themselves, picking up anything that could be used as a weapon, snatching each other's spoils, taking possession of all they could lay hands on, even the most useless objects, then dropping them and running after some other plunder. What they could not take away they destroyed. They had a senseless mania for destruction, for tearing to shreds, smashing to smithereens, trampling underfoot.

A senior army officer appeared in the street and blew a whistle to summon the police. Striding towards the looters, he shouted orders in a fierce military voice, blew repeated blasts on the whistle. His face was dark with rage, framed by the astrakhan collar of his fine overcoat. The main mass of the crowd fled at the sight of him. But some, bolder than the rest, stayed skulking among the wreckage. Furious, he strode towards them, threatened them with his cane, shouted to them to clear off, swore at them. They took no notice at first; then formed a rough circle, rushed at him from several points simultaneously, in groups of three or four together. He pulled out his revolver, fired it over their heads. A mistake: he should have fired at them. They swarmed round him, trying to snatch the weapon. The police were a long time coming. There was a scuffle. In the course of it, either by accident or intention, the gun was dropped through a grating. Its owner was a man in the late fifties, tall, vigorous. But I could see him panting. They were young toughs with faces of a sinister blankness. They attacked cunningly, with bits of metal and broken glass, pieces of smashed furniture, whatever came to hand. He fended them off with his cane, keeping his back to a wall. Their numbers and their persistence were gradually wearing him down; his movements were getting slower. A stone was thrown. Then a shower of stones. One of them knocked his cap off. The sight of his hairless skull produced ribald shouting, and for a second he seemed disconcerted. They took advantage of this, closed in, set on him like a pack of wolves. Blood trickling down his face, back to the wall, he still managed to fight them off. Then I saw something flash; someone had used a knife. Others followed suit. He clutched his chest, blindly staggered forward. The moment he left the wall he was done for, they were on him from every side. They knocked him down, sprang on top of him, tore his coat off, beat his head on the frozen ground, stamped on him, kicked him, slashed his face with chains. Finally he lay still on the snow. He had had absolutely no chance. It was murder.

It was not my affair, but I could not see it and stand there doing nothing. They were society's dregs, they would never have dared come near him in normal times, far less touch him. A little jeering fellow had draped himself in the fine overcoat and was dancing about, tripping over the trailing hem. I was disgusted, furious. In uncontrollable fury I charged at him, stripped off the coat, twisted his arms, punched and pummelled him, slung him across the pavement, heard a satisfactory crunch when his screaming face hit the wall. Turning, I confronted a man twice his size, half saw a boot flick out. Acute pain in my leg made me stumble: I recovered just in time to see his arm swing up in a practised curve, and reacted as I had been trained. A textbook fall; flat on my back, one foot locking his ankle, I caught the glint of the falling knife, as my other leg bashed the trapped kneecap until it cracked. In a moment I would have the entire crew swarming all over me. I had no more chance than the officer against the lot of them with their knives; but I meant to do some damage before they finished me off. Suddenly there were shots, shouts, the sound of running feet: the police had arrived at last. I watched them chase the looters round a corner into another street; then limped over to the man on the ground.

He lay on his back, bleeding from many wounds. Not much past the prime of life, he had looked impressive, a tall, vital, imposing man, still desirable physically. Now his nose had been flattened, his mouth slit at the corners, one eye was half out of its socket, his whole face and head discoloured with blood and dirt, the shapes lost and distorted. Blood was everywhere. They had almost torn off his right arm. He did not move. I could not see his breathing. I knelt down, opened his tunic, his shirt, put my hand on his chest. The heart was not to be felt, and my hand came out sticky with blood. I wiped it on my handkerchief, then went for his coat, spread it over him, hiding the mess. I wanted to leave him some dignity. He was a stranger to whom I had never spoken; but he was my sort of man; we were not like that rabble. It was an outrage that they should have killed him. They must have cringed before him in his strength and power. This was how they treated him when they caught him alone, no longer young, and at a disadvantage. It was disgusting. I regretted not having inflicted more punishment on them.

I remembered the revolver, stooped over the grating. There was just room for my fingers between the bars, and I pulled it up, put it into my pocket, moved on. I was still limping badly, my leg was painful. Suddenly someone shouted, a shot zipped past. I stopped, waited until the police overtook me.

'Who are you? What are you doing here? Why did you touch the body? It's not allowed.' Before I could answer, there was a rasping noise and a ground floor window burst open, dislodging masses of snow from the sill, a woman's head stuck out just beside me. 'This man's brave. He deserves a medal. I saw what happened. He rushed in and tackled the lot of them singlehanded, although they had knives and he was unarmed. I saw everything from this window.' A policeman wrote down her name and address in his notebook.

Their attitude became more friendly; but they insisted that I should go to the station and make a report. One of them took my arm. 'It's only in the next street. You look as if you could do with some first aid.' I had to go in. It was unfortunate: I did not want to give an account of myself and my movements and motives. Besides, the revolver would make things awkward if it was noticed; they were bound to recognize the service pattern. When I took off my coat, I arranged it carefully so that the bulge did not show. They patched me up, strapped my leg with plaster. I had a wash, drank some strong coffee with rum in it. The chief interviewed me alone. He glanced at my papers, but gave the impression of being preoccupied with something else: it was not possible to ask if he had any precise information about the advancing ice. We exchanged cigarettes, discussed the food problem. He said rations were short, and distributed according to the value to the community of each individual's work: 'No work, no food.' His face showed signs of strain while he was talking; the crisis must be nearer than I had supposed. Planning my questions deliberately, I asked about refugees. Gangs of starving fugitives from the ice were a problem in all the surviving countries. 'If they're able to work we let them stay. We need all the workers we can get.' I said: 'Doesn't that create difficulties? How do you manage to house them all?' 'There are camps for the men. We put the women in hostels.' I had been leading up to this point. Pretending to take a professional interest, I enquired: 'Would I be allowed to look over one of these places?' 'Why not?' His smile was tired. I could not tell whether he was exceptionally civilized or merely indifferent. Before I left he gave me an address. Things had turned out very much better than I had expected. I had got the information I wanted, and a good army revolver.

I went to look for her. It was snowing again, the wind was colder and stronger. The streets were deserted, there was nobody to direct me. I thought I had found the house, but saw no sign. Perhaps I was too late: through an unaccountable failure of impulse had waited too long ... I tried the street doors as I passed them; they were all locked.

The door of one house was unfastened. I entered without hesitation. Inside, the place was bare and shabby, had the look of an institution. The rooms were unheated. She sat wearing her grey overcoat, her legs wrapped in something that looked like a curtain. As soon as she saw me she threw this aside and sprang up. 'You! I suppose he sent you – didn't you get my message?' 'No one sent me.

What message?' 'I left a message telling you not to follow me.' I said I had not received it, but if I had it would have made no difference, I should have come just the same. Her big distrustful eyes gazed at me, indignant and frightened. 'I don't want anything to do with either of you.' I ignored this. 'You can't stay here alone.' 'Why not? I'm getting on all right.' I asked what she was doing. 'Working.' 'How much do they pay you?' 'We get our food.' 'No money?' 'Sometimes people are given money when they've worked specially hard.' Defensively she went on: 'I'm too thin for the really hard jobs. They say I haven't got enough stamina.' I had been watching her: she looked half-starved, as if for some time she had not had enough to eat. Her thin wrists had always fascinated me; now I could scarcely take my eyes off them, emerging like sticks from the heavy sleeves. Instead of enquiring into the nature of the work she was doing, I asked her plans for the future. When she snapped 'Why should I tell you?' I knew that she had no plans. I said I very much wished she would look on me as a friend. 'Why, I've no reason to. Anyhow, I don't need friends. I can manage alone.' I told her I had come hoping to take her away with me to a place where life would be easier, somewhere in a better climate. I felt her beginning to weaken, waved my hand at the window covered in heavy frost, snow banked on the sill to half its whole height. 'Haven't you had enough of the cold?' She could no longer hide her nervousness, her hands twisted together. I added: 'Besides, you're in the danger zone here.' Her face was starting to have its bruised look, she was gradually losing control. 'What danger?' The pupils of her eyes dilated as I watched her. 'The ice . . .' I meant to say more, but the two words were sufficient. Her whole appearance indicated fear, she began to tremble.

I moved closer to her, touched her hand. She jerked it away. 'Don't do that!' I held a fold of her coat, looked at her angry, frightened face of a child betrayed, the look of faint bruising around the eyes like a child that has cried a long time. 'Leave me alone!' She tried to drag the heavy material out of my hand. 'Go away!' I did not move. 'Then I'll go!' She tore herself free, dashed to the door, threw her whole weight against it. It crashed open so violently that she lost her balance and fell. The bright hair spread on the floor, quicksilver, brilliant, stirring, alive, on the dark, dull, dead, dirty floor. I picked her up. She struggled, gasped: 'Let me go! I hate you, I hate you!' She had no strength at all. It was like holding a struggling kitten. I shut the door and turned the key in the lock.

I waited a few days although waiting was difficult. It was time to go. It was only a matter of hours before a disaster of the greatest magnitude. In spite of the secrecy which enveloped the subject, news must have leaked out. Agitated activity suddenly spread through the town. From my window I watched a young man running from house to house, delivering a message of terror. In an astonishingly short time, minutes only, the street was full of people carrying bags and bundles. Disorganized, and showing every sign of acute fear, they set off in great haste, some going one way and some another. They seemed to have no definite destination or plan, just the one overwhelming urge to fly from the town. I was surprised that the authorities took no action. Presumably they had failed to evolve a workable scheme for evacuation, so simply decided to let things take their course. The chaotic exodus was disturbing to watch. Everybody seemed on the verge of panic. People clearly thought I was mad to sit in a bar instead of preparing for flight. Their fears were infectious; the atmosphere of impending catastrophe made me uneasy, and I was thankful to get the message I was expecting. A ship was about to anchor outside the harbour, somewhere beyond the ice. It was the last one that would call, and it would stay at anchor for one hour only.

I went to the girl, told her this was our last chance, and that she had to come. She refused, refused to stand up. 'I'm not going anywhere with you. I don't trust you. I shall stay here where I'm free.' 'Free for what? To starve? To be frozen to death?' I lifted her off the chair bodily, stood her on her feet. 'I won't go – you can't force me.' She backed away, wide eyed, and stood against the wall, waiting for someone or something to rescue her. I lost patience, dragged her out of the building, went on holding her arm; I had to pull her along.

It was snowing so hard I could barely see to the other side of the street; a stark, white, deathly, pre-polar scene. The arctic wind drove floods of snow past us like feathers. Walking was difficult, the wind slammed the snow in our faces, hurled it at us from different sides, whirled it round us in crazy spirals. Everything was muffled, blurred, indistinct, not a person to be seen. Then suddenly six mounted policemen rode out of the blizzard, hooves soundless and bridles jingling. The girl cried, 'Help!' when she saw them. She thought they would save her, tried to struggle free, made an imploring gesture with her free hand. I held on to her tight, kept her close beside me. The men laughed and whistled at us as they passed, disappearing in the blowing white. She burst into tears.

I heard a bell ringing, slowly coming nearer. An old priest shuffled round the corner, black cowled, bent double against the storm, leading a rabble of people. The bell was the sort used to call children from the playground; as he walked, he kept ringing it feebly. When his arm tired, he gave it a brief rest, calling out in a quavering voice: 'Sauve qui peut!' Some of his followers took up the cry, chanting it like a dirge: one or two paused long enough to bang on the doors they were passing. From some of the houses muffled figures crept out to join them. I wondered where they were going; it did not look as if they would get very far. They were all old and infirm, decrepit. The young and able-bodied had left them behind. They moved with weak tottering steps in a slow, shambling procession, their movements uncoordinated, their faded faces reddened by the blast.

The girl kept stumbling in the deep snow. I had to half carry her, although I could hardly breathe. The frost tore my breath away, tried to stop me breathing; my breath froze in icicles on my collar. The frozen mucous membranes plugged my nose with ice. Each time I took a mouthful of polar air I coughed and gasped. It seemed hours before we got to the harbour. She renewed her feeble struggles at the sight of the boat, cried 'You can't do this to me . . .' I pushed her in, jumped in after her, seized the oars, shoved off, started rowing with all my might.

Voices screamed after us, but I ignored them; she was my one concern. The open channel had narrowed considerably, its edges frozen; soon it would be solid ice. Extraordinarily loud, long cracks, like shots, like thunderclaps, came from the thickening ice of the harbour. My face felt raw, my hands were blue and burning with cold, but I kept on rowing towards the ship, through the churning white of the blizzard, through flying spray, booming ice, shrieks, crashes, blood. A small boat foundered beside us, the water seethed with frantically lashing limbs. Desperate drowning fingers clawed at the gunwale; I beat them off. A pair of lovers floated past, locked together by frozen arms, rocking and rolling deliriously in the waves. Suddenly the boat gave a violent lurch; I swung round, pulling out my revolver. I knew what had happened. Behind my back a man had climbed over the side. I fired, thrust him into the water again, watched it turn red. The ship's side loomed steep as a cliff above us, the companion-ladder only reached to my shoulder.

Somehow or other, by a colossal effort, I managed to hoist the girl on to the wooden steps, climbed up after her, pushed her up to the deck. We were allowed to stay. No one else came aboard. The ship started moving immediately. It was a triumph.

We travelled on, changing from ship to ship. She could not stand the intense cold, she shivered continually, broke in pieces like a venetian glass. The disintegration could be observed. She grew thinner and paler, more transparent, ghostlike. It was interesting to watch. She did not move more than was absolutely essential. Her limbs seemed too brittle for use. The seasons ceased to exist, replaced by perpetual cold. Ice walls loomed and thundered, smooth, shining, unearthly, a glacial nightmare; the light of day lost in eerie, iceberg-glittering mirage-light. With one arm I warmed and supported her: the other arm was the executioner's.

The cold abated slightly. We went ashore to wait for a different ship. The country had been at war, the town had suffered severe damage. There was no accommodation available; only one hotel was being rebuilt, only one floor was finished, every habitable room occupied. I could not persuade or bribe anybody to take us in. Travellers were disliked and discouraged: it was natural, in the circumstances. We were told we could stay at some sort of centre for strangers outside the town, drove there through the ruined suburbs, everything flattened, no trace of trees or gardens remaining, nothing left standing upright. The country beyond had been a battlefield and was now a desert, covered in shapeless rubbish.

We were deposited at a place which had been a farm. All around was indescribable chaos. Bits of broken carts, tractors, cars, implements, lay about, bits of old tyres, bits of unrecognizable tools, all mixed up with the debris of shattered weapons and war supplies.

Our escort walked cautiously, told us to look out for mines, unexploded bombs. Inside, the rooms were littered with fragments of all kinds of rubbish, too smashed to identify. They took us to a room with an earth floor and no furniture, holes in the walls, roof roughly boarded over, where three people sat on the ground propped against the wall. They were silent, unmoving, hardly seemed alive, took no notice when I spoke to them. I learnt later that they were deaf, their eardrums had burst. There were many in the same state all over the country, their faces ripped and lips torn by the same deadly wind. A desperately sick man lay on the floor under a thin blanket. Great tufts of his hair had fallen out, strips of skin hung from his hands and face, his loose teeth rattled in black bleeding gums every time he coughed, he never stopped coughing and groaning and spitting blood. Emaciated cats wandered in and out, licked the blood with delicate pointed pink tongues.

We had to stop there until the ship came. I longed for something to focus my eyes on, there was nothing inside or out; no fields, houses, or roads; only vast quantities of stones, rubbish, the bones of dead animals. Stones of all shapes and sizes were spread thick all over the ground to a depth of two or three feet, often piled up in enormous mounds, which took the place of hills in a normal landscape. I managed to obtain a horse and rode ten miles inland, but the awful featureless scene did not change, the same derelict stony waste extended to the horizon in every direction, no sign of life or water. The whole country seemed stone dead, grey in colour, no hills except hills of stones, even its natural contours destroyed by war.

The girl was exhausted, worn out by travel: she did not want to go on. She kept saying that she must rest, begged me to leave her and continue the voyage alone. 'Don't drag me any farther!' Her voice was fretful. 'You only do it to torture me.' I replied that I was trying to save her. Anger showed in her eyes. 'That's what you say. I was fool enough to believe you the first time.' In spite of all attempts to please her, she persisted in treating me as a treacherous enemy. Hitherto I had tried to comfort, to understand. Now her protracted antagonism had its effect, I followed her into the tiny cabin. She struggled, there was no room, the boat rolled, she fell from the berth, her shoulders struck the floor and the soft flesh was hurt. She cried, 'You're a brute! A beast! I detest you!' tried to hit me, to struggle up; but I forced her under, forced her to stay down in that hard cold place. She cried out, 'I wish I could kill you!' began to sob and struggle hysterically. I slapped the side of her face.

She was afraid of me, but her hostility continued unchanged. Her white, stubborn, frightened child's face got on my nerves. She was still always cold, although the days were gradually getting warmer. She refused my coat. I was obliged to watch her incessant shivering.

She grew emaciated, the flesh seemed to melt off her bones. Her hair lost its glitter, was too heavy, weighed her head down. She kept her head bent, trying not to see me. Listless, she hid in corners or, avoiding me, staggered round the ship, stumbling, her weak legs unable to balance. I no longer felt any desire, gave up talking to her, adopted the warden's silences as my own. I was well aware how sinister my wordless exits and entrances must have seemed, and derived some satisfaction from this.

We were near the end of the journey.

eleven

The gay, undamaged town, full of light and colour, freedom, the absence of danger, the warm sun. The faces were happy. The sense of escape brought euphoria. The past was forgotten, the long, hard, dangerous voyage and the preceding nightmare. Nothing but the nightmare had seemed real while it was going on, as if the other lost world had been imagined or dreamed. Now that world, no longer lost, was here the one solid reality. There were theatres, cinemas, restaurants and hotels, shops where goods of all sorts were sold freely, without coupons. The contrast was staggering. The relief overwhelming. The reaction too great. A kind of delirium was induced, a mad gaiety. People sang and danced in the streets, strangers embraced one another. The whole town was decorated as for a festival: flowers everywhere, chinese lanterns and fairy lights strung from trees, buildings floodlit, elaborate arrangements of coloured lights in the parks and gardens. The throb of dance music never stopped. Every night firework displays. All night long fiery stars and rockets burst in the sky, and sank reflected in the dark harbour. The festivities went on and on: carnivals, battles of flowers, balls, regattas, concerts, processions. Nobody wanted to be reminded of what was happening in other parts of the world. Rumours coming from outside were suppressed by order of the consul, who had assumed responsibility for the maintenance of law and order, 'pending the restoration of the status quo'. To speak of the catastrophe was an offence under the new regulations. The rule was to choose not to know.

Remembering how I myself had wished to forget on another occasion, I understood the euphoric blindness without condoning it. I did not take part in the general rejoicing; I did not feel gay. I had no wish to spend my time dancing or looking at fireworks. Very soon I was utterly sick of bands playing and people in fancy dress. The girl loved all the gaiety, was absolutely transformed by it, her life miraculously renewed. Her weakness and lassitude vanished, she rushed to the shops, bought clothes and cosmetics extravagantly, visited hairdressers, beauty parlours. She seemed a different person. No longer shy, she made friends with people I did not know, drew confidence from their approval, became independent and gay. I scarcely saw anything of her; most of the time I had no idea where she was. She came to me only when she needed money, which I always gave her. For me it was an unsatisfactory situation. I wanted to end it.

I could not remain isolated from the rest of the world. I was involved with the fate of the planet. I had to take an active part in whatever was going on. The endless celebrations here seemed both boring and sinister, reminiscent of the orgies of the plague years. Now, as then, people were deluding themselves; they induced a false sense of security by means of self-indulgence and wishful thinking. I did not believe for one moment they had really escaped.

I observed the weather carefully; it was fine and warm, but not warm enough. I noted particularly how the temperature fell after sunset, producing a definite chill. It was a bad sign. If I mentioned it, I was told this was the cool season. All the same, the sun should have had more power. Looking about, I found other signs of changing climate. Plants in the tropical gardens were starting to look unhealthy, and I asked a man working there why this was. He gave me a suspicious glance, mumbled an evasive answer: when I persisted, he pretended to hear the head gardener calling, and ran away. I commented on the chilly evenings to some townspeople I saw going about in peculiar wrappings. They were obviously unused to even this mild degree of cold, and possessed no suitable clothing. They too answered evasively and looked at me in alarm. In view of the new regulations, they probably took me for an agent provocateur.

An acquaintance of mine, employed in an official capacity by his government, stopped to refuel his plane. I made contact with him, questioned him about events elsewhere. He was uncommunicative. I understood the reason and did not press him. He could not be certain of my affiliations. Mistakes were not tolerated. An absolute standard of loyalty was demanded. The speaker of an incautious phrase would be eliminated, given no chance to correct an error of judgement. Somewhat reluctantly, he agreed to take me as a passenger when he left, but only as far as another island in the archipelago. I saw on the map that the island inhabited by the Indris was not far away, and though I had decided to go back to my old profession, I promised myself a short visit to the lemurs before proceeding to the theatre of military operations.

I went to inform the girl of my plans. Earlier in the day, waiting to cross a street, I had been held up while a procession went past. She was at its head, standing beside the driver of a big open car decorated with parma violets. She did not see me, she had no reason to look. Her hair shone like pale fire in the sun, she was smiling and throwing violets to the crowd. It was hard to recognize her as the girl who had travelled with me. When I entered her room, she was still wearing the same parma violet dress; the delicate colour suited her fragile paleness, she looked extremely attractive. Her sparkling hair, sprinkled with silver and parma violets, had been touched with a matching dye; the slight touch of fantasy was especially charming.

Telling her to open it later, I presented her with a small package containing a bracelet she had admired, and a cheque on my personal account. 'I've brought you some good news, too. I've come to say goodbye.' She looked disconcerted, asked what I meant. 'I'm leaving tonight. By plane. Aren't you pleased?' As she only stared silently, I went on: 'You've always wanted to get rid of me. You must be glad I'm going at last.' A pause, then her voice, cold, resentful. 'What do you expect me to say?' I was puzzled by this reaction. She continued to survey me coldly, asked with sudden bitterness: 'What sort of a man do you think you are?' The tone was meant to be scathing. 'Now perhaps you see why I've never trusted you. I always knew you'd betray me again ... go off and leave me, just as you did before.' I protested: 'That's grossly unfair! You can't blame me for going after you've told me to go, made it completely clear that you've no time for me – I've hardly set eyes on you since we got here.' 'Oh ...!' With a disgusted exclamation, she turned her back, took a few steps away from me.

The full skirt swirling, a silky shimmer like moonlight on violets; the bright heavy hair swinging, scintillating with violet highlights. I followed, touched her hair with the tips of my fingers, felt it ripple with life. Her arms had a soft satin sheen, the skin smooth and scented, a chain of violets round the thin wrist. I put my arms round her and kissed her neck. Instantly her whole body tensed up in violent resistance, she twisted herself away. 'Don't touch me! I don't know how you have the nerve ...' Her voice seemed to fail on the edge of tears, then rose again thinly: 'Well, what are you waiting for? Why don't you go? And don't come back this time. I never want to see you again, or be reminded of you!' She pulled off her watch and a ring I had given her, flung them wildly in my direction; began trying to unfasten her necklace, hands at the back of her head, the raised arms giving her slight body a hint of voluptuousness it did not really possess. With an effort I refrained from embracing her again, pleaded with her instead. 'Don't be so angry. Don't let's part like this. You must know how I've felt about you all this time. You know how I've always followed you, forced you to come with me. But you've said so consistently that you hated me, wanted nothing to do with me, that I've finally had to believe you.' I was only being half honest, and knew it. Tentatively I took her hand; it was stiff, unresponsive, but she did not take it away, let me go on holding it while she gazed at me fixedly. With doubt, criticism, accusation her eyes rested ... serious, innocent, shadowed eyes; the hand behind her head still engaged with the necklace; the glittering hair, the scent of violets, close to my hand; then the grave voice . . . 'And if I hadn't said those things, would you have stayed with me?'

This time it seemed important to speak the whole truth: but I could not be certain what that was, and in the end, the only true words seemed to be: 'I don't know.'

Immediately she became furious, tore her hand out of mine; the other hand tugged at the chain round her neck, broke it, beads shot all over the room. 'How can you be so utterly heartless – and so brazen about it! Anyone else would be ashamed . . . but you . . . you don't even pretend to have any feelings . . . it's too horrible, hateful . . . you simply aren't human at all!' I was sorry, I had not wanted to hurt her: I could understand her indignation in a way. There seemed nothing that I could say. My silence enraged her still more. 'Oh, go on! Go away! Go!' She turned on me suddenly, pushed me with a force for which I was unprepared, so that I stumbled back, ran my elbow into the door. It was painful, and I asked in annoyance: 'Why are you so anxious to get me out of the room? Are you expecting somebody else? The owner of the open car you were in?' 'Oh, how I loathe and despise you! If only you knew how much!' She pushed me again. 'Get out, can't you? Go, go, go!' She took a deep breath, lunged at me, started pounding my chest with her fists. But the effort was too much, she abandoned it at once and leant against the wall, her head drooping. I saw that her shadowed face looked bruised by emotion, before the bright hair swung forward, concealing it. There was a brief pause, long enough for me to feel a chilly sensation creep over me; the adumbration of emptiness, loss . . . of what life would be like without her.

Action was needed to drive away this unpleasant feeling. I put my hand on the door knob, and said, 'All right; I'll go now,' half hoping to be detained at the last moment. She did not move or speak, made no sign. Only, as I opened the door, a funny little sound escaped from her throat; a sob, a choke, a cough, I could not tell which. I went out into the passage, walked quickly past all the closed doors, back to my own room.

There was still a little time left. I rang for a bottle of Scotch and sat drinking. I felt uncertain, divided in myself. My bag was already packed and had been taken downstairs. In a few minutes I would have to follow ... unless I changed my plans, stayed here after all ... I remembered that I had not said goodbye, wondered whether to go back, could not make up my mind. I was still undecided when it was time to go.

I had to pass her door again on the way down. I hesitated outside it for a second, then hurried on to the lift. Of course I was leaving. Only a madman would waste this almost miraculous chance of getting away. I could not possibly hope for another.

twelve

The news I heard during the flight confirmed my worst fears. The world situation seemed to be entering its last fatal phase. The elimination of many countries, including my own, left no check on the militarism of the remaining big powers, who confronted each other, the smaller nations dividing allegiance between them. Both principals held stocks of nuclear weapons many times in excess of the overkill stage, so that the balance of terror appeared to be nicely adjusted. But some of the lesser countries also possessed thermo-nuclear devices, though which of them was not known: and this uncertainty, and the resulting tension, provoked escalating crises, each of which brought nearer the final catastrophe. An insane impatience for death was driving mankind to a second suicide, even before the full effect of the first had been felt. I was profoundly depressed, left with a sense of waiting for something frightful to happen, a sort of mass execution.

I looked at the natural world, and it seemed to share my feelings, to be trying in vain to escape its approaching doom. The waves of the sea sped in disorderly flight towards the horizon; the sea birds, the dolphins and flying fish, hurtled frenziedly through the air; the islands trembled and grew transparent, endeavouring to detach themselves, to rise as vapour and vanish in space. But no escape was possible. The defenceless earth could only lie waiting for its destruction, either by avalanches of ice, or by chain-explosions which would go on and on, eventually transforming it into a nebula, its very substance disintegrated.

I went through the jungle alone, searching for the Indris, believing their magic influence might lift the dead weight of depression which had fallen on me. I did not care whether I saw or dreamt them. It was hot, steamy; the mad intensity of the sun pouring down all its force on the equator for the last time. My head was aching, I was exhausted: unable to stand the burning sun any longer, I lay down in black shade, shut my eyes.

At once I felt that the lemurs were near me. Or *was* it their nearness that abolished despair and dread? It seemed more as if I received a message of hope from another world; a world without violence or cruelty, in which despair was unknown. I had often dreamed of this place, where life was a thousand times more exciting and splendid than life on earth. Now one of its inhabitants seemed to stand beside me. He smiled at me, touched my hand, spoke my name. His face was calm and impartial, timelessly intelligent, full of goodwill, impossible to associate with any form of pretence.

He told me about the hallucination of space-time, and the joining of past and future so that either could be the present, and all ages accessible. He said he would take me to his world if I wanted to go. He and others like him had seen the end of our planet, the end of the human race. The race was dying, the collective death-wish, the fatal impulse to self-destruction, though perhaps life might survive. The life here was over. But life was continuing and expanding in a different place. We could be incorporated in this wider life, if we chose.

I tried to understand. He was a man, but seemed more; he was not what I was. He had access to superior knowledge, to some ultimate truth. He was offering me the freedom of his privileged world, a world my inmost self longed to know. I felt the excitement of the unimaginable experience. From the doomed dying world man had ruined, I seemed to catch sight of this other one, new, infinitely alive, and of boundless potential. For a second I believed myself capable of existing on a higher level in that wonderful world; but saw how far it was beyond my powers when I thought of the girl, the warden, the spreading ice, the fighting and killing. I was part of all that, irrevocably involved with events and persons upon this planet. It was heart-breaking to reject what a part of me wanted most. But I knew that my place was here, in our world under sentence of death, and that I would have to stay and see it through to the end.

The dream, the hallucination, or whatever it was, had a powerful effect on me afterwards. I could not forget it, could not forget the supreme intelligence and integrity of that dream-face. I was left with a sense of emptiness, loss, as if something precious really had been in my grasp, and I had thrown it away.

It did not seem to matter what I did now. I was committed to violence and must keep to my pattern. I managed to reach the mainland where the guerrilla fighting was going on, and, indifferent to everything, joined a company of mercenaries in the pay of the west. We fought in the marshes, in the delta of a tidal river with many mouths, thigh-deep in mud most of the time. More men had been lost in the mud than through enemy action when finally we were withdrawn. It seemed to me we were fighting against the ice, which was all the while coming steadily nearer, covering more of the world with its dead silence, its awful white peace. By making war we asserted the fact that we were alive and opposed the icy death creeping over the globe.

I still felt I was waiting for something fearful to happen, but in a curious sort of suspended state. There was an emotional blockage. I recognized it in others besides myself. In suppressing food riots, our machine-guns indiscriminately cut down rioters and harmless pedestrians. I had no feeling about it and noticed the same indifference in everyone else. People stood looking on as at a performance, did not even attend to the wounded. I had to share a sleeping tent with five other men for a time. They had fantastic courage, but no idea of danger, of life, death, anything; were satisfied as long as they got a hot meal every day with meat and potatoes. I could not make any contact with them; hung up my overcoat as a screen and lay sleepless behind it.

Presently I began to hear the warden mentioned again. He was attached to western headquarters, held an important post there. I remembered his wish to cooperate with the big powers, and admired the way he had achieved it. Thinking of him made me restless. It seemed idiotic to spend my last days in a hired fighting unit, and I decided to ask him to find me a job in which I would have more scope. The problem was how to reach him. Our leader was the only person who occasionally had direct dealings with the higher command, and he refused to help me, interested in nothing but his own advancement. For days we had been attacking a strongly defended building said to contain secret papers. He would not ask for reinforcements, determined to get the credit for taking the place unaided. By a simple trick, I enabled him to capture the building and send the documents to headquarters, for which he was highly praised.

Impressed by my ingenuity, he asked me to have a drink with him, offered me promotion. He was making a personal report the next day, and I said that the only reward I wanted was to go to headquarters with him. He replied that he couldn't spare me, I must give him more of these tips. He was half drunk. I deliberately encouraged him to go on drinking until he passed out. In the morning, when he was about to start, I jumped into his car, pretending he had promised to take me, relying on his having been too drunk the previous night to remember what had been said. It was a nasty moment. He clearly suspected something. But he did not have me thrown out of the car. I drove with him to headquarters, neither of us speaking a word the whole way.

thirteen

They had built their headquarters far away from the battlefields, a large clean new building, flying a large clean flag. Stone and concrete, it stood out solid, massive, expensive, indestructible looking, among the low, old, rickety wooden houses. Apart from the sentries at the main entrance, it seemed to have nothing to do with war. No other guards were visible. Inside there appeared to be no security precautions at all. I recalled the commander's drunken remark: perhaps these people really were too soft to fight; relying on their technological supremacy, on the gigantic size and wealth of their country, believed they need not dirty their hands with the actual fighting, paid their inferiors to do that.

I was directed to the warden's suite. The place was air-conditioned. Elevators rose smoothly, silently, swiftly. Thick carpets stretched from wall to wall of the wide corridors. After the squalid discomfort in which I had been living, it was like a luxury hotel. Lights blazed everywhere in spite of the sunshine outside. Windows were hermetically sealed, not made to open. The resulting atmosphere was slightly unreal.

A woman secretary in uniform told me the warden could see no one. He was leaving immediately on a tour of inspection and would be away some days. I said: 'I must see him before he goes. It's urgent. I've come all this way specially. I won't keep him a minute.' She pursed her lips, shook her head. 'Absolutely impossible. He has important papers to sign and gave orders that nobody was to disturb him.' Her well-made-up face was adamant, uncomprehending. It annoyed me. 'To hell with that! I tell you I must see him! It's a personal matter. Can't you understand?' I wanted to shake her, to get some human expression into her face. Instead, I made my voice calm. 'At least tell him I'm here and ask whether he'll see me.' I felt in my pockets for some means of identification, then wrote my name on a pad. While I was doing so, a colonel came in. The secretary went over and whispered to him. At the end of their confabulation the man said he would give the message himself, took the paper with my name on it, and left the room by the same door through which he had just entered. I knew he had no intention of telling the warden about me. Only decisive action on my part would get me an interview. Soon it would be too late.

'Where does that door lead?' I asked the secretary, pointing to one at the far end of the room. 'Oh, that's strictly private. You can't go in there. It's forbidden.' For the first time she began to lose her superior calm and to look flustered. She had not been trained to deal with a direct approach. I said: 'Well, I'm going in,' moved towards the door. 'No!' She flew to stand in front of it, barring my way. The country she belonged to was so firmly convinced of world power that its nationals could not conceive of real opposition from anyone, even over the smallest issue. I smiled, pushed her aside.

She clung to my clothes, holding me back. There was a brief scuffle. I heard a voice I recognized beyond the closed door. 'What's going on there?' I went in. 'Oh, it's you, is it?' He seemed singularly unsurprised. In the doorway the secretary was talking fast and apologetically. He waved her away. The door shut. I said: 'I must speak to you.'

We were alone in the rich room. Persian rugs on the parquet floor, period furniture, on the wall a full-length portrait of him by a well-known painter. My worn, shabby, unpressed uniform emphasized, by contrast, the elegant grandeur of his, which had gold emblems on cuffs and shoulders, and, on the chest, the ribbons of various orders. He stood up; I had not remembered him as being so tall. The touch of the grand manner he had always had was more marked than when I last saw him. I was not at ease. His presence affected me in the usual way; but, with such obvious differences between us, the idea of contact, however obscure, seemed inappropriate and embarrassing. When he said coldly, 'It's no use forcing your way in here. I'm just leaving,' I felt confused, and could only repeat: 'I must speak to you first.' 'Impossible. I'm late as it is.' He glanced at his watch, started towards the door. 'Surely you can wait just a moment!' In my anxiety, I hurriedly stepped in front of him. I should have known better. His eyes flashed; he was angry; I had thrown away my one chance. I cursed myself for a fool. Perhaps my downcast expression amused him: at all events, his attitude suddenly seemed to change, he half smiled. 'I can't hold up the entire war just to talk to you. If there's something you *must* say, you'll have to come with me.' I was delighted. This was better than anything I had expected. 'May I? That's wonderful!' I thanked him enthusiastically. He burst out laughing.

The road to the airfield was lined with people waiting to catch a glimpse of him as we drove past. They stood six deep at the roadside, watching from gardens, windows, balconies, roofs, trees, hoardings, telegraph poles. Some of them must have waited a long time. I was impressed by the force of his immediate impact on the crowd.

Sitting beside him on the plane, I was conscious of curious glances from its other occupants. It was strange to look down and see the earth, not flat or gently curved, but as a segment of a round ball, the sea light blue, the land yellowish green. Overhead it was dark blue night. Drinks were brought, I was handed a tinkling glass. 'Ice! What luxury!' He glanced at my dilapidated uniform, made a grimace. 'You can't expect luxury if you insist on being a hero.' The words were mocking, but the smile had some degree of charm. He might even have been taking a friendly interest. 'May I ask why you have suddenly become one of our heroic fighters?' I knew I should have spoken about a job. Instead, for some reason, I told him I'd had to do somehing drastic to cure my depression. 'Funny sort of cure. More likely to kill you.' 'Perhaps that's what I wanted.' 'No, you're not the suicide type. Anyway, why bother, when we're all going to be killed next week?' 'As soon as that?' 'Well, perhaps not literally. But certainly very soon.' I recognized the trick of blinking his eyes, making the bright blue pupils flash as if they reflected a dazzling blue light. It was the sign that something had not been said. Of course, he had secret information. He always knew everything before anyone else.

An enormous dinner was served. It seemed altogether too lavish, I could not eat half of it. I had got out of the way of eating big meals. Afterwards I tried again to say what I had come to say, but the sentences would not take shape in my head. I found myself thinking of him, and remarked on how little surprise he had shown over my arrival. 'I was almost expecting you.' His expression was rather odd. 'You have a way of turning up just before things happen.' He seemed to speak quite seriously. 'You really expect the catastrophe within weeks or days?' 'Looks like it.'

Blinds were drawn, shutting out the sky. A film was to be shown. He muttered in my ear: 'Wait till their attention's fixed on the screen. Then I'll show you something more interesting. It's supposed to be kept secret.' I waited, curious. We left our seats quietly, went through a door, faced an uncovered window. I was confused about time. It had been night overhead all along, but below it was still daylight. There were no clouds. I saw islands scattered over the sea, a normal aerial view. Then something extraordinary, out of this world: a wall of rainbow ice jutting up from the sea, cutting right across, pushing a ridge of water ahead of it as it moved, as if the flat pale surface of sea was a carpet being rolled up. It was a sinister, fascinating sight, which did not seem intended for human eyes. I stared down at it, seeing other things at the same time. The ice world spreading over our world. Mountainous walls of ice surrounding the girl. Her moonwhite skin, her hair sparkling with diamond prisms under the moon. The moon's dead eye watching the death of our world.

When we left the plane we were in a remote country, a town I did not know. The warden had come to attend an important conference, people were waiting for him, all sorts of urgent affairs. I was flattered because he seemed in no hurry to leave me. He said: 'You should have a look round, it's an interesting place.' The town had only lately changed hands, and I asked if the troops had not done a lot of damage; received the reply: 'Don't forget some of us are civilized people.'

In his splendid uniform he strolled beside me in beautifully kept gardens, attended by armed guards in black and gold. I was proud to be with him. He was a fine-looking man who kept himself in every way at the height of his powers, all his muscles exercised like an athlete's, his intellect and his senses deliberately sharpened. He radiated tremendous dominance, besides an intense physical vitality, zest for living. His aura of power and success seemed to fill the surrounding air, and even extend to me. Walking past artificial cascades, we came to a lily pool where the stream widened. Giant willow trees trailed long green hair in the water, made an inviting grotto of cool green shade. We sat on a stone seat, watched a kingfisher tracing jewelled parabolas. Motionless grey shadows, herons stood here and there in the shallows. It was a private, peaceful, idyllic scene; violence was worlds away. I thought, but did not say, that it seemed a pity people were not allowed to enjoy all this tranquil beauty. As if he read my mind, he told me: 'The public used to be admitted on certain days. But we had to suspend the practice on account of vandalism. Hooligans did the damage the armies refrained from doing. There are people you can't teach to appreciate beauty. They're sub-human.'

On the far side of the river a troop of small gazelle-like creatures had come to drink, lifting and lowering graceful horned heads. The guards stood at a distance. Alone with my companion, I felt closer to him than ever before; we were like brothers, like identical twin brothers. Drawn to him more strongly than I had ever been, I had

to give my feelings some expression, told him how much I appreci-
ated his kindness, how greatly I was honoured to be his friend.
Something was wrong. He did not smile or acknowledge the compliment, but abruptly stood up. I got up too, while across the water
the animals fled, alarmed by our movements. The atmosphere was
changing round me; suddenly there was a chill, as if the warm air
had passed over ice. I felt a sudden uncomprehended terror, like
the sensation that comes in nightmares just before one begins to
fall.

In a moment he had turned on me, his eyes flashing blue danger,
his face a grim mask. 'Where is she?' His voice was fierce, curt, icy.
It was as if he had whipped out a gun and pointed it at me. I was
horrified; confused by the sudden switch from one emotion to
another totally different, I could only stammer stupidly: 'I suppose
where I left her . . .' He gave me a look of ice. 'You mean you don't
know?' His accusatory tone froze. I was too appalled to reply.

The guards came closer, formed a circle round us. To shade
their eyes, prevent recognition, or inspire dread, they wore as part
of their uniform black plastic visors which covered the upper part of
the face so that they looked masked. I vaguely remembered hearing
about their toughness, that they were convicted thugs and murderers, whose sentences had been remitted in exchange for their
absolute loyalty to his person.

'So you've abandoned her.' Arrows of blue ice piercing a blizzard, his eyes narrowed and struck. 'I hardly expected that, even of
you.' The abysmal contempt in his voice made me wince and
mutter: 'You know she's always been hostile. She sent me away.'
'You don't know how to handle her,' he stated coldly. 'I'd have
licked her into shape. She only needs training. She has to be taught
toughness, in life and in bed.' I could not speak, could not collect
myself: I was in a state of shock. When he asked, 'What do you
propose to do about her?' I found nothing to say. His eyes were
watching me all the time with a frigid scorn and remoteness that was
too painful, too humiliating. Their blue blaze seemed to stop me
thinking. 'I shall take her back then.' In half a dozen dry words he
disposed of her future, she had no say in the matter.

At that moment I was more concerned with him, linked to him so
closely, as if we shared the same blood. I could not bear to be

alienated from him. 'Why are you so angry?' I went a step closer, tried to touch his sleeve, but he moved out of my reach. 'Is it only because of her?' I could not believe this, the bond between him and myself seemed so strong. Just then she was nothing to me by comparison, not even real. We could have shared her between us. I may have said something of the kind. His face was carved in stone, his cold voice hard enough to cut steel, he was thousands of miles away. 'As soon as I can make time I shall go and fetch her. And then keep her with me. You won't see her again.'

There was no bond, never had been, except in my imagination. He was not my friend, had never been close to me, identification was nothing but an illusion. He was treating me as someone beneath contempt. In a feeble attempt to re-establish myself, I said I had tried to save her. His eyes were terribly hard and blue, I could hardly meet them. His face was a statue's, stony, it did not change. I forced myself to go on looking him in the face. Only his mouth finally moved to say: 'She will be saved, if that's possible. But not by you.' Then he turned and strolled off in his grand uniform with gold epaulettes. A few paces away he paused, lit a cigarette keeping his back towards me, strolled on again without giving me a glance. I saw him lift one hand and make a sign to the guards.

They closed in, inhuman in their black masks. Rubber truncheons crashed into me, I was kicked in the groin, in falling my head must have struck the stone seat, I passed out. This was lucky for me. Apparently it did not amuse them to beat an unconscious body. There was no sign of them when I came round. My head throbbed and rang, even to open my eyes was a fearful effort, every inch of my body ached, but nothing was broken. Pain confused me, made me uncertain of what had happened, of the length of time that had elapsed, of the sequence of events. In my confusion I could not understand being let off so lightly, until it occurred to me that the guards meant to come back later to finish the job. If they found me here I was done for. I could hardly move, but with infinite labour, dragged myself down to the river, everything swaying round me, fell among rushes and lay for some time with my face in the mud.

When a far-off sound roused me it was almost dark. In the distance a semicircle of dark shapes was slowly advancing, as if searching. I got a fright, I thought they were people looking for me and kept quite motionless. They must have been animals grazing, for when I next looked up they had gone. The shock made me realize that I had to get moving. I crawled on to the water's edge, let the river run over the wound in my head, washed another deep gash on my cheekbone, washed off some of the blood and mud.

The cold water revived me. Somehow or other I managed to reach the park gates, even started walking along a street, but collapsed after a short distance. A cartload of noisy young people coming back from a celebration saw me lying in the road and stopped to investigate. They thought I was one of their party who had fallen down drunk. I persuaded them to drive me to the hospital, where a doctor attended to me. I invented some story to account for my injuries and was given a bed in the casualty department. I slept for two or three hours. The clanging bell of an ambulance woke me. Stretcher-bearers came tramping in. To move was appallingly difficult, all I wanted was to lie still and go on sleeping. But I knew it was too dangerous, I dared not stay any longer.

While the night staff were occupied with the new arrival, I crept through a side door into a dark corridor and left the building.

fourteen

My head was aching, everything was confused inside it. I knew only that I had to get out of the town before daylight. I could not think. The hallucination of one moment did not fit the reality of the next. In a narrow alley, a car came tearing towards me to run me down, filling the whole space between Alp-high houses. With bleeding knuckles I staggered from door to locked door, at the last moment crushed myself up against one. In uniform, immensely grand, the warden drove past in his great black car. The girl was with him, her hair shimmering violet like the shadows of trees on snow. They drove through the snow together under a white fur rug, wide as a room, deep as a snowdrift, edged with cabochon rubies.

Lit by the dazzling cold fire of the aurora borealis, they walked among glittering icebergs; a blizzard blew arctic white, his bone-white forehead and icicle eyes, her silver-frosted hair bright with ice flowers under the pole star. A thunderclap boomed in the ice. He fought a polar bear, strangled it with his hands, to train her in toughness taught her to take the skin with his wicked knife. When it was done, she crept close for warmth. The huge skin covered them both, its long white hairs tipped with blood. The snowy thickness hid their two bodies; blood dripping from the tips of the dense fur turned the snow blood-red.

I saw her standing in torchlight with dreaming eyes. I watched her, wanted her, wanted to take her away with me. But that other had claimed her; her white girl's body fell through the smoke of smouldering torches across his knees. I was out searching for her, marauders were sacking the town. I searched everywhere, could not find her, stumbled over her in the rubble, her head awry. Through the smoke and dust filling the air, I saw her skin white against dirt and debris, the blood first red and then black on the white, her head twisted sideways by the unbelievable hair, the slender neck broken. Victimization in childhood had made her accept the fate of a victim, and whatever I did or did not do, this fate would ultimately achieve itself. To leave her to it was one thing. To leave her to that man was quite a different thing. It was something I could not do.

I had to get to her before he did. But the difficulties were overwhelming. The total absence of transport meant resorting to bribery, every kind of deception, worse. In my mind's eye I kept seeing the ice-line moving across the ocean, towards the islands, towards that particular island I had not identified on the map. I thought of her at the centre, not knowing she was encircled, while we advanced towards her from different sides, I from one point, he from another, and then the ice ... My chances of arriving first seemed almost non-existent. Every mile would be slow and difficult for me. He could get to her by plane in just a few hours, whenever he felt inclined. I could only hope for the important conference he was now attending and other military matters to detain him as long as possible. But I was not optimistic.

My head wound and slashed face had begun to heal normally, but I did not feel normal. My head ached all the time, I was pursued by horrific visions, disasters exploding in violent death, universal destruction. I was always aware that I was going to execution. Not that my own death seemed to matter. I had lived, I had done things, I had seen the world. I did not want to grow old, deteriorate, lose my intelligence and my physical faculties. But I had this compulsive urge to see the girl once more; to be the first to reach her.

I had to travel an enormous distance. Because I could not risk crossing the frontier openly, for two days I went on foot through wild country, without shelter, without food or drink. Later I had the luck to be taken some of the way by helicopter. A naked woman, life size, was painted on the side in crude colours; pop art in the midst of war. A person in occupation had to be disposed of; I was not going to lose the chance of a lift. The luck did not last. In a frenzy I searched the wreckage for the man who had been shot down. Only the painted face simpered at me among the debris, round pink circles for cheeks, black eyes blankly serene as a painted doll's.

In a country at war I tried to keep away from the fighting, came to a town unexpectedly quiet, except for the lorries that thundered through, crammed with troops or workers. A dull grey day and a dull grey town, sickly women languidly slapping their dirty washing on flat river stones. I was worn out and started to lose heart. Without some form of transport I would never complete my journey. I saw nothing encouraging here. Passers-by averted their eyes when I looked at them; they were suspicious of strangers, and with my scarred face, my old torn muddy guerrilla's outfit, my appearance could not have been reassuring. I went about searching for someone who looked approachable, found no such person. I talked to the owner of a garage, offered him money, a new foreign rifle with telescopic sights; he threatened to call the police, would do nothing to help me.

At dusk it began to rain, rained harder as night came on. A curfew was in force: no light showed from the houses, the streets were empty. I was taking a risk by staying outside, but was too despondent to care. A siren howled, distant crashes, gradually coming nearer, followed at intervals, alternating with bursts of gunfire. Rain fell in sheets, the streets had become a river. I sheltered under an archway, shivered, could not think what to do; my brain seemed paralysed by discomfort. I felt desperate, in despair.

A big military car swished past, stopped on the opposite side of the road. Impregnable in steel helmet, overcoat and high boots, the driver got out and went into a house. The desultory bombardment was still going on. There was no need for silence. In desperation, I prised up one of the granite cobbles, hurled it through a ground-floor window, put my hand in, pushed up the glass, swung myself over the sill. Before my feet touched the floor, the door of the room opened, I faced the man from the car. A sudden much louder explosion rocked everything, filled the dark room with a fiery blaze, reflected on cheekbones, eyeballs. Blood gushed from the wound, ran in dark rivers I tried to check, while I dragged off his uniform, put it on, forced him into my tattered clothes. By good luck we were about the same size. I went round hurriedly, wrecking the room, threw the furniture about, smashed mirrors, opened drawers, ripped pictures with my knife, to make it look as if a looter had broken in and been shot by the householder. I could not stand the weight of the metal helmet on my head. Carrying it in my hand, I went out, dressed as the other man, got into the armoured car, drove away. I had not succeeded in keeping his blood off the uniform, but with the fur-lined coat fastened the stains did not show.

I was stopped at a checkpoint on the outskirts. A bomb obligingly dropped near by. There was chaos, the guards had no time to interrogate me. I bluffed my way through and drove on. I knew I had not satisfied them, that they suspected something; but I thought they were too busy to worry me. I was wrong. I had only gone a few miles when searchlights spotlit the car, I heard the roar of super-charged motorcycles behind me. One rider hurtled past, ordering me to stop. Just ahead, he braked hard, stayed straddled in the middle of the road, suicidal, his gun pointed at me, spitting bullets which bounced off like hailstones. I put on speed, hit him squarely, glanced back, saw a black shape fly over handlebars and another crash down, as the next two machines skidded into the wreck and piled up. The shooting went on for a bit, but no one came after me. I hoped the survivors would stay to clean up the mess and give me time to get right away. The rain stopped, warlike noises died out, I began to relax. Then my headlights caught figures in uniform hurrying off the road, patrol cars blocking it, parked right across. Somebody must have telephoned on ahead. I wondered why they thought me important enough to send out all these people; decided they must already have found the man who should have been driving, and that the importance was his. They started firing. I accelerated, vaguely recalling the warden's story of crashing a frontier barrier, as the car burst through the obstruction like tissue paper. More shots followed harmlessly. Soon all was quiet, I had the road to myself, no further sign of pursuit. When I crossed the border half an hour afterwards, I knew I was clear at last.

The chase had a bracing effect on me. Singlehanded I had defeated the organized force which had been used against me. I was stimulated, as if I had won a fast and exciting game. At last I felt normal again, my old self, no longer a despairing traveller in need of help, but strong, independent, powerful. The mechanical power I controlled had become my own. I stopped to examine the car. Except for a few dents and scratches it was none the worse. The tank was still three-quarters full, the back packed with numerous cans of petrol, far more than I needed to get to my destination. I discovered a large package of food: biscuits, cheese, eggs, chocolate, apples, a bottle of rum. I should not have to bother about stopping to get supplies.

Suddenly I was on the last lap of the journey. In spite of difficulties which had seemed insurmountable, my objective was almost in sight. I was pleased with my achievement, and with myself. I did not think about the killing involved. If I had acted differently I should never have got here. In any case, the hour of death had only been anticipated slightly, every living creature would soon perish. The whole world was turning towards death. Already the ice had buried millions; the survivors distracted themselves with fighting and rushing about, but always knew the invincible enemy was advancing, and that wherever they went, the ice would be there, the conqueror, in the end. The only thing was to extract what satisfaction one could from each moment. I enjoyed rushing through the night in the high-powered car, exhilarated by the speed and my own skilful driving, by the feeling of excitement and danger. When I got tired I pulled up at the roadside, slept for an hour or so.

The cold woke me at dawn. All night long freezing stars had bombarded the earth with ice-rays, which penetrated its surface and were stored beneath, leaving only a thin crust over a reservoir of ice cold. In this sub-tropical region, to see the ground white with rime and feel it frozen hard underfoot gave the impression of having stepped out of everyday life, into a field of strangeness where no known laws operated. I ate a quick breakfast, put the engine in gear, and sped towards the horizon, towards the sea. On a good road, I drove fast, at ninety miles an hour, flying over the desolate land, at long intervals passing the remains of a house or a village. Although I never saw anyone, I could feel eyes watching me from the ruins. People saw the army car and kept quiet, did not reveal themselves; they had learnt that it was safer to remain hidden.

The day got colder as it went on, the sky darkened. Rising beyond the mountains behind me, ominous masses of black cloud were converging upon the sea. I watched these clouds, understood their meaning; felt the intensifying cold with increasing dread. I knew it meant only one thing: the glaciers were closing in. Instead of my world, there would soon be only ice, snow, stillness, death; no more violence, no war, no victims; nothing but frozen silence, absence of life. The ultimate achievement of mankind would be, not just self-destruction, but the destruction of all life; the transformation of the living world into a dead planet.

In a sky which should have been cloudless and burning blue, the sombre, enormous structures of storm cloud looked inexpressibly sinister, threatening, like monstrous ruins on the point of collapse, hanging impossibly overhead. Icy crystalline shapes began to flower on the windscreen. I was oppressed by the sense of universal strangeness, by the chill of approaching catastrophe, the menace of ruins suspended above; and also by the enormity of what had been done, the weight of collective guilt. A frightful crime had been committed, against nature, against the universe, against life. By rejecting life, man had destroyed the immemorial order, destroyed the world; now everything was about to crash down in ruins.

A gull flew close and cried; I had reached the sea. I sniffed the salt smell, looked over the dark waves to the horizon, saw no wall of ice. But the air was full of the deadly coldness of ice, it could not be far away. I raced across fifty miles of bare land to the town. Above it, the clouds hung lower, blacker, more ominous, waiting for me to arrive. The cold made me shiver: perhaps *he* had already been there. When I slowed down and entered the streets where people had danced all night, I could hardly believe this was the same gay place. The streets were all deserted and silent; no pedestrians, no traffic, no flowers, no music, no lights. I saw sunken ships in the harbour; demolished buildings, closed shops and hotels; a cold grey light that belonged to another climate, a different part of the world; everywhere the imminent threat of a new ice age.

I saw what was in front of my eyes, and at the same time I saw the girl. Her picture was always with me, in my wallet and in my head. Now her image appeared in the open wherever I looked. Her white lost face was everywhere with its too-large eyes, her albino paleness flared like a torch beneath the malignant clouds, drew my eyes like a magnet. She was a shimmer among the ruins, her hair a glittering in the dark day. Her wide eyes of a wronged and terrified child accused me from the black holes of smashed windows. Like a perverted child she ran past, soliciting me with big eyes, tempting me with the pleasure of watching her pain, elaborating the worst imaginings of my desire. The ghostly gleam of her face lured me into the shadows, her hair was a cloud of light; but as I came near her she turned and fled, the silver shifting suddenly on her shoulders, a waterfall glinting in moonlight.

The remains of a roadblock obstructed the entrance to the hotel at which we had stayed. I had to leave the car and walk up the drive. A strong wind, cruelly cold, blew straight off the ice, tore my breath away. I kept glancing at the anthracite-coloured sea to make sure the ice itself was not already in sight. At ground level the exterior of the hotel was unchanged, but higher up the walls were full of great gaping holes, the roof sagged. I went inside. It was cold and dark, no heating, no light, dilapidated chairs and tables arranged as in a café. In spite of fragments of gilt decoration surviving amidst the destruction, I did not recognize the wrecked room.

I heard uneven steps, the tap of a stick, was approached by someone who knew my name. The young man's appearance was vaguely familiar, but at first I could not place him in the dim light. Suddenly it came back to me while we were shaking hands. 'Of course, you're the proprietor's son.' The lameness was new and had put me off. He nodded. 'My parents are dead. Killed in the bombing. Officially I'm dead too.' I asked what had happened. He grimaced, touched his leg. 'It was in the retreat. All the wounded were left behind. When I heard I'd been reported killed I didn't bother to contradict. . . .' He broke off, gave me a nervous glance. 'But what on earth brings you back? You can't stay here, you know. We're in the area of immediate danger. Everyone's been told to get out. There are only a few of us old inhabitants left.'

I looked at him; did not understand why he was uneasy with me. He told me the crowds of people I had seen here had left long ago. 'They almost all got away before war broke out.' I said I had come in the hope of finding the girl. 'But I ought to have realized that she would have gone.' I waited for him to say something about the warden. Instead, he looked awkward, hesitated before he spoke. 'As a matter of fact, she's one of the very few who did *not* go.' My emotions had been disturbed during the last few seconds; to disguise the fact as much as to make sure my present relief was justified, I asked if any inquiries had been made about her. 'No.' He looked blank, seemed to be speaking the truth. 'Does she still live here?' Again the reply was 'No'. He went on: 'We've been using this part as a restaurant, but the whole building's unsafe. There's nobody left to do repair work. Anyhow, what's the use?' I agreed that the approach of the ice made all such activities futile. But I was only interested in the girl. 'Where is she living now?' His hesitation was longer this time, more marked. He was obviously embarrassed by the question, and when he finally answered it, I at once saw why. 'Quite near. At the beach house.' I stared at him. 'I see.' Everything was clear now. I remembered the house well, it was his home, where he had lived with his parents. He continued uncomfortably: 'It's convenient for her. She's been doing some work here.' 'Really? What sort of work?' I was curious. 'Oh, helping in the restaurant.' He sounded evasive, vague. 'Do you mean waiting on people?' 'Well, she sometimes dances. . . .' As if to avoid the topic, he said: 'It's a great pity she didn't go to a safe place like everyone else, while it was still possible. She had friends who would have taken her with them.' I replied: 'Evidently she had friends here she preferred to stay with.' I watched him closely, but his face was in shadow, his back to the fading light. I could not make out his expression.

All at once I became impatient. I had already wasted too much time on him. She was the one I had to talk to. On my way to the door I asked: 'Have you any idea where I'd be likely to find her?' 'I should think she'd be in her room. She's not due here till later.' He limped after me, leaning on the stick. 'I'll show you a short cut through the garden.' I got the impression he was trying to delay me. 'Many thanks: but I can find my own way.' I opened the door and went out; shut it between us before he had time to say anything more.

fifteen

An ice-cold air-stream hit me outside. Dusk was falling, the wind brought crumblings of frozen snow. I did not look for the short cut, but took a path I knew led down to the beach. Frost had killed off the exotic plants I remembered growing beside it: the leaves of palm trees were shrivelled, moribund, blackened, furled tight like rolled umbrellas. I should have been inured to climatic changes; but I again felt I had moved out of ordinary life into an area of total strangeness. All this was real, it was really happening, but with a quality of the unreal; it was reality happening in quite a different way.

Snow began to fall steadily, driven into my face by the arctic wind. The cold scorched my skin, froze my breath. To keep the snow out of my eyes I put on the heavy helmet. By the time the beach came in sight, a thick crust of ice had formed on the brim, making it still heavier. Through the white shifting curtain the house dimly appeared ahead; but I could not make out whether waves or a huge uneven expanse of pack ice lay beyond. It was heavy going against the wind. The snow thickened, inexhaustibly falling, incessantly sifting down, spreading a sheet of sterile whiteness over the face of the dying world, burying the violent and their victims together in a mass grave, obliterating the last trace of man and his works.

Suddenly, through the churning white, I saw the girl running away from me, towards the ice. I tried to shout, 'Stop! Come back!' but the polar air corroded my throat, my voice was whirled away by the wind. Snow powder blowing round me like mist, I ran after her. I could hardly see her, hardly see out of my eyes: I had to pause, painfully wipe away the crystals of ice forming on my eyeballs, before I could continue. The murderous wind kept hurling me back, the snow heaped up white hills that fumed like volcanoes, blinding me again with white smoke. In the awful dead cold I lurched on, staggered and stumbled, slipped, fell, struggled up, reaching her somehow at last, clutched her with numbed hands.

I was too late, I saw at once that we had no chance. A mirage-like arctic splendour towered all around, a weird, unearthly architecture of ice. Huge ice-battlements, rainbow turrets and pinnacles, filled the sky, lit from within by frigid mineral fires. We were trapped by those encircling walls, a ring of ghostly executioners, advancing slowly, inexorably, to destroy us. I could not move, could not think. The executioner's breath paralysed, dulled the brain. I felt the fatal chill of the ice touch me, heard its thunder, saw it split by dazzling emerald fissures. Far overhead the iceberg-glittering heights boomed and shuddered, about to fall. Frost glimmered on her shoulders, her face was ice white, the long eyelashes swept her cheek. I held her close, clasped her tightly against my chest, so that she should not see the mountainous masses of falling ice.

In her grey loden coat, she stood on the verandah surrounding the beach house, waiting for someone. At first I thought she had seen me coming, then realized that her eyes were fixed on a different path. I stopped and stood watching. I wanted to make sure who it was she expected, though I did not think the hotel man was likely to come now, knowing I would be here. She seemed to feel she was no longer alone, started looking about, and finally saw me. I was not close enough to distinguish the dilating pupils that made her eyes huge and black in her white face. But I heard her sharp exclam-ation, saw the hair swirl and glint as she swung round, pulled the hood over her head, and started towards the beach. I could hardly see her once she was off the veranda. She was trying to become invisible in the snow. Sudden terror had seized her: the thought of the man whose ice-blue eyes had a magnetic power which could deprive her of will and thrust her down into hallucination and horror. The fear she lived with, always near her, close behind the world's normal façade, had become concentrated on him. And there was another connected with him, they were in league together, or perhaps they were the same person.

Both of them persecuted her, she did not understand why. But she accepted the fact as she accepted all the things that happened to her, expecting to be ill-treated, to be made a victim, ultimately to be destroyed, either by unknown forces or by human beings. This fate seemed always to have been waiting for her, ever since time began. Only love might have saved her from it. But she had never looked for love. Her part was to suffer; that was known and accepted. Fatality brought resignation. It was no use fighting against her fate. She knew she had been beaten before the start.

She had gone only a few steps when I overtook her and pulled her back to the shelter of the veranda. Wiping the snow off her face, she exclaimed, 'Oh, it's *you*,' stared at me in surprise. 'Who did you think it was?' I remembered the uniform I was wearing. 'These clothes aren't mine, by the way. I borrowed them.' Her apprehension vanished, she showed relief, her manner became quite different, suddenly she seemed self-possessed. I was familiar with the air of confidence and independence she could assume when people or circumstances made her feel secure. The young man at the hotel must have done this. 'Let's go in quickly. Why are we standing here?' She spoke casually, acted as though my return had been planned and expected, pretending there was nothing unusual about the situation. It was annoying, after all I had been through. I knew it was meant to make me feel small.

She led the way to her door, invited me in with a social gesture. The little room was bare and cold, an old-fashioned oil heater barely took off the chill. But everything was clean and tidy, I saw that affectionate care had been expended, there were decorations of drift-wood and shells from the beach. 'I'm afraid it's not very comfortable; not up to your standard.' She was trying to make fun of me. I said nothing. She undid her coat and put back the hood, shaking her hair free. It had grown longer, sparkled and shimmered with life. Under the coat she was wearing an expensive-looking grey suit I had not seen, which had evidently been made to measure. So she had not been short of money. To see her looking attractive and well dressed for some reason added to my annoyance.

Like a conventional hostess making conversation, she said: 'It's nice to have a place of one's own after so much travelling about.' I stared at her. I had come so far to find her, through so many deaths and dangers and difficulties: now at last I had reached her; and she was talking to me like a stranger. It was too much. I felt hurt and resentful. Exasperated by her off-hand pose and her determination to deprive my arrival of its importance, I said indignantly: 'Why are you putting on this act? I didn't come all this way just to be treated as a casual caller.'

'Did you expect me to put out the red carpet for you?' The feeble flippant retort sounded offensive. I was becoming angry, knew I would not be able to control myself much longer. When, still keeping up the farce, she inquired in the same artificial tone what I had been doing, I answered coldly: 'I've been with someone you know,' giving her a long, hard, meaning look at the same time. She understood at once, dropped her affectations and showed signs of anxiety. 'When I first saw you … I thought you … he … I was afraid he'd arrived here.' 'He will be here at any moment. I came to tell you that. To warn you, in case you have other plans, that he means to get you back—' She interrupted, 'No, no – never!' shaking her head so vigorously that the hair flew out with a sheen like spray. I said: 'Then you must leave immediately. Before he comes.'

'Leave here?' It was cruel. She looked round in dismay at the home she had made. The sea shells comforted, the little room was so reassuring, so safe, the one place on earth she could call her own. 'But why? He'll never find me …' Her wistful, pleading voice did not touch me; mine remained adamant, cold. 'Why not? *I* found you.' 'Yes, but you knew …' She looked at me with suspicion, I was not to be trusted. 'You didn't tell him, did you?' 'Of course not. I want you to come with *me*.'

All of a sudden her confidence was restored, she reverted to her former disparaging attitude, gave me a derisive glance. 'With *you*? Oh, no! Surely we haven't got to go through all *that* again!' Attempting sarcasm, she rolled her big eyes, turned them up to the ceiling. It was a deliberate insult. I was outraged. Her slighting tone belittled my desperate efforts to reach her, ridiculed everything I had endured. In a furious rage suddenly, I took hold of her roughly, gave her a violent shake. 'Stop it, will you! I can't stand any more! Stop being so damned insulting! I've just been through hell for your sake, travelled hundreds of miles under ghastly conditions, run fantastic risks, almost got myself killed. And not the slightest sign of appreciation from you . . . not one word of thanks at the end of it . . . you don't even treat me with ordinary common politeness . . . I only get a cheap sneer . . . Charming gratitude! Charming way to behave!' She was gazing at me speechlessly, her eyes all black pupil. My rage did not become any less. 'Even now you haven't got the decency to apologize!'

Still infuriated, I went on abusing her, called her insufferable, impertinent, insolent, vulgar. 'In future you might at least be civil enough to thank people who do things for you, instead of displaying your stupid conceited rudeness by laughing at them!' She seemed stricken, dumb; stood before me in silence, with hanging head, all trace of assurance gone. In the last few moments she had become a withdrawn, frightened, unhappy child, damaged by adult deviations.

A pulse at the base of her neck caught my eye, beating rapidly like something under the skin trying to escape. I had noticed it on other occasions when she was frightened. It had its usual effect on me now. I said loudly: 'What a fool I've been to worry about you. I suppose you moved in with your boy friend as soon as I left.' She looked up at me quickly, apprehensively, stammered: 'What do you mean?' 'Oh, don't pretend you don't understand – it's too sickening!' My voice sounded aggressive, got louder and louder. 'I mean the owner of this house, of course. The fellow you're living with. The one you were waiting for on the veranda when I arrived.' I could hear myself shouting. The noise terrified her. She had begun to tremble, her mouth was shaking. 'I was *not* waiting for him—' She saw what I was doing, broke off. 'Don't lock the door . . .' I had locked it already. Everything had turned to iron, to ice, to hard, cold, burning impatience. I grasped her shoulders, pulled her towards me. She resisted, cried, 'Keep away from me!' kicked, struggled, her hand shot out, dislodging a bowl of delicate wing-shaped shells, which smashed on the floor: our feet ground them to rainbow powder. I forced her down, crushed her under the blood-stained tunic, the sharp buckle of the uniform belt caught her arm.

Blood beading the soft white flesh ... the iron taste of blood in my mouth ...

She lay silent, unmoving, avoiding me by turning her face to the wall. Perhaps because I could not see her face, she seemed like someone I did not know. I felt nothing whatever about her, all feeling had left me. I said I could not stand any more, and that was the truth. I could not go on; it was all too humiliating, too painful. I had wanted to finish with her in the past, but had been unable to do so. Now the moment had come. It was time to get up and go, to end the whole wretched business. I had let it go on far too long, it had always been painful and unrewarding. She did not move when I stood up. Neither of us said a word. We were like two strangers accidentally in the same room. I was not thinking. All I wanted was to get into the car and drive and drive, until I was somewhere far away where I could forget all this. I left the room without looking at her or speaking, and went out into the arctic cold.

Outside it had got quite dark. I paused on the veranda for my eyes to get used to the blackness. By degrees the snow became visible as it fell, a sort of faint shimmer like phosphorescence. The hollow roar of the wind came in irregular bursts, the snowflakes whirled madly in all directions, filled the night with their spectral chaos. I seemed to feel the same feverish disorder in myself, in all my pointless rushing from place to place. The crazily dancing snowflakes represented the whole of life. Her image flew past, the silver hair streaming, and was instantly swept away in the wild confusion. In the delirium of the dance, it was impossible to distinguish between the violent and the victims. Anyway, distinctions no longer mattered in a dance of death, where all the dancers spun on the edge of nothing.

I had grown used to the feeling that I was going towards execution. It was something in the distance, an idea with which I had become familiar. Now it suddenly sprang at me, stood close to my elbow, no longer an idea, but a reality, just about to happen. It gave me a shock, a physical sensation in the pit of the stomach. The past had vanished and become nothing; the future was the inconceivable nothingness of annihilation. All that was left was the ceaselessly shrinking fragment of time called 'now'.

I remembered the dark blue sky of noon and midnight which I

had seen above, while below a wall of rainbow ice moved over the ocean, around the globe. Pale cliffs looming, radiating dead cold, ghostly avengers coming to end mankind. I knew the ice was closing in round us, my own eyes had seen the ominous moving wall. I knew it was coming closer each moment, and would go on advancing until all life was extinct.

I thought of the girl I had left in the room behind me, a child, immature, a glass girl. She had not seen, did not understand. She knew she was doomed, but not the nature of her fate, or how to face it. No one had ever taught her to stand alone. The hotel proprietor's son had not impressed me as particularly reliable or protective, but rather a weak unsatisfactory type, and disabled as well. I did not trust him to look after her when the crisis came. I saw her, defenceless and terrified, amidst the collapsing mountains of ice; above the crashes and thunder, heard her feeble pathetic cries. Knowing what I knew, I could not leave her alone and helpless. She would suffer too much.

I went back indoors. She did not seem to have moved, and though she looked round when I came into the room, at once twisted away again. She was crying and did not want me to see her face. I went close to the bed, stood there without touching her. She looked pathetic, cold, shivering, her skin had the same faint mauve tinge as some of the shells. It was too easy to hurt her. I said quietly: 'I must ask you something. I don't care how many different men you've slept with – it's not about that. But I must know why you were so insulting to me just now. Why have you been trying to humiliate me ever since I arrived?' She would not look round, I thought she was not going to answer; but then, with long gaps between the words, she brought out: 'I wanted . . . to get . . . my . . . own . . . back . . .' I protested: 'But what for? I'd only just got here. I hadn't done anything to you.'

'I knew . . .' I had to bend over her to catch the accusing voice, speaking through tears. 'Whenever I see you, I always know you'll torment me . . . kick me around . . . treat me like some sort of slave . . . if not at once, in an hour or two, or next day . . . you're sure to . . . you always do . . .' I was startled, almost shocked. The words presented a view of myself I much preferred not to see. I hurriedly asked her another question. 'Who *were* you waiting for on the veranda, if it wasn't the hotel fellow?' Once more a totally unexpected answer disconcerted me. 'For you ... I heard the car ... I thought ... I wondered ...' This time I was astounded, incredulous. 'But that can't possibly be true – not after what you've just said. Besides, you didn't know I was coming. I don't believe it.'

She twisted round wildly, sat up, flung back the mass of pale hair, showed her desolate victim's face, features dissolved in tears, eyes black as if set in bruises. 'It *is* true, I tell you, whether you believe it or not! I don't know why ... you're always so horrible to me ... I only know I've always waited ... wondered if you'd come back. You never sent any message ... but I always waited for you ... stayed here when the others left so you'd be able to find me ...' She looked a desperate child, sobbing out the truth. But what she said was so incredible that I said again: 'It's not possible – it can't be true.' Face convulsed, she gasped in a voice choked by tears: 'Haven't you had enough yet? Can't you *ever* stop bullying me?'

Suddenly I felt ashamed, muttered: 'I'm sorry ...' I wished I could somehow obliterate past words and actions. She had thrown herself down again, flat on her face. I stood looking at her, not knowing what to say. The situation seemed to have gone beyond words. In the end I could think of nothing better than: 'I didn't come back only to ask those questions, you know.' There was no response at all. I was not even sure she had heard me. I stood waiting, while the sobs slowly died away. In the silence, I watched the pulse on her neck, still beating fast, presently put out my hand, gently touched the spot with the tip of one finger, then let the hand fall. A skin like white satin, hair the colour of moonlight ...

Slowly she turned her head towards me without a word; her mouth appeared out of the shining hair, then her wet brilliant eyes, glittering between long lashes. Now she had stopped crying; but at intervals a shudder, a soundless gasp, interrupted her breathing, like an interior sob. She did not say anything. I waited. The seconds passed. When I could not wait any longer, I asked softly: 'Are you coming with me? I promise I won't bully you any more.' She did not answer, so after a moment, I was obliged to add: 'Or do you want me to go?' Abruptly she sat up straight, made a distraught movement, but still did not speak. I waited again: tentatively held out my hands; lived through another long silence, interminable suspense.

At last she gave me her hands. I kissed them, kissed her hair, lifted her off the bed.

While she was getting ready I stood at the window, staring out at the snow. I was wondering whether I ought to tell her that I had seen the sinister ice-wall approaching across the sea, and that in the end it was bound to destroy us and everything else. But my thoughts were muddled and inconclusive and I reached no decision.

She said she was ready, and went to the door; stopped there, looking back at the room. I saw her psychologically bruised face, her extreme vulnerability, her unspoken fears. This little room the one friendly familiar place. Everything outside terrifyingly strange. The huge alien night, the snow, the destroying cold, the menacing unknown future. Her eyes turned to me, searched my face: a heavy, doubting, reproachful look, accusing and questioning at the same time. I was another very disturbing factor; she had absolutely no reason to trust me. I smiled at her, touched her hand. Her lips moved slightly in what, in different circumstances, might have become a smile.

We went out together into the onslaught of snow, fled through the swirling white like escaping ghosts. With no light but the snow's faint phosphorescent gleam, it was hard to keep the path. Even with the wind behind us, walking was hard labour. The distance to the car seemed much greater than I had thought. I held her arm to guide her and help her along. When she stumbled I put my arm round her, steadied her, held her up. Under the thick loden coat she was cold as ice, her hands felt frozen through my heavy gloves. I tried to rub some warmth into them, for a moment she leaned on me, her face a moonstone, luminous in the dark, her lashes tipped white with snow. She was tired, I sensed the effort she made to start walking again. I encouraged her, praised her, kept my arm round her waist, picked her up and carried her the last part of the way.

When we were in the car, I switched on the heater before doing anything else. The interior was warm in less than a minute, but she did not relax, sat beside me silent and tense. Catching a sidelong suspicious glance, I felt myself justly accused. After the way I had treated her, suspicion was all I deserved. She could not know that I had just discovered a new pleasure in tenderness. I asked if she was hungry; she shook her head. I produced some chocolate from the food parcel, offered it to her. No chocolate had been available for civilians for a long time. I remembered she used to like this particular brand. She looked at it doubtfully, seemed about to refuse, then relaxed suddenly, took it, thanked me with a timid and touching smile. I wondered why I had waited so long to be kind to her, until it was almost too late. I said nothing about our ultimate fate, or about the ice-wall coming nearer and nearer. Instead, I told her the ice would stop moving before it reached the equator; that we would find a place where we would be safe. I did not think this was remotely possible, did not know whether she believed it. However the end came, we should be together; I could at least make it quick and easy for her.

Driving the big car through the glacial night I was almost happy. I did not regret that other world I had longed for and lost. My world was now ending in snow and ice, there was nothing else left. Human life was over, the astronauts underground, buried by tons of ice, the scientists wiped out by their own disaster. I felt exhilarated because we two were alive, racing through the blizzard together.

It was getting more and more difficult to see out. As fast as the frost-flowers were cleared from the windscreen they re-formed in more opaque patterns, until I could see nothing through them but falling snow; an infinity of snowflakes like ghostly birds, incessantly swooping past from nowhere to nowhere.

The world seemed to have come to an end already. It did not matter. The car had become our world; a small, bright, heated room; our home in the vast, indifferent, freezing universe. To preserve the warmth generated by our bodies we kept close to each other. She no longer seemed tense or suspicious, leaning against my shoulder.

A terrible cold world of ice and death had replaced the living world we had always known. Outside there was only the deadly cold, the frozen vacuum of an ice age, life reduced to mineral crystals; but here, in our lighted room, we were safe and warm. I looked into her face, it was smiling, untroubled; I could see no fear, no sadness there now. She smiled and pressed close, content with me in our home.

I drove at great speed, as if escaping, pretending we could escape. Although I knew there was no escape from the ice, from the ever-diminishing remnant of time that encapsuled us. I made the most of the minutes. The smiles and the minutes flew past. The weight of the gun in my pocket was reassuring.

Franz Kafka
The Trial £3.99

At his death, Kafka bequeathed a number of manuscripts to his friend, Max Brod, with the instruction that they were to be destroyed. Brod disregarded this instruction and thus *Der Prozess* – translated as *The Trial* – was published a year later. Probably written in 1914, it follows Josef K. from the morning when he wakes to find himself inexplicably arrested, through a labyrinth of bureaucratic persecution, to his execution by two men in black. A work of powerful – and prophetic – symbolism, it remains one of the most influential and widely interpreted fictions of the twentieth century.

Translated by Douglas Scott and Chris Waller
This translation – specially commissioned by PICADOR – adheres with scrupulous fidelity to the tone and the style of the original German.

Charles Baudelaire
Les Fleurs du Mal £5.95

These 'flowers of evil' are Baudelaire's supreme creation. Their recurring images of sea-voyage and the Orient stem from the poet's own journey to the East in 1841. Their inspiration was in no small part provided by his mulatto mistress, the coarse and rapacious Jeanne Duval. Their decadent vision and distinctive voice inspired the work of Mallarmé, Rimbaud and Verlaine, lighting the touch-paper for the whole Symbolist movement. This bi-lingual edition contains the first-ever English translation of the complete text of a work that has changed the course of European literature.

Translated from the French by Richard Howard
'Will bring Baudelaire vigorously alive for English readers, and in the full range of his extraordinary gifts' THE GUARDIAN

All Pan books are available at your local bookshop or newsagent, or can be ordered direct from the publisher. Indicate the number of copies required and fill in the form below.

Send to: **CS Department, Pan Books Ltd., P.O. Box 40,**
             Basingstoke, Hants.   RG21 2YT.

or phone: 0256 469551 (Ansaphone), quoting title, author
             and Credit Card number.

Please enclose a remittance* to the value of the cover price plus: 60p for the first book plus 30p per copy for each additional book ordered to a maximum charge of £2.40 to cover postage and packing.

*Payment may be made in sterling by UK personal cheque, postal order, sterling draft or international money order, made payable to Pan Books Ltd.

Alternatively by Barclaycard/Access:

Card No. ☐☐☐☐☐☐☐☐☐☐☐☐☐☐☐☐☐☐

Signature:

Applicable only in the UK and Republic of Ireland.

While every effort is made to keep prices low, it is sometimes necessary to increase prices at short notice. Pan Books reserve the right to show on covers and charge new retail prices which may differ from those advertised in the text or elsewhere.

NAME AND ADDRESS IN BLOCK LETTERS PLEASE:

....

Name——————————————————————————

Address——————————————————————————

————————————————————————————

————————————————————————————

————————————————————————————

3/87